The Design and Construction of British Warships 1939-1945

The Design and Construction of British Warships 1939-1945

The Official Record

Major Surface Vessels

Edited by

D K Brown

CONWAY
MARITIME PRESS

Frontispiece:
Vanguard, *Britain's last battleship, in September 1950.*

First published in Great Britain in 1995 by
Conway Maritime Press,
an imprint of Brassey's (UK) Ltd,
33 John Street,
London WC1N 2AT

British Library Cataloguing in Publication Data
Design and Construction of British Warships, 1939-45:
Official Record – Vol. 1: Major Surface Ships
 I. Brown, D. K.
 623.8250941

ISBN 0 85177 673 6

Typesetting and page make-up by TypeBright, Burton upon Trent
Printed and bound by Butler and Tanner Ltd, Frome

Contents: Major Surface Ships

Introduction

At the end of World War I, the Naval Construction Department of the Admiralty produced a two-volume history of its wartime activities.[1] Though originally 'Confidential', copies of this work can be found in a few libraries and have proved invaluable to historians. When World War II came to an end in August 1945 it was decided to produce a similar record but, though largely complete, it was never printed or issued, even internally. A number of chapters were slightly re-shaped and published as papers to the Institution of Naval Architects in 1947.[2] In 1983 a carbon copy of the typescript came to light and a few copies were made for naval libraries and it is from these that the current work has been produced. There are indications on the original that one or two chapters were never completed, notably the introduction on the effect of naval limitation treaties (now covered briefly in this introduction) and on wartime damage to ships. This book is published as it was written and no attempt has been made to correct any errors there may be (except obvious spelling mistakes), though manuscript notes suggest that it was very carefully checked. A limited number of footnotes have been added to supplement the information given, mainly as references to other sources.

With rare exceptions, the text mentions only those designs which were actually built and the many designs progressed but abandoned are not mentioned. Few records remain of these designs which are frequently the 'missing link' between apparently unrelated ships which entered service.[3]

The Director of Naval Construction and the Naval Construction Department

The Director of Naval Construction (DNC) was the key figure, indicated by the opening words of his terms of reference:

> He is the principal technical adviser to the Board of Admiralty, and the final authority on the design of warships and other vessels of HM Navy, and will be directly responsible to the Controller for all matters of design, stability, strength of construction, weights built into the hulls of ships, armour, boats, masting and all nautical apparatus for all ships whether building in HM Dockyards or by contract.

There were two limitations on his authority. He had no formal input into the Staff Requirements though discussion on various options for a new ship often meant that DNC had a substantial input in practice. Though DNC was tasked with the design of the whole ship, he had only moral authority over the key Departments of the Engineer-in-Chief (E-in-C) and the Director of Electrical Engineering (DEE) and, at the time, relations were not as good as they should have been.

The two leaders, Sir Stanley Goodall, the taller of the two, and Sir Charles Lillicrap, Directors of Naval Construction, who had a very personal responsibility for every ship described in this book.

There were two Directors during the war, Sir Stanley Goodall (1936-44) and Sir Charles Lillicrap (1944-51). Goodall's distinguished career included the design of the *Arethusa* class cruisers in 1912, an appointment to Washington after the USA entered World War I, the design of postwar capital ships such as the G3 battlecruisers,[4] culminating in the early studies leading to the *King George V* class. His diaries reveal that some section heads were trusted to get on without much supervision whilst the work of others was closely monitored. Lillicrap had designed the monitors of World War I after which he spent most of his career on cruiser design before taking over from Goodall. At his own request, a new, 'elder statesman' post, that of Assistant Controller, was created for Goodall as he wished to step aside and make way for Lillicrap whilst the latter was at the peak of his powers.

[1] *Records of Warship Construction, 1914-1918.*

[2] These were reprinted by Conway Martime Press as *British Warship Design* in 1983.

[3] See, for example, G Moore's study of cruiser designs, to appear in *Warship 1996.*

[4] J Campbell, 'Washington's Cherrytrees', *Warship 1-4 (1977).*

[5] D K Brown, *A Century of Naval Construction* (London 1983).

[6] D K Brown, 'The Design of HMS *Arethusa*', *Warship International* (1/1983).

[7] D K Brown, 'Naval Rearmament, 1930-1941: the Royal Navy', *Revue Internationale d'Illistoire Militaire* (Stuttgard 1991).

The senior staff of DNC Department, alternatively known as the Naval Construction Department, were all members of the Royal Corps of Naval Constructors (RCNC).[5] Until the late 1930s, almost all members of the RCNC had entered a Royal Dockyard as an apprentice and, after four very competitive years in the Dockyard School had won a cadetship to the three-year Warship Design Course at the RN College. A list of members of the Royal Corps in August 1945 is appended. The draughtsmen had a similar background and many had completed four years Dockyard School, considered the equivalent of a pass degree. The gulf between the Constructor and his draughtsmen was wide though a few were promoted across it. The total staff of the department numbered some 250 when war broke out.

The design section for a ship type was responsible from cradle to grave and took immense pride in the performance of their ships.[6] There was a direct feedback from the performance and maintenance experience of existing ships into the next new design. Sections had a considerable degree of autonomy and there were differences in the definition of loading conditions and even in what weights constituted 'Hull' between sections. (Annex)

On 17 September 1939 a special train took 500 staff of DNC, E-in-C and DEE to Bath, the design office being set up in the Grand Pump Room Hotel, where most of the work described in this book took place. Later in the war, the Departments moved into brick huts on the outskirts of Bath where they remain today (1995).

Between the Wars

In 1918 the general public believed that the war that had ended was 'the war to end all wars' and the pacifist movement became increasingly powerful; even as late as 1937 a Gallup poll showed a large majority in favour of disarmament. The Treasury realised that the war had seriously damaged the economy and imposed severe curbs on expenditure. On the other hand, the Admiralty realised that the pace of development had left much of the vast Royal Navy obsolescent or worn out by hard wartime steaming whilst the USN and Japanese Navy had big building programmes of ships which were larger and more powerfully armed than any British ships.

These conflicting views led to a number of constraints on spending and, by Treaty, both on the size of the navy and on individual ships. Though much criticised by naval enthusiasts, both at the time and later, these treaties probably worked to the advantage of the navy by keeping competing navies to a level which the United Kingdom could afford and also setting a level for the RN which helped in debate with the other two services.[7] The

The Grand Pump Room Hotel, Bath, the temporary design office for most of the war.

effect of the treaty limits and of expenditure limits considerably affected the design of ships between the wars.

In 1918 the RN was in the middle of a technological revolution[8] which lasted until about 1923 when impetus was lost. The reasons why so many developments were dropped about that date are unclear; shortage of funds and the return of temporary staff to civilian life were part of the problem while Admiral le Bailly has suggested[9] an increasing anti-technology bias on the Board of Admiralty. In anti-submarine warfare the very success of Asdic led to most other developments being abandoned and to a complacent attitude which may be simplified as saying that the World War I U-boat offensive was defeated without Asdic and that any new submarine war should be much easier.[10]

Finance

In 1919 the Treasury laid down that no war was likely for ten years, which in the circumstances was very reasonable. In 1925 the Admiralty tried to argue that this meant war was likely in 1929 and a big building programme was requested. Again, quite reasonably, the Treasury made the 'ten year rule' a floating guideline (from 1928) which was abandoned following the Japanese invasion of Manchuria in 1932. The great depression limited funds for all defence work but even at it lowest, expenditure on the navy was 77% of that of 1913, a peak year.[11]

When re-armament began, the Admiralty repeatedly demanded an increase of funds but the Treasury was able to point out that industrial capacity and not funds was the limiting factor and that the Admiralty was unable to spend what money had been allocated.[12]

Treaties

In 1921 the US government, concerned over the rising cost of their naval programme, suggested a conference on naval limitation, offering a big reduction of their own programme. This was welcomed by the governments of leading naval powers and a treaty was agreed in 1922. As far as the Royal Navy was concerned, the treaty had the following effects:

The total tonnage of capital ships was to be limited to 525,000 tons, the same as that of the USN and 40% greater than that allowed to Japan. It is most unlikely that the country's economic position would have allowed more and this clause guaranteed Britain's position viz-a-viz its main rivals.

Individual capital ships were limited to 35,000 tons with 16 inch guns. This was somewhat larger than the RN wanted but was not a serious problem. Aircraft carriers were limited to 27,000 tons and 8in guns. Cruisers were limited to 10,000 tons and 8in guns, figures supported by the RN so as to include the new *Frobisher* class. The definition of 'Standard Displacement', roughly full load without oil and water, seems to have been suggested by the RN to conceal the advanced torpedo protection, using water spaces, in its latest designs. It did, however, end development of diesel engined surface warships as the engines were heavy and fuel economy no longer seemed very important.

No new battleships were to be laid down until the end of 1936 with the exception of two for the RN to redress their lack of 16in gun battleships. (Until these completed, four old ships could be retained.) In the long term, this was the only damaging clause; the long building holiday led to the collapse of much supporting industry such as armour making, gun mounting capacity, etc.

A further treaty was signed in London in April 1930 which divided cruisers into two categories, those with guns above or below 6.1in with separate limits in total tonnage. The RN were to have 146,800 tons of heavy cruisers and 192,000 of 6in gunned ships. This enabled the RN to increase the total number of cruisers by building small ships whilst allowing the USN to keep to the bigger ships which it needed in fewer numbers in the Pacific. Destroyers were limited to 1500 tons and 5.1in guns (16% were allowed to reach 1850 tons) with a total permitted tonnage of 150,000 tons. There were also strict definitions of minor war vessels in an attempt to prevent them from becoming as powerful as major warships. It should be noted that the Admiralty made every effort to keep to the letter of these treaties; only in the last few months of peace was the displacement of ships under construction allowed to rise and, even then, the technical breaches were trivial compared with the violations by the Axis powers.

Another limitation conference was held in London in 1936 but, though a draft was agreed, it was never ratified. This had a most unfortunate consequence as the United Kingdom, hoping it would be ratified, and desperate to re-commence battleship building on 1 January 1937, was forced to adopt the proposed limit of 14in for guns.

Some of the less well understood consequences of these treaties were explained by Goodall in an important but little known paper called 'Uncontrolled Weapons and Warships of Limited Displacement'[13] making the obvious point that though ships were limited by the treaties, there

[8] D K Brown, 'Revolution Manqué', *Warship 1994* (London 1994).

[9] Sir Louis le Bailly, *From Fisher to the Falklands* (London 1991). See also the author's *Man about the Engine* (Emsworth 1990).

[10] D K Brown, 'Atlantic Escorts, 1939-1945', in *The Battle of the Atlantic* (London 1995).

[11] P Pugh, *The Cost of Sea Power* (London 1986).

[12] G C Peden, *British Rearmament and the Treasury* (Edinburgh 1979).

[13] S V Goodall, 'Uncontrolled Weapons and Warships of Limited Displacement', *Transactions of the Institution of Naval Architects* (1937).

14 H B Peebles, *Warship Building on the Clyde* (Edinburgh 1987). See also the frontispiece to I L Buxton, *Big Gun Monitors* (Tynemouth 1978).

15 J English, *The Hunts* (Kendal 1987).

16 Germany had made similar advances and these two navies had armour some 25% more resistful than World War I armour (and World War II USN armour).

17 The RN had 4in, 4.5in, two very different 4.7in and the 5.25in for roles filled very well by a single version of the 5in gun in the USN: see J Campbell, *Naval Weapons of World War Two* (London 1985).

18 It was possible to make a weld in D quality steel and this was often done for emergency repairs in the war. Usually, the joint would be brittle and crack soon. Good welds could only be made in laboratory conditions.

19 Cammell Lairds were an honourable exception with an all-welded merchant shiip in the early 1920s and extensive welding in the *Ark Royal*.

20 D K Brown, 'Early Welding for the RN', *Journal of Naval Engineering* 34/1 (1992). This Journal can be obtained via the National Library and is held in the Science Museum.

were no such limits on bombs and torpedoes. Requirements for deck armour, which is very heavy, grew rapidly as did the requirement for AA weapons, torpedo protection and for the carriage of aircraft. Indeed, the Admiralty no longer considered it possible to produce a properly balanced design with 16in guns on 35,000 tons.

Industry

Jane's Fighting Ships for 1914 and 1939 list shipbuilders which built or could build warships. In 1914 there were twenty major yards, reduced to fourteen in 1939. The most prominent casualties were Beardmore and Palmer whilst Armstrongs had been absorbed by Vickers. In addition, the Royal Dockyards, which prior to World War I had built the majority of major warships, had largely lost that capability and the specialist building yard, Pembroke, had closed. The number of smaller yards listed had reduced from 111 to 19 though these figures may not be truly comparable. The 1914 book listed thirty-three marine engine works (excluding shipyards which built engines) many of which had closed by 1939 when there was no such list given.

The real reduction in capability was much greater than suggested by these figures. Company directors, naturally, put survival first so there was strong opposition to new technology, seen as risky, such as welding and longitudinal framing. Even when income increased rapidly in the late 1930s there was very little investment in the shipyards.[14] While less easy to prove, it is likely that the best young men did not seek a career in shipyards during the long depression. Goodall's wartime diaries are full of complaints about poor management and, in particular, old men. In turn, one may see this as a major cause of the very poor labour relations in the shipbuilding industry. DNC department was not immune from these troubles: one of Goodall's first act as DNC was to retire a few constructors who were not pulling their weight, whilst overwork probably accounted for the design error of the *Hunt* class.[15]

During World War I industry was able to supply a very large number of geared turbine sets for destroyers but much of this capacity was lost and in World War II escorts had to accept triple expansion engines; and even these were in short supply. Early in the re-armament programme it was discovered that the supply of armour plate was inadequate and, after an embarrassing search, a considerable quantity was ordered from Czechoslovakia. It is interesting that only non cemented armour was ordered abroad since it was believed, rightly, that the UK developments in

cemented armour had put Britain well ahead of most other countries.[16] Gun mountings were a particular problem, made worse since they had to be ordered in advance of the ship. Some imaginative treatment of the rules by the Admiralty, abetted by a Treasury blind eye, overcame the ordering problem.

The lack of capacity remained, exacerbated by the large number of designs of medium calibre guns in production,[17] an amazing self inflicted wound.

Technology

A number of decisions made between the wars left the RN well behind the leaders in technology, the consequences being that ships were burdened with unnecessary weight leaving less for armament. Some of the more important aspects will be considered in the following paragraphs. It should be noted that most, if not all, these decisions were reasonable in the context of the day and most other navies made even more serious errors.

Welding and High Tensile Steel

At the end of World War I the Admiralty was a leader in electric arc welding and it was thought that the all-welded ship was not far off. The Washington Treaty put an emphasis on weight saving and DNC decided to use a new high tensile steel, D Quality, extensively in hulls to save weight. Unfortunately, D quality was not suitable for welding[18] and this, combined with conservatism in most shipyards[19] led to very slow progress in the use of welding and that mainly in the Royal Dockyards.[20] Hindsight suggests that welding with mild steel would have offered bigger weight saving than D steel.

The Admiralty can be criticised for being slow in the introduction of longitudinal framing in destroyers, but when this was finally proposed for the *Javelin* there was intense opposition from industry.

Little attention was given to habitability between the wars. In part, this can be attributed to the peacetime fleet's way of working. Exercises were held when conditions were favourable and not in the north Atlantic winter or the tropical summer. Under wartime conditions, more and more men were crammed into mess spaces further reduced by new equipments. Ventilation was inadequate, air conditioning almost unknown. Little attention was paid to diet; *ie* good, well cooked food. There was a widespread impression that plenty of cold air helped to keep lookouts alert which caused a great deal of discomfort and led to exhaustion which had the reverse effect to that intended.

The biggest failing in British ships lay in their machinery. Things got off to a good start with the adoption of superheating in all postwar ships but there was a major setback when an experimental high pressure, high temperature machinery plant in *Acheron* gave persistent problems. It is often said that these were teething problems which could have been overcome with more determination. Admiral Bowen USN[21] claims that the cause was more fundamental: that Parsons' design team had failed to understand the problems of turbine blade vibration. Whatever the cause, the RN entered the war with machinery which was much heavier, more bulky, less reliable and far less (25%) economical than that used in the USN. It is often claimed that RN machinery was very reliable but Admiral le Bailly[22] has shown this was achieved only at the expense of frequent, lengthy maintenance periods and hard work by officers and artificers. Even so, British ships were plagued by steam leaks and oil leaks, almost unknown in the USN.

British electrical installations were also very heavy in comparison with USN ships, the difference in a cruiser being equivalent to the weight of an automatic twin 6in mount by the end of the war.

However, in the decade 1935-45 the RN lost no undamaged destroyers from stress of weather: the USN had four capsize, the Italian Navy two, Russia and Japan one each whilst the French Navy had a small destroyer break in half.

Anti-Aircraft Weapons and Control

Admiral Chatfield has written[23] that the decision to abandon the tachymetric anti-aircraft fire control system, then well advanced, was the biggest mistake between the wars. A recent study[24] suggests that even the best fire control system would have made little difference to the effectiveness of AA fire before the introduction of the proximity fuse.

The AA capability of the fleet in 1939 was inadequate in a number of respects as a result of decisions made many years earlier. There was a big review of naval AA measures in 1931 which concluded that the threat lay in formations of high level bombers, flying straight and level. The advice from the RAF representative was that dive bombing posed no threat. Against the high flying plane, simple control was adequate, there was no need for destroyer guns to have high elevation and that there was little urgency in providing better close range weapons than the pom-pom.

Damage and Survival

One of the most interesting chapters of the World War I equivalent to this book was that on action damage, but no such chapter was completed for the later war. To the mind of the editor, it would seem that too much publicity has been given to a few disasters – *Hood*, *Ark Royal* – and not enough to the survival of very heavily damaged ships – *Illustrious*, *Javelin*.[25] Some idea of the scale of action damage is given in the tables below.[26]

Too much has been written about disasters; British ships were tough. Javelin *under the command of Lord Mountbatten had both ends blown off by torpedoes on 28 November 1940 but was towed back to Devonport and repaired.*

Major Warships sunk or damaged

	Sunk	Seriously Damaged	Slightly Damaged	Sinkings as Percentage of Total Incidents
Battleships	9	18	14	13.5
Carriers	7	14	7	25.0
Cruisers	27	83	69	15.1
Destroyers	127	171	198	25.6
Sloops, Corvettes, Frigates, M/S	85	88	53	37.6
Total	251	374	341	26.0

The full seriousness of these figures may not be immediately apparent; for example, the number of incidents of damage to destroyers in each of the early war years was greater than the number of

[21] H G Bowen, Vice Admiral, USN, *Ships, Machinery and Mossbacks* (Princeton 1954).

[22] le Bailly, as 9.

[23] Lord Chatfield, *It might Happen Again* (London 1947).

[24] P Pugh, Unpublished study.

[25] D K Brown, 'Attack and Defence, 4,' *Warship* 27 and 28 (1983).

[26] J D Brown, *Warship Losses of World War Two* (London 1990).

[27] G A Bassett, 'Repair and Upkeep of HM Ships and Vessels in War', *Transactions of the Institution of Naval Architects* 88 (1946).

[28] There is an interesting note in Goodall's diary to the effect that any fool (overseer) can reject some item as not fully meeting a specification; a wise man will know when it is good enough.

such ships in commission. The torpedo was the principal sinking weapon accounting for 124, roughly half, of the sinkings. Bombs came second, particularly in the smaller ships, followed by mines and, last, the shell. Bombs scored heavily in causing damage.

Effectiveness of Weapons (Per cent)

Weapon	Sinking	Seriously Damaged	Slightly Damaged
Shell	9	14	32
Bomb	28	45	63
Mine	14	24	5
Torpedo	49	17	–
	100	100	100

Amongst the smaller ships, destroyers and below, structural collapse – back breaking – was the most common cause of sinking (41% of losses). Sinking was often rapid, the majority going down in under 10 minutes.

Nearly three-quarters of the ships hit, survived, a tribute to their toughness, but repair work imposed a major load on dockyards and shipyards.[27] Since a considerable amount of new equipment was usually fitted at the same time, repair times varied considerably while, late in the war, when ships were fairly plentiful, a number of damaged ships were written off as not worth repairing.

The main lesson learnt was the need for systems - engines, lights, pumps etc - to work after damage. This led to a big increase in the number of diesel generators, battery lamps and in damage control training. The wing spaces abreast the after boiler rooms in most modern cruisers were a mistake, excused by the difficulty of estimating the effects of serious flooding before computers. Some destroyers would have come home if the machinery had been arranged on the unit system as in modern USN destroyers, but this had been ruled out between the wars on the grounds of cost. Interestingly, the USN had reached the same conclusion prior to the introduction of advanced machinery which, because it was more compact, was easier to arrange as units.

Achievement

Ships designed and built during the war are listed individually in each chapter but it may not be obvious how large was the total effort. Major ships completed during the war are listed in the following table (omitting those built for the RN in the Dominions and the USA).

Battleships		6
Monitors		2
Aircraft Carriers	Fleet	8
	Light Fleet	17
	Escort	6
Cruisers		33
Destroyers		258
Submarines		193 + 33 Midgets
Sloops		27
Corvettes		183
Frigates		110
Fleet Minesweepers		96

Then there were the conversions: some 50 armed merchant cruisers, 695 minesweepers, 328 A/S vessels, 300 auxiliary patrol and many more not listed here.

All these ships, new construction or conversion, required a design input, if only as a basic check on stabilty and strength. DNC department also operated the overseeing service, ensuring that the ships and their equipment were fit for the job.[28] The constructors and technical officers of the Royal Dockyards came from a common personnel pool and there was a considerable interchange of staff to the benefit of both organisations.

Conclusions

The editor, a retired Constructor, may be biased, but the performance of the vast fleet described in this volume does seem very creditable. There are many indications of careful prewar planning, such as the development of prototype trawlers and boom defence vessels leading to wartime production and in the plans for armed merchant cruisers and escort carriers. Of course there were mistakes in all departments, particularly in machinery, AA armament and in the proliferation of medium calibre guns, but these were few in comparison with the successes.

It is perhaps a general lesson that many mistakes were made in areas of greatest success. Asdic was one such: its value was truly great but its operational capability was over-valued, leading to a belief that the submarine was no longer a threat and hence the development of passive sonar and ahead throwing weapons were abandoned.

On the DNC side one can see that the success of the V & W destroyers and the improvements in the A class may have led to complacency with failure to develop welded construction and longitudinal framing.

Editor's Note

The original photographs intended for this book cannot be identified. Those chosen have been selected as clear, not too well known and, with a few exceptions, representing the ship on completion, more or less to the original design. A few later photos have been used to show the extent of wartime alterations. Likewise the general arrangement drawings are not available and only those which would reproduce with reasonable clarity have been copied from the surviving typescript.

Many of the footnotes are in the form of references to other books. In the limited time available, I have only been able to refer to those readily available and apologise for any omissions and also for the too frequent references to my own papers.

This first volume covers major surface ships; the second is devoted to submarines, escorts and small craft; and the third covers amphibious warfare vessels, the fleet train and other auxiliaries.

David K Brown, RCNC

Appendix – Weight Groups

The total weight of the ship – deep displacement – was divided into 'Groups' for convenience in design estimating. These group weights are quoted for most of the designs mentioned in the text and their headings seem self explanatory but practise varied from time to time and from one section to another. Such small differences are not usually important - unless you are trying to use the data in estimates for a new ship. Explanations are offered below in groups where confusion was likely, the others seem self explanatory.

Hull. This was usually subdivided into:
Structure. This is fairly clear except that thin protective decks and bulkheads could be treated as structure rather than protection and, sometimes, a portion of a thick deck was treated as structure.
General fittings included such items as ventilation, pumping and fire fighting systems, electric light and power (excluding gunnery circuits), hatches, doors, W/T offices, paint cement and tiles, stabilisers (it seems likely that early radar was often included in this sub group), etc, etc.
Incidentals to equipment, armament, machinery and fuel; seats, brackets, pipes etc.

Protection. There was the overlap with the hull group mentioned above and it was sometimes unclear if some turret plating appeared under Armament.

Machinery. Dynamos would appear as Machinery; the rest of the electrical system as General Fitting.

Oil Fuel.

Reserve Feed Water.

Armament.

General Equipment included fresh water and provisions, the crew and their possessions, masts, yards and rigs, anchors and cables, boats, naval stores, etc.

Aircraft Equipment.

ROYAL CORPS OF NAVAL CONSTRUCTORS IN 1945

Director of Naval Construction – C S Lillicrap, Esq, CB, MBE

Deputy Directors of Naval Construction – A P Cole, MBE (*act*) – (*a*) W G Sanders, MBE (*act*) and
L C Williamson (*act*), Esqrs

Director of Warship Production – S A McCarthy, Esq (*act*)

Director of Contract Work (Ships) – (*a*) C Hannaford, Esq, MBE (*act*)

Director of Contract Work (Supplies) – C J W Hopkins, Esq, MBE (*act*)

Assistant Directors of Naval Construction – F Hickey (*act*) and (*a*) A W Watson, MBE, Esqrs

Deputy Director of Dockyards – G A Bassett, Esq (*act*)

‡ *Senior Staff*

Bartlett J L (ADNC) (*act*),
Blackman, F T, MCD (*act*) (*tempy*),
Curphey, E S, MBE (Assistant D of D) (*act*),
Davies, W J A, OBE (*Assistant DWP*)
Forbes, W A D (ADNC) (*act*),
Gawn, R W L (Supt, Haslar),
Holt, N G, CBE (ADNC) (*act*),
Horley, A E (WPS NW Area)
Hudson, G, MBE (MCD) (*act*),

(*a*) Joughlin, J C, CBE (*Assistant DCW (s)*)
Kennett, E G (MCD) (*act*),
McCloghrie, G OBE (ADNC) (*act*),
Mathias, J E (*WPS Scottish Area*) (*act*),
Mathias, T L (ADNC) (*act*),
Merchant, C F (*Assistant D of D*) (*act*),
Moon, J E P (MCD) (*act*),
Offord, D E J, (*Superintendent, Undex, Rosyth*),
Payne, S, MBE (MCD) (*act*),

Pengelly, H S (ADNC) (*act*),
Shepheard, V G (ADNC) (*act*),
Stanley, H (*WPS North East Area*) (*act*),
Stantan, A G W (ADNC) (*act*),
Steed, F H (ADNC),
Sutcliffe, F (MCD) (*act*),
(*a*) Walker, J F, MBE (MCD)
Wallond, W H (*WPS NW Area*) (*act*),
(*a*) Woollard, L, MA (ADNC), Esqrs

‡ *Chief Constructors.*

(*a*) Adams, A (*act*),
Baker, R (*act*),
Bentley, T H (*act*),
(Bessant, J L, BSC (*act*),
Constr Capt F G Bogie, (*FNCO East Indies Station*),
Bryant, G (*act*),
Cannon, S R (*act*) (*Deputy WPS, Scottish Area*)
Carter, L T (*act*),
Chapman, J H B (*act*),
Constr Capt E F Craggs, BSC, *Lyness* (*act*),
Constr Capt V W Hall (*act*), (*tempy*) *For duty in Australia*
Hatchard W J (*act*),
Constr Capt S I Hill, *Colombo* (*act*),
Holt, W J (*act*),

W H Jackman, (*act*),
John, W G (*act*),
Johnson, H T (*act*),
King, I E, CBE (*act*),
Leddra, C H (*act*),
Lemmon, A T
McCammon, G W R MBE (*act*),
Mann, H R, OBE (*act*), (*tempy*),
May, H (*act*), (*Deputy WPS, NE Area*)
Constr Capt A J Merrington, OBE, BSC (*SCO Staff of ANCXF*) (*act*),
Monk, R J (*act*),
Narbeth, J H, BSC (*Eng*) (*act*),
Newnham, H E (*act*),
(*a*) Nicholls, A CBE, OBE,
(*a*) Noble, W E,
Constr Capt Paige, C V (*Bombay*) (*act*),

Constr Capt G W Pamplin (*Staff of RAFT*) (*act*),
Peake, H S (*act*), (*Deputy WPS NW Area*)
Perrett, W R (*act*),
Perry, C H, BSC (*act*),
Pound, F J A (*act*),
Richards, R H (*act*),
(*a*) Scott, C
Skinner, H E, OBE, BSC (*act*),
Sims, A J, OBE (*act*),
Constr Capt D W Smithers (*FNCO Mediterranean Fleet*) (*act*),
Stevens, L G (*act*),
Sutherby, F S (*act*),
Trevan, S N (*act*),
Watson, H J (*act*),
Watson, S H (*act*) Esqrs
Constr Capt R H Wright, *Kilindini* (*act*),

Tempy. Chief Constructors, H J Cox,

‡ *Senior Constructors*

Penwill, C H *(act),*   Sherwin, C E *(act),* Esqrs
Pether, R P *(act),*

‡ *Tempy. Senior Constructors*

Mitchell, C C H P,   P G Rouse, BA, MINA *(Supt of Conversions),*   Whiting, W R G, MBE, MA Esqrs

‡ *Constructors.*

Andrew, W R, *(M Eng) (act),*
Barrett, L J *(act),*
Brooks, L J *(act),*
Chislett, H W J *(act),*
M C Dunstan *(act),*
Contr Com G S Ferris, BSC (ENG) *(act) (Lent to RIN)*
French, A W *(act),*
Gibbons, A J T *(act),*
Hancock, N *(act),*
Harrington, J W *(act),*
Constr Capt A N Harrison *(Lent to Royal Canadian Navy),*
Constr Com W R N Hughes *(Staff of VA(D)) (act),*

Constr Com L Kirkpatrick *(act),*
McCalin, E *(act),*
Mason, H R *(act),*
Matthews, F W *(act),*
Constr Com J R F Moss *(act),*
Mowatt, H M, BSC *(act),*
Newton, R N *(act),*
Constr Com S J Palmer, *(duty in Australia) (act),*
Perry, W G *(act),*
Constr Com T H Pilfold, *(duty at SHAEF) (act),*
Pound, E C, BSC (ENG) *(act),*
Purvis, M K *(act),*

Rayner, L W A *(act),*
Rogers, F C C,
Spanner, W F *(act),*
Constr Com J F Starks, *(Staff Admiral (S)) (act),*
Stewart, A, BSC *(act),*
Stunden, G J *(act),*
Tabb, H J *(act),*
Thorpe, T *(act),*
Tozer, R E *(act),*
Constr Com J E S Vincent, *(Freetown) (act),*
Vosper, A J *(act),*
Wood, R K, BSC (ENG) *(act),*

---

‡ *Arranged alphabetically*   (*a*) *Re-employed*   (*act*) *Acting*   (*tempy*) *Temporary*

‡ Temporary Constructors

Allen, T E,
Baker, D M,
Bedford, C A,
Constr Com J A Bonnyman, MBE (*duty in India*),
Boulton, T J,
Brookshaw, S W,
Bugler, A R,
Burrell, L W J,
Bush, F R,
Campaign, H H,
Chandler, C,
Coombes, L C,
Corfield, W A H,
Constr Com N J Coscoros,
Constr Com J Craig (*Staff of C-in-C, EIS*),
Constr Com R G Craig (*duty in Australia*),
Cross, T S,
Crossley, E,
(*a*) Cumbe, E. R,
(*a*) Daniels, S G,
Davey, S J,
Dwelly, E,
Eddey, J F J,
Grant, R C,

Constr Com F W Gray (*N Africa*),
Grinyer, A L,
Hankins, P H,
Constr Com A C Hardy,
Harris, C H L,
Hickish, J R,
Holloway, A H E,
Jago, E G,
Jeffery, W A,
Kicks, E,
King, P,
Langford, A T,
Littlejohns, F,
Constr Com C Lloyd-Roberts (*India*),
McMurray, M, BSC,
Mann, W J,
Martin, F J,
Matthews, A J,
Constr Capt J A Mavor (*PBCO, Italy*),
Mitchell, A BSC
Morley, F,
(*a*) Morris, R,
Constr Com H H Mutch (*Colombo*),
Nancarrow, G C,
New, H J C,

Norrington, E C,
North, D H,
O'Keeffe, W,
Osborne, A H,
Patridge, A,
Patterson, A P, BSC
Payne, R L,
Constr Com N H Perkin,
Phillips J,
Pitcher, H A
(*b*) Sears, F H,
Sedgwick, H E,
Smart, F J,
Constr Com W B Strang (*Staff of ANCXF (PH)*),
Thomas, A W,
Tillett, F L,
Turner, F,
(*a*) Turner, H A,
Constr Com A G Wearn (*Italy*),
Webb, W J,
Wolfe, A J M,
Wyatt, R,
Young, F, Esqrs

‡ Assistant Constructors, First Class

Constr Lieut-Com R Anscomb,
Constr Lieut-Com I McD Black, (*Staff of C-in-C, EIS*)
E C S Hepden, Esq

Constr Lieut-Com D R King,
Constr Lieut-Com R F Lofft, (*For special duty*),

Constr Lieut-Com E P Skinner (*Staff of C-in-C, BPF*),
Constr Lieut-Com W H Winn,

‡ Assistant Constructors, Second Class

Austin, A A,
Bell, L G,
Boulter, G J (*act*) (*tempy*),
Brinton, L J,
Brokensha, E A,
Chatten, H R P,
Cope, A J,
Dale, S D,
Constr Lieut-Com R J Daniel, (*Staff of RA(D), BPF*),
Davis, S M, M.ENG,
Evans, K G,
Constr Lieut-Com L H Evans, (*Staff of C-in-C, BPF*),

Farrell, K P,
Constr Lieut-Com J H Froud, (*For duty in Australia*),
Gibbons, E S,
Gundry, N E (*act*),
Hawkes, R,
Honey, N W,
Constr Lieut-Com R H Howorth,
Jolliffe, F V,
Constr Lieut-Com D B Kimber,
Constr Lieut J C Lawrence (*Staff of C-in-C, Med*),
Constr Lieut-Com C G Nace (*Staff of C-in-C, EIS*),

Constr Lieut A H Matthews (*duty in Australia*), (*act*),
North, E R (*act*),
Oldridge, C P (*act*),
Padbury, A E W,
Phillips, A E W,
Constr Lieut D S Radford (*Staff FOCT*),
Reeves, A E, (*act*),
Revans, J T,
Warren, W G,
Wood, E F,
Yearling, F H J, Esqrs

‡ Temporary Assistant Constructors

Blake, G D,
Crawford, J B,
Davies, J B,
(*a*) Froude, W,
(*a*) Hackney, G,

Lawson, D F,
Lees, J A H,
Constr Lieut L A Oliver,
Peel, R W,
Robinson, L M C,

Spanner, D C,
Lieut-Com P J Thornycroft,
Constr Lieut R J Tirard,
Watson, R H M,
Williams, F, Esqrs

‡ Temporary Acting Assistant Constructors

Constr Lieut-Com J P Allsopp,
Algate, E F,
Benoy, W H,
Chester, R,
Clews, C E,
Collecott, W B,
Davies, J J,
Dean, F D'A,
Dowden, A G,
Dunstall, J C,

Foot, F G,
Fuller, J V,
George, J,
Hastings, W A W,
Hosking, W H,
Jones, W,
King, J H,
Kingcome, F J,
Mason, T J,
(*a*) Merriman, T P,

Nightingall, V H,
Paradise, R,
Parsons, C H,
Price, J A,
Price, T L,
(*a*) Roberts, F C,
Rowe, J P,
Tippins, H G W,
Truscott, A G Esqrs

Honorary Member of the Corps
H B W Evans, Esq, MBE (*Assistant Constructor*)

---

‡ Arranged alphabetically (*a*) *Re-employed* (*b*) *On loan from other Government Departments*

(From Vol. III of the "Navy List" for July 1945 (corrected to 30 June)).

Key to Abbreviations and Terms

This book was written by naval constructors who probably expected that most readers would also be naval architects and other Admiralty officers who would be familiar with the many abbreviations and initials used. This glossary defines and explains most of them; though one or two sets of initials beat even the editor's 40 years of experience. Many of the entries relate to stability or strength and two short notes are included which explain the problems and define the terms used.

A   Aft

ACNS (W)   Assistant Chief of Naval Staff (Warfare)

Advance   The distance the ship moves in the direction of the original course during a turn.

AE   After End

AEW   Admiralty Experiment Works, at Haslar, near Portsmouth, where all hydrodynamic model testing was carried out.

Angle of max righting lever (GZ)
See Stability note.

Angle of vanishing stability
See Stability note.

AP   After perpendicular, at this date taken as the centre of the rudder stock.

AQ   Cannot be recognised. It clearly refers to cemented armour (C) and may be an error in the original.

BATM   British Admiralty Technical Mission – in Washington, USA.

BD   Between Deck. Of gun mounting refers to mountings, mainly twin 4.5in, worked from a gun bay between decks.

Bending Moment   See Strength note

BP   Between perpendiculars (of length) The fore perpendicular (FP) was the intersection of the design waterline with the stem, AP as above.

BTU   British Thermal Unit – an old, Imperial measure of heat.

Buster   A twin Bofors mount under development late in the war but never put into service, mainly because its weight of 20 tons was excessive.

C   Cemented, of armour. Armour with a very hard face produced by heating for a long period in contact with carbon.

Crush (of dock blocks)   During the war, most dock blocks were of timber which would compress (crush) under the weight of a ship.

D (quality), D1, D1HT   D Quality steel was a high strength steel introduced in the 1920s, D1 and D1HT were slight variations on D. It was not possible to make good, lasting welds on any of them.

DB   Double Bottom.

DC   Depth Charge.

DCHQ   Damage Control Headquarters, primary (1), secondary (2).

DCT   Director Control Tower.

Developed (blade) area   The total area of all blades outside the boss on the face of a propeller. (The face is the high pressure side, facing aft.)

Disc   The circle swept by the blades of a propeller.

Displacement   The total weight of a ship. Deep is fully laden, everything on board; standard is defined by the Washington Treaty, roughly deep without all liquids, water, fuel etc.

DTSD   Director of Tactical and Staff Duties. Responsible for co-ordinating the views of naval staff divisions and issuing the Staff Requirement for a ship.

DW   A development of D quality steel which could be welded.

Endurance   Normally given with fouling corresponding to the average effect, six months out of dock in temperate waters. This conventionally added 1/4% per day to the frictional resistance (20-25% in six months). The effect was doubled in tropical waters. The quoted endurance was a comparative figure only, and true endurance was much less.

Expansion joint   A long superstructure will be strained by the flexing of the main hull in a seaway. It can either be made strong enough to accept the resulting load or the superstructure can be divided into short lengths. The joints between these lengths are known as expansion joints and will have a splash-proof cover.

F   Forward (sometimes used for Freeboard).

^{o}F   Temperature, degrees Fahrenheit

(fl)   Fluid, refers to the effect of liquid movement on metacentric height, see Stability note.

g   The acceleration due to gravity – 32.2 ft/sec^2 – used as a measure of acceleration.

GM   Metacentric height. See Stability note.

HA   High Angle (gun mounting).

HADT   High Angle Director Tower

HA/LA   Combined High Angle/Low Angle mounting

Haslar   Site of AEW (*qv*), the ship model tanks.

Hogging   See Strength Note.

HP   High Pressure, as of a high pressure turbine stage or of a compressed air system

HT   High Tensile steel. Usually used in this book to describe high strength steels earlier than D quality.

Inclining (experiment)   See stability – an experiment to measure GM.

Inertia (in^{2}ft^2)   See Strength note

Lbs (Plate thickness)   Naval architects have to be very conscious of weight and to keep this in mind, the thickness of plates was given in lbs/sq ft. A 1 inch thick plate weighed 40lbs per sq ft (approximately) and was referred to as '40lb' plate. A similar approach was used for sections such as angle bars which were described by their weight ft run.

lbs/in^2   Pressure or stress in pounds per square inch, can also be written as psi.

Legend   In submitting a design for approval, DNC would complete a standard 4-page form setting out the main particulars of the design. This form was known as the Legend and quantities such as displacement given thereon became the Legend Displacement. After the Washington Treaty, the Legend Displacement would be the Standard (Washington) displacement. Prior to Washington the Legend displacement would include some fuel, usually one third.

Length (Between perpendiculars BP), (Overall)   See BP, length overall was from the furthermost points forward and aft (excluding the ensign staff but including stern galleries).

LP   Low pressure.

Maximum righting lever, Max GZ   See Stability note,

Metacentric Height   See Stability note.

ML   Middle Line.

NC   Non Cemented armour. Lacking the hard face of cemented armour which could not be made in thin plates. NC was generally preferred for turret roofs of any thickness because of its toughness.

NMMPP   Non Magnetic Protective Plating, used near the magnetic compass.

OB   Outer Bottom.

Peace Tanks   Fuel tanks carried high up in the machinery spaces of destroyers. Only used in peace because of the risk of fire in war.

Pitch   The face of a propeller of the type used in World War II was part of a helical screw – like a wood screw. The pitch of the propeller is the distance such a screw would move forward along its axis if turned through one revolution without slipping (again as in wood rather than water).

Propulsive coefficient (PC)   This is not an efficiency. It is the ratio of the power required to tow the hull, without appendages (bilge keels, shaft brackets etc) and without propellers to the power put into the shafts by the engines. It is a very useful shorthand to the naval architect, particularly in giving a first estimate of power for a new ship by comparison with a similar, existing ship. However, definitions and usage differ and it is a trap for the unwary.

psi   Pounds per square inch.

Rabbetted   Two plates slotted together at their edges in similar fashion to 'tongue and groove' floorboards.

Range (of stability)   See Stability note.

rpm   Revolutions (of shaft) per minute.

Sagging   See Strength note.

Speed   This may be given at deep displacement or standard. For a destroyer, there would be about 5 knots difference. Speed is quoted with a 'clean bottom' – no fouling.

STAAG   Twin Bofors mounting introduced late in the war. Acronym for 'Stabilised Tachymetric Anti Aircraft Gun'.

Standard   Displacement as defined by Washington; also used for corresponding draught and freeboard.

Stress   See Strength note.

SWL   Standard Water Line – see Standard.

Tactical Diameter   The diameter of the turning circle of the ship; unless otherwise stated, is full rudder angle.

Trim   Difference in draught between bow and stern. It was usual to design for about 2ft trim by the stern which would give good directional stability, sufficient draught for the propellers and would ensure that, in dry docking, the ship would settle on the blocks stern first, where the structure had been reinforced to take the heavy loads involved.

UD, UDk   Upper Deck.

UP   Unrotated Projectile. A rocket device which it was hoped would deter or even destroy attacking aircraft.

USK   Under Side of Keel.

Vote 8 cost   The cost without guns and stores.

WA   Warning Air (of Radar or, as it was then known, RDF – Radio Direction Finding).

WPS   Warship Production Superintendent.

WT   Wireless Telegraphy, radio using morse.

W/T   Water Tight.

Y   See strength note.

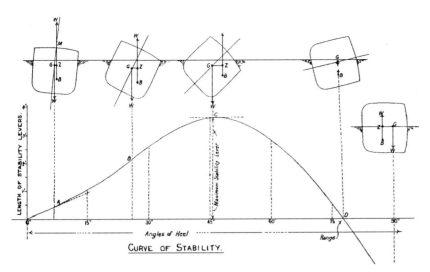

CURVE OF STABILITY.

Stability

To the naval architect, stability is a measure of the moment of force trying to bring the ship upright from a heeled position. The weight force acts downwards through the centre of gravity (G) which is (almost) a fixed point. The buoyancy force acts upwards through the centre of buoyancy (B) which is the centre of the underwater volume of the ship, which clearly moves as the ship is heeled.

The five small sections at the top of the diagram show how the centre of buoyancy B first moves outward as the ship is heeled, increasing the leverage bringing the ship upright and then, for extreme angles, moves back until the righting moment is zero and then becomes negative, causing capsize. Weight (W) equals buoyancy and hence the righting moment is measured by

$$\text{Weight (W) x GZ}$$

The stability characteristics were – and are – set out in the curve of stability or 'GZ curve' in which GZ, the righting lever, is plotted against angle of heel. The key parameters, which are given for each class in the text, are shown on the diagram.

Maximum stability lever, commonly called maximum GZ, defines the maximum steady heeling moment which the ship can withstand.

The angle at which the maximum GZ occurs is also important as if it is too small a sudden gust of wind may cause heel which exceeds the angle at which GZ is a maximum and lead to capsize (as in the loss of the *Captain* in 1870).

The extreme angle at which there is a positive righting moment is called the range. It is a less important parameter as, in a real ship, water will be pouring in down ventilators and other openings well before this angle is reached.

At small angles of heel (θ) GZ is given approximately by

$$GZ = GM. \sin(\theta) \quad - \text{See Diagram}$$

where GM is the metacentric height and θ is the angle of heel.

The values of most of the parameters used differ with changes in loading and are normally given for deep and light condition, the latter usually giving the worst results since the weight of fuel low down in the deep condition acts as ballast. It was frequently necessary to add water ballast if the ship approached the light condition. During World War II it was customary to base design values of GM, GZ etc on previous practice rather than on rigid standards. With the experience gained from operating a large navy this was a perfectly acceptable procedure, shown by the fact that no British warship was lost due to stress of weather. The chosen values would have to be justified in formal debate with increasingly senior – and experienced – officers concluding with the DNC himself, who was not easily satisfied.

In the first paragraph it was said that the centre of gravity (G) was (almost) fixed. The effect of liquids, fuel or water, which are free to move in partially filled tanks does cause some movement of G except in the light condition where there are no liquids. This movement can be calculated and an effective position of G determined. This is known as G (fluid) usually written in this book as Gfl. Care would be taken in the design to minimise the possible movement of liquids and operators were warned to minimise the number of partially filled tanks.

It is possible to measure metacentric height directly in an inclining experiment. Known weighs (w) are moved a specified distance (x) across the deck and the heel (θ) measured. Then

$$w.x = W.GM.\sin\theta$$

Since the position of M can be calculated precisely, that of G can be deduced.

Strength

Ships are loaded, even in still water, by the uneven distribution of weight and buoyancy along the length and this is made worse in waves. The worst case is when the ship is end on to waves of its own length and from a paper of 1870 by Edward Reed this was formalised into a standard calculation which was gradually refined. By World War II the waves considered were of the same length, crest to crest, as the ship with a height equal to 1/20 of the length.

Two conditions were considered:
Hogging with a wave crest amidships and the ends relatively unsupported and
Sagging with crest at either end.

The loading of the ship – stores, fuel etc – would be adjusted to give a worst case in either condition. (Note, in some tables the different displacement used for Hogging and Sagging is given.) With the ship 'balanced' (weight = buoyancy) on the wave it was a simple, if lengthy, task to calculate the differential vertical force, the difference between weight and buoyancy, at each point along the length. This could be integrated to give the bending moment from which the stress (load per unit area of cross section) in deck and keel could be obtained with a knowledge of the properties of the structural section.

The resistance of the section to bending is given by the 'moment of inertia' in which the area (in^2) of each longitudinally continuous member – plate or frame bar – is measured from the axis and multiplied by the square of this distance. Moment of Inertia (MI) or inertia has dimensions in^2 ft^2. In riveted ships 2/11 of the section in tension was deducted to allow for rivet slip.

When the ship is hogging, the deck will be in tension and the keel compressed whilst if sagging the deck will be compressed and the keel in tension. The neutral axis, roughly at half depth, is where there is no stress, either compressive or tensile, and the distance Y given in some tables is the distance of the deck or keel from this axis.

Such a calculation is an approximation to what happens in a real seaway but, given experience from many previous results for similar ships, its use can be quite reliable; indeed today's calculations, with a much greater theoretical background, are little different in principle. It was recognised that there were few long waves with a height of 1/20 their length and this was compensated for by accepting higher nominal stresses in long ships.

In ships of World War II the first warning of over-stressing was failure of rivets which was an all too common event, particularly in destroyers. However, there were no total failures of the structure of British ships as in some other navies. It should be noted that 'back breaking' was the commonest cause of sinking following action damage for destroyers and smaller ships. Appreciation of this problem led the designers to calculate stresses in battleships with all unarmoured structure destroyed.

For ships which are similar in both shape and loading it is reasonable to assume that bending moment is a constant fraction of Displacement x Length (= W.L/k where k is a constant derived from the previous ship) and reference will be found to estimates 'based on previous ships' in which this approximation has been used.

The tables usually give, both for hogging and sagging, values of bending moment and the stresses amidships in deck and keel. In one or two cases, stresses are calculated at other points along the length. There would also be a large number of calculations of the strength of detail portions of the hull and of items such as the rudder stock, shaft brackets, machinery seats etc but these are not reported in the book.

Howe in 1943.

CHAPTER 1

Battleships & Battlecruisers

Editorial Note

The modernisation of the older battleships and the development of the King George V *have been described in greater detail elsewhere.*[1,2] *The importance of this chapter is that it emphasises the topics which seemed important to the design team; in particular, the consequences of moving the armour deck from middle to main deck is brought out, involving an additional 8ft of side armour, and the effect on stability of raising the very heavy armour deck. One may also note the difficulty of maintaining the shape of the older ships during modernisation when much of the structure was cut away, particularly in the case of* Valiant *in floating dock.*

Strength is rarely considered by authors, perhaps a tribute to the lack of serious failures, but it was a continuing problem. In battleships the worst problem was where the relatively flexible ends met the citadel beginning with an extremely rigid barbette. Cracking and leaks in this area were almost inevitable.

A considerable number of the capital ships built during 1914-1918 survived to see service in the second World War.

Queen Elizabeth Class Battleships
    Queen Elizabeth   Valiant
    Warspite   Malaya
    Barham

Royal Sovereign Class Battleships
    Royal Sovereign   Resolution
    Royal Oak   Ramilles
    Revenge

Battlecruisers
    Renown   Repulse   Hood
These ships are described in *Records of Warship Construction 1914-1918*;[3] below is a brief summary of their subsequent history, together with an account of the battleships *Nelson* and *Rodney* built under the 1922-3 programme.

When the Government decided in 1936 to re-arm to maximum peacetime capacity, International Treaty prevented them laying down new capital ships before 1 January 1937, and it was known that these ships would take about four years to build. Trials had shown that all the old capital ships were vulnerable to attack from modern shells, mines, bombs and torpedoes. Accordingly it was decided to reconstruct all of them except the *Royal Sovereign* class ships, which had older underwater protection than the *Queen Elizabeth* class and also, being smaller and

Modernisation of *Queen Elizabeth*

	As orginally designed	*As completed in 1940*
15in Main Armament	Range 23,400yds	Range 32,200yds firing improved shell[4]
Secondary Armament	16-6in guns	20-4.5in (high angle, low angle)
Minor Armament	2-3in HA	32-2pdr HA guns in 4 mountings 16-0.5in HA guns in 4 mountings
Torpedo tubes	4	Nil
Aircraft armament	Nil	Catapult & 2 Walrus aircraft in hangars
Propelling machinery	24 in number, Babcock & Wilcox type boilers. Turbine-direct drive to propeller shafts	8 in number, Admiralty 3 drum type boilers. Geared turbines.
Oil fuel	3400 tons	3570 tons
Endurance	4400 miles at 10kts	13,500 miles at 10kts
Deck projection (over magazines)	1in HT plating	4in armour on 1in HT plating
Deck protection (over machinery spaces)	1in HT plating	2½in armour on 1in HT plating[5]

[1] A Raven & J Roberts, *British Battleships of World War Two* (London 1976).

[2] R A Burt, *British Battleships 1919-1939* (London 1993).

[3] *Records of Warship Construction 1914-1918* was the official history of the Naval Construction Department in World War I on which the present volume was modelled. Originally 'Confidential', copies are to be found in a few libraries, such as those of the National Maritime Museum and the Ministry of Defence.

[4] 'Improved shell' refers to the 6crh head. They were slightly heavier at 1938lbs: see N J M Campbell, *Naval Weapons of World War Two* (London 1985).

[5] A layer of 2½in over a 1in plate is less effective than a single 3½in plate.

shorter, were not so easy to adapt to meet requirements. By 1939 *Malaya*, *Barham* and *Repulse* had been partially reconstructed; *Warspite* and *Renown* had been completely reconstructed; *Queen Elizabeth* and *Valiant* were in hand.

Queen Elizabeth Class Battleships

Starting with *Warspite* in 1926, bulges were fitted in each vessel of the class, also water protection compartments abreast the magazines. Concurrently certain modifications to the bridges were carried out.

To prevent back draught carrying funnel gases to the bridge, the forward funnel was united with the after one.

Many improvements were considered desirable from time to time, but it was not until reconstruction was started in 1936 that these were undertaken. The work involved in complete reconstruction can be understood from the particulars in table above of *Queen Elizabeth* as originally completed in 1915 and as reconstructed in 1940.

The underwater protection at the sides remained as it was when the ship was bulged in 1927, but the watertight subdivision inboard of the protective bulkheads was greatly improved; at the same time the old inner bottom and main bulkheads were almost entirely renewed and strengthened.

Space for the much larger quantity of ammunition carried was provided by the surrender of submerged torpedo tubes and the much smaller area

necessary for modern propelling machinery.[6] Indeed, reconstruction of such a drastic nature was only rendered possible by the advances in marine engineering practice during the previous quarter of a century; as can be seen from the comparison in the table below the machinery weight was halved, the space it occupied reduced by one-third, and the endurance at 10kts was trebled.

The additional weight involved by the heavier deck protection and armament was compensated for by the lighter machinery, the surrender of the heavy conning tower and the 6in battery armour. The removal of the old conning tower enabled space to be found for the large modern bridge, director control towers, aircraft hangars, and athwartships catapult.

Other improvements were:
(1) Electric generators: 8 in number, total capacity 2400kW. As originally designed there were 4 in number, total capacity 700kW.
(2) Pumps for dealing with leaks, fires and bilge water: total maximum capacity 9050 tons per hour. As originally designed 950 tons per hour.
(3) New steering gear (electro-hydraulic).
(4) New forward capstan machinery.
(5) Up-to-date wireless telegraphy.
(6) Ventilation, accommodation, and equipment generally were brought up to date.

The standards of strength and stability adopted when the ship was first designed were maintained.

[6] The class, as built, had large and heavy boilers and the success of the modernisation rested largely on the savings in weight made possible by their replacement by much lighter and more compact boilers. It should be noted that the replacements were still old fashioned by World War II standards – see note 18.

Propelling Machinery (80,000shp)

	As originally designed	*As completed in 1940*
Weight of main engines and boilers	3080 tons	1570 tons
Floor space occupied by main engines and boilers	13,150sq ft	8610sq ft
Steam consumption at full power	12.8lb per shp per hour	9.4lb per shp per hour
Steam consumption at one-fifth full power	20lb per shp per hour	12.7lb per shp per hour

A major conversion of this type is both makeshift and expensive. The cost of this particular case was about £1,750,000.

The reconstruction involved almost gutting the vessel amidships and great care was required to preserve the ship's form when the main bulkheads were removed. To avoid deformation the ships were opened up to a pre-arranged programme and the decks stiffened by large fore and aft girders well shored. The behaviour of *Warspite*, the first ship so treated, gave the Portsmouth Dockyard Officers considerable anxiety, but later they had the satisfaction of knowing that both this ship and *Queen Elizabeth* stood up to very severe tests. *Valiant*, reconstructed at Devonport, required special precautions as much of the work had to be done in a floating dock.[7]

Royal Sovereign Class Battleships

| *Royal Sovereign* | *Resolution* | *Revenge* |
| *Royal Oak* | *Ramilles* | |

This 1918 class survived to see service in the Second World War. An account of these ships is given in *Records of Warship Construction 1914–1918*; below is a brief summary of their subsequent history.

In October 1917 it was decided to fit bulges to the remaining four ships of the class (*Ramilles* having been already fitted) partly to improve the trim and to obtain more initial stability, and partly to give additional protection against underwater explosions. The bulge consisted of a single watertight chamber without any tube compartments or water chambers as in most of the other bulged vessels, completed at the upper portion by filling in with a composition of cement and wood. The additional buoyancy thus obtained decreased the draught in the deep load condition by about 16in.

The following table shows the final conditions which were deduced from an inclining experiment on *Revenge* after bulging:

Condition	Draught	Displacement	GM*	Range
	(ft-in)	(tons)	(feet)	(degrees)
Extreme deep (3400 tons of OF 95%)	32–3	32,820	5.16	68.3
Deep (85% oil fuel)	31–10	32,460	5.10	67.2
Legend (900 tons oil fuel)	29–3½	29,590	5.24	62.3
Light	28–4	28,410	5.25	59.3

*Metacentric height

Protection

In 1929 water protection compartments abreast the magazines were introduced as further protection against torpedo attack. In 1935 addition 4in NC armour was fitted in *Royal Oak* on the main deck over magazine and 2½in HT plating over the engine rooms. In 1941 the question of increasing deck protection, considered in 1939, was again raised and it was decided to fit additional 80lb NC armour on the main deck over the magazines, which was completed in *Royal Sovereign* and *Ramilles* and partially in *Resolution*.

Armament

Various modifications were made to keep the close range armament up to date. In 1942 the two forward 6in guns were removed from the upper deck to provide extra accommodation. Flying-off platforms, and later catapults, were fitted to some ships of the class, but were subsequently removed. In 1930, the after submerged torpedo tubes were removed, and later, the forward ones also. Approval was given to fit four above-water fixed tubes in 1937, but these were fitted in *Royal Oak* only. In 1944, the *Royal Sovereign* was transferred on loan to the USSR. No large scale reconstruction was carried out on any ships of the class, although *Royal Oak* was partially reconstructed when taken in hand for a large refit in 1936.[8]

Battlecruisers *Renown, Repulse* and *Hood*

Repulse commenced a large refit in December 1918 which was completed in January 1921. During this period bulges were fitted, also additional armour and protection, and eight above-water torpedo tubes were fitted on the upper deck.

Another large refit of *Repulse* was commenced in April 1933 and completed about May 1936. The principal items of work carried out were:

(1) Bulges - buoyancy tubes were removed from upper and lower bulges. The upper bulges were strengthened and forward and after ends reconstructed.
(2) Additional deck protection, NC armour, fitted on main and lower decks.
(3) Two 4in between-deck twin HA mountings were fitted.
(4) Catapult and aircraft crane were installed.
(5) Bridge was modified.
(6) Aircraft hangars were fitted.

Renown was not taken in hand for large refit until May 1923. This refit was completed in August

[7] The special problem in a floating dock is that the dock, as well as the ship, is flexible and to a different extent. Keeping everything straight was difficult.

[8] A number of designs were prepared for the *Royal Sovereigns* as bombardment ships, primarily for 'Operation Catherine'. Typically, these involved removing two 15in turrets, fitting enormous bulges which would increase the beam to 140ft whilst reducing draught by 9ft, fitting 4–5in additional deck armour and many more AA weapons. No trace of these plans have been found: see D K Brown, 'Operation Catherine', *Warship* 40 (October 1986).

1926, and the work carried out was generally similar to that for *Repulse*.

In 1936 *Renown* was again taken in hand, for a large refit and reconstruction, when modernisation was carried out similar to that described for *Queen Elizabeth* and *Valiant*. It is interesting to note that after this reconstruction, when eight boilers were substituted for the original forty-two, she remained during the whole of the war the fastest capital ship in the fleet, and was capable of developing 130,000shp with ease.

Hood was completed in April 1920. Despite efforts made to compensate for the additional protection added since approval of the design, by fitting twelve instead of sixteen 5.5in guns and the omission of protective plating to the uptakes, the ship completed with a legend displacement of 42,670 tons and a deep displacement of 46,680 tons, draught 32ft 0in. The metacentric height allowed for in the design was about 4.15ft in the legend and 4.9ft in the deep condition with a range of stability of 69° and 76° respectively. On completion an inclining experiment gave metacentric heights of 3.25ft and 4.2ft respectively.

The increase in draught gave rise to some anxiety regarding future dockings and the loss of freeboard resulted in the ship being always regarded as 'wet'.

The freeboards as designed and completed in legend condition were:

	As Designed (ft-in)	As Completed (ft-in)
To forecastle deck at side forward	29 - 0	29 - 0
To forecastle deck at side amidships	21 - 11	21 - 0
To upper deck at side aft	18 - 9	17 - 0

In the programme for reconstruction of capital ships considered in 1938 and 1939, the following was proposed for the *Hood*, the estimated cost being £4½m and the time required three years:

(a) New machinery.
(b) Increased horizontal and vertical protection.
(c) Improved underwater protection.
(d) Improved HA armament.
(e) Up-to-date aircraft arrangements.

War intervened, however, and the work was not undertaken.

During a refit in 1940 all the 5.5in armament was removed. Three additional 4in twin HA mountings were fitted.

The *Hood* was sunk on 24 May 1941 by shellfire during the *Bismarck* action.

Battleships of the *Nelson* Class

1922 Programme
Nelson
Rodney

At the conclusion of the 1914-18 War investigations were made into capital ship designs to incorporate the lessons of the war. A battlecruiser design of 48,000 tons displacement was approved by the Board in 1921, but orders were cancelled in 1922 as the Washington Treaty limited the standard displacement of capital ships to 35,000 tons.

Investigations into a battleship design with a standard displacement of 35,000 tons were then progressed, and in December 1922 the keels of two ships - *Nelson* and *Rodney* - were laid down. The main particulars of the ships are given in

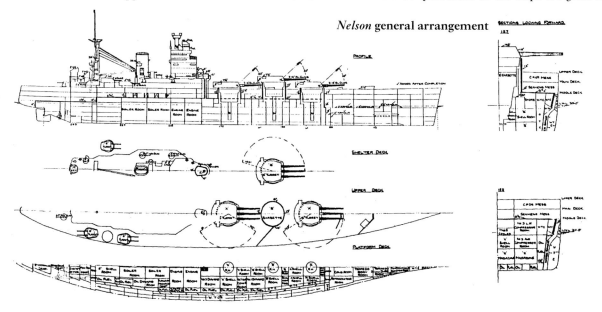

Nelson general arrangement

Appendix I. For the manner in which the Treaty limitations influenced the various features of the design see *King George V* class.

Armament

The main armament consisted of three triple 16in turrets (maximum elevation 40°) and the secondary armament of six twin 6in turrets (maximum elevation 60°).

The concentration of the three triple 16in gun mountings in the middle portion of the length was adopted as a means of getting the heaviest protection over the main magazine and shell rooms with the minimum length of horizontal and vertical armour. An amidships position was also best from the point of view of underwater protection.

The maximum after bearing was 165° Red and Green from the centre mounting 'B' which was superimposed over the other two 'A' and 'X'. The restriction of after fire was much discussed during the design stage, but was accepted as the grouping of the main armament resulted in a saving of weight in armour protection.

The three twin 6in gun mountings each side were arranged well aft so that interference between 16in and 6in armament groups was a minimum. As in the 16in mountings the centre mounting was superimposed over the other two.

The grouping of the main armament was a distinctive feature in the design, and a marked departure from the 15in gun ships preceding *Nelson*.

The statement below shows a comparison between the main armament of *Nelson* and a 15in gun ship:

	Nelson	*Queen Elizabeth* Class
Number of guns carried	9-16in	8-15in
Total weight of broadside	18,432lb	15,360lb
Revolving weight of mounting	1500 tons (triple)	840 tons (twin)

Provision for the large increase in revolving weight and barbette diameter required very considerable investigation and extensive calculations. The ring bulkheads and supports in particular received very careful and detailed investigation to meet the effect of recoil of three 16in guns firing simultaneously.

Armour Protection

In arranging the armour protection the lessons learnt from the firing trials carried out on HMS *Superb* were incorporated.[9] The armoured citadel was 384ft in length. The side armour was 14in thick abreast the main armament magazines, 13in abreast the machinery spaces and secondary armament magazines, and was sloped at 75°.

Each butt of armour was keyed and individual plates were as large as possible, with heavy bars fitted behind the butts. Chock castings housing the lower edge of armour deflected shells or shell fragments from the belt. The arrangement of armour inside the outer hull reduced the armoured waterplane, but sufficient reserve of buoyancy was available to ensure that the ship was safe in the ordinary fighting condition, with spaces between side armour and bulge plating, and also the unprotected ends, opened up.

Deck protection against bombs and shellfire was arranged on the middle deck, 6¾in over the main magazines and 4½in over machinery; also on the lower deck aft 4¾in maximum.

The middle deck armour was given a slight slope of about 2° at the sides, and was recessed into the side armour. The slope of 2° had the effect of slightly reducing the height of the side armour belt. The deck plates were rabbeted into each other. Principal supports were girders under the butts and edges, with strong top plates to supporting bulkheads.

As a further protection against shell fragments penetrating to the main 16in magazines, these were arranged below the 16in shell rooms.

9 See Burt, note 2.

Rodney seen in May 1944. She and her sister incorporated most lessons of World War I and early postwar tests whilst fully complying with the Washington Treaty. Weight saving was so effective that she completed well under the design displacement.

[10] D K Brown, 'Attack and Defence, Part 3', *Warship* 24 (October 1982). Includes a drawing of the Chatham Float.

[11] This seems to have been unsuccessful; the two ships always suffered from smoke on the bridge.

[12] It seems that this work was not carried out in *Rodney*.

[13] Great attention was paid to weight saving during the building of these two ships as a result of which they completed at a much lower displacement, around 33,300–33,700 tons.

Underwater Protection

Improved defence against underwater attack and near-miss bombs and mines was developed. The lessons of Chatham Float experiments were embodied to provide protection against the explosion of a 750lb charge.[10]

A sloping protection bulkhead 1½in thick was fitted the full length of the citadel and arranged behind the armour belt as far from the outer hull as practicable. The bulkhead was of two thicknesses of special quality plating 30lb each worked vertically and faced on the outboard side with two thicknesses of fir, 3in inner and 2in outer with ½in felt between. Sea experience with these bulkheads showed that leakages from and into the oil spaces inboard of the water spaces were very difficult to stop.

Outside the thick bulkhead was a water space with an air space outboard of this space extending to the outer hull. A bulge as fitted in earlier ships was not practicable without increasing the extreme beam of the ship and the internal form of protection was therefore adopted. Venting arrangements were provided from the water space at top and bottom by bolted plates (on the outer hull). Later experiments showed that these vents would not be effective during the time maximum pressure was exerted, and they were sealed off.

The framing of the air space was kept as light as possible consistent with strength considerations. A 5ft deep double bottom was adopted.

Machinery

Two shafts were driven by geared turbines arranged in four engine rooms, with eight water-tube boilers (working pressure 250lb per sq in) arranged in four boiler rooms.

The machinery was designed for 45,000shp to give a speed of 23kts at the legend displacement of 35,000 tons.

A departure from previous practice was made by arranging the engines forward of the boilers in order to obtain the following advantages:

(i) The engine rooms, which required more width than the boiler rooms, were in a less fine section of the ship and were consequently better protected.

(ii) The large openings for uptakes and boiler room fans were further from the main magazines.

(iii) The great space required for the main armament and controls could be provided without funnel smoke trouble.[11]

The steering gear in *Nelson* and *Rodney* marked the first departure from the more usual type of screw gear with a long lead of shafting from the [steering] engine, which was generally fitted in the engine room, to a self-contained unit situated in the steering compartment itself and of electro-hydraulic type. The gear was installed by Messrs Brown Bros.

Manoeuvring capabilities of these vessels were affected at speeds below 7 or 8kts by the high superstructure aft. The rudder area of 360sq ft was relatively smaller than in any previous battleship, but the large propellers (16ft 6in diameter) helped to compensate for this when manoeuvring.

Period of building

This is shown in the table below. Building was delayed by shipyard strikes.

	Nelson	*Rodney*
Where built	Armstrong Whitworth & Co.	Cammell Laird & Co.
Engines	Wallsend Slipway	Cammell Laird & Co.
Laid down	Dec 1922	Dec 1922
Launched	Sept 1925	Dec 1925
Completed	Oct 1927	Dec 1927

Additions after completion

In 1937 additional protection against long range shell attack was provided by fitting NC armour to the lower deck forward and portion of the platform deck were so fitted in 1941.[12]

Close range armament developments resulted in many changes and in 1945 the close range armament of *Nelson* was as follows:

6 in number Mk VI (8-barrel) pom-poms
4 in number quadruple Bofors
61 in number single-barrel Oerlikons

A larger structure was built up from the director control tower platform to take modern directors and two calculating stations were arranged below protection.

No large schemes of reconstruction were undertaken for these ships, however.

APPENDIX I

Dimensions and Weights etc of Nelson and Rodney as designed

Dimensions, etc.

Length between perpendiculars	660ft 0in
Length, overall	710ft 0in
Breadth, extreme	106ft 0in
Legend draught, forward	30ft 0in
Legend draught, aft	30ft 0in
Displacement in tons	35,000[13]
Freeboard to top of deck at side, forward	29ft 0in
Freeboard to top of deck at side, amidships	25ft 6in
Freeboard to top of deck at side, aft	27ft 0in

Deep load draught, mean	35ft 0in
Shaft horsepower	45,000
Speed (kts)	23
Oil fuel capacity (tons)	4000
Complement of officers and men as squadron flagships	1560

Armament	Number	Rounds per gun
16in (45 calibre) guns in 3 turrets	9	80
6in (50 calibre) guns in 6 turrets	12	100
4.7in (43 calibre) HA guns	6	100
2pdr pom-poms	8	1000
Torpedo tubes 24½in submerged	2	10 torpedoes

Stability

Metacentric height in legend condition	7ft
Range of stability in legend condition	65°
Metacentric height in deep condition	10.2ft
Range of stability in deep condition	77½°

Weights	Tons
General equipment	1050
Armament	6900
Machinery (including engineers stores but not reserve feed water)	1924
Other machinery weights	10,250
Armour and protective plating, hull	14,250
Total displacement	35,000

King George V Class Battleships

General

King George V class were designed to comply with Treaty limitations of 35,000 tons standard displacement and 14in calibre of largest gun. The 14in gun limit (London Naval Treaty 1936) was subject to Italy and Japan also agreeing to the 14in gun not later than 1 April 1937. Great Britain, however, decided to lay down two capital ships at the earliest date permitted by the Treaty, namely 1 January 1937, and this necessitated the completion of the design about the middle of 1936. Great Britain thus became committed to the 14in gun although, in the event, Japan refused to signify acceptance of this limitation. Consideration was given to designing the ships to permit of a changeover from 14in quadruple to 16in triple mountings if Japan failed to agree to the 14in gun, but this would have involved an appreciable increase in citadel length and armour weight and considerable delay in the design and production of new 16in turrets. It was therefore decided to design for 14in guns only.

Many sketch designs were prepared before approval was given to proceed with the detailed design. The early sketch designs included 12–14in guns in three quadruple mountings and 20–4.5in HA/LA guns in 10 twin BD mountings. The middle deck was the armour deck. In later sketch designs the secondary armament became 16–5.25in HA/LA guns in eight twin turrets, and the armour deck was raised to main deck level, increasing the depth of the side armour belt by about 8ft.[14] To meet this increase in weight, whilst adhering to the Treaty limit of 35,000 tons standard displacement, it was found necessary to reduce the main armament to 10–14in guns by making 'B' turret a twin; this involved some delay in the design and production of a 14in twin turret. A further reduction in weight was necessary and it was decided to economise in armour weight by reducing deck heights and freeboard. The sheer of the upper deck forward was limited to 5ft to enable 'A' turret to fire right forward at a small angle of elevation without raising 'B' turret and the bridge with considerable increase in weight of barbette armour and structure. The reduction in freeboard and limitation of sheer forward contributed greatly to the ships being 'wet' in a seaway and adversely affected habitability.

Every effort was made during design and building to economise in weight but, when war was declared, the Treaty restrictions lapsed and additions were to protection, HA armament, radar, etc. In consequence, the ships exceeded 35,000 tons standard displacement on completion, with the result that the freeboard was further reduced.

Another important restriction imposed on the *King George V* design was the requirement that the ships should be capable of docking at Portsmouth and Rosyth. This limited the beam and made more difficult the problem of providing good underwater protection.

Principal Dimensions

On 28 May 1936, approval was given to the sketch design known as '14 P', which had the following principal dimensions and particulars:

Length bp	700ft 0in
Length overall	745ft 0in
Breadth extreme	103ft 0in
Draught to SWL	28 ft 0in
Standard displacement	35,000 tons
Freeboard to top of deck at side amidships	22ft 9in
Depth of ship from USK to upper deck beam at middle	56ft 9in fore / 51ft 9in amidships / 52ft 9in aft

[14] This class had the most extensive as well as the thickest armour of the '35,000-ton' battleships.

[15] It is usual to start with the form of an existing ship of roughly the same speed/length and length/(cube rt displaced volume) ratio. LK was the designation of the model in a sequence which began with AA in 1872.

Power of engines

(shp)   100,000 (110,000 overloaded)

Speed   28½kts (29¼kts) standard

                         27½kts (28¼kts) deep

Oil fuel   4000 tons

Endurance   4000 mils at 10kts (trial condition)

Armament:

10-14in guns in two quadruple and one twin
mounting

16-5.25in HA/LA guns in twin mountings

4-2pdr Mk VI pom-poms

4-D.II H catapult

4 Aircraft

Seven models were tried at Haslar before adopting the final form (LK), the curve of areas of which closely followed the curve of areas of HMS *Tiger*.[15] The effect of a bulbous bow and a square cut stern were investigated but not adopted.

The largest section was not shaped to follow the batter of dock entrances as in *Nelson* class. The docks capable of taking *King George V* class were:

Admiralty Graving Docks: Devonport, No 10 Dock

Portsmouth, C & D Docks

Rosyth, Nos 1, 2 and 3
Docks and Lock

Gibraltar, No 1 Dock

English Private Docks: Liverpool, Gladstone Dock

Southampton, King
George V Dock

Empire Docks: Africa { Durban, Prince Edward
Dock

Capetown, Sturrock Dock

Canada { Esquimalt, British
Columbia

Quebec, Champlain Dock,
St Johns (NB)

Australia   Sydney, Captain Cook Dock

Passage through the Suez and Panama Canals could be made but, as completed to carry aircraft, the catapult sheaves and supporting brackets were made portable to give clearance in passing through the Panama Canal.

On 29 July 1936 two ships, *King George V* and *Prince of Wales*, were ordered in the 1936 programme.

The Board drawings were completed, approved and delivered to the shipbuilders on 30 September 1936.

On 28 April 1937 three more ships, *Anson*, *Jellicoe* and *Beatty*, were ordered in the 1937 programme. Subsequently the names of these three ships were changed to *Duke of York*, *Anson* and *Howe*, respectively.

Speed, Power and Endurance

It was estimated from experimental data than an shp of 100,000 was required on four shafts in order to obtain the required speed of 28kts in the standard condition. The machinery was designed to develop 100,000shp and was capable of being forced to 110,000shp. It was estimated that speeds of 27½kts and 28¼kts respectively could be attained with these powers with the ship in the deep condition.

Manganese bronze three-bladed propellers of 14ft 6in diameter, 15ft 0in pitch and 112sq ft developed area capable of transmitting 25,000shp

Duke of York *on completion in March 1942. She is seen very nearly in design configuration except for the radar aerials at the mastheads.*

Building Particulars and Costs

Ship	Where Built	Engine Makers	Ordered	Laid Down	Launched	Commis-sioned	Completed	Cost[16]
King George V	Vickers	Vickers	29 Jul 1936	1 Jan 1937	21 Feb 1939	30 Sep 1940	11 Dec 1940	£7,398,408
Prince of Wales	Cammell Laird	Cammell Laird	29 Jul 1936	1 Jan 1937	3 May 1939	19 Jan 1941	31 Mar 1941	£7,413,045
Duke of York	John Brown	John Brown	28 Apr 1937	5 May 1937	28 Feb 1940	20 Aug 1941	4 Nov 1941	£7,374,015
Anson	Swan Hunter	Wallsend Slipway	28 Apr 1937	22 Jul 1937	24 Feb 1940	14 Apr 1942	22 Jun 1942	£7,439,023
Howe	Fairfield	Fairfield	28 Apr 1937	1 Jun 1937	9 Apr 1940	2 Jun 1942	29 Aug 1941	£7,415,003

at 230rpm were fitted. Variations in pitch and area were introduced in *Duke of York* and *Howe* in order to obtain data from trials. The disc overlap was 1ft 6in and the tip clearances from the hull were 2ft 11in at the inner and 2ft 4in at the outer propellers.[17]

The resistance of appendages was checked by experiment and adjustments subsequently made to the run of the ends of the bilge keels resulted in a reduction of 40% in bilge keel resistance, equivalent to 1¾% of naked hull resistance.

A balanced rudder of 360sq ft with 27½% of the area before the axis was decided upon, after experiments had been carried out with three designs of rudder. The maximum torques anticipated from model experiments were 125 ton ft at 18° and 29kts ahead and 555 ton ft at 24° and 12¾kts astern. A steering gear capable of developing torque of 600 ton ft was fitted.

The staff requirements for endurance called for:

(I) (a) 200 hours at 16kts with steam available for 18kts.

 (b) 8 hours at full speed
 +16 hours at 18kts with steam available for full speed
 +12 hours at 16kts with steam available for full speed
 assuming ship 6 months out of dock.

(II) An addition of 35% to the above to allow for bad weather, damage, fuel left in tanks etc.

(III) Fuel additional to (I) and (II) to give 14,000 miles at 10kts under trial conditions.

Initially it was estimated that 3700 tons of oil fuel would meet these requirements and, as the total capacity of wing and double bottom tanks was of the order of 4000 tons, it was decided that some of the less suitable tanks would not be fitted with fill-ing arrangements. A total stowage of 3770 tons was provided.

To use the oil in the wing tanks, whilst still maintaining protection, it was necessary to displace it to the DB tanks by admitting sea water. It was found that 150 tons of oil became contaminated; 100 tons of this could be slowly settled out but 50 tons was lost. This water-displacement system was very complex and involved opening WT hatches and doors and required extra stokers to operate the valves.

To meet war demands for increased endurance arrangements were made to carry oil in the DB tanks before the citadel and in the wing tanks between the armour shelf and the lower deck. This involved some reduction in the effectiveness of the wing protection system and the increased weight still further reduced the freeboard.

On completion of the above additions in *Anson*, she carried 4202 tons of oil fuel plus 183 tons of diesel fuel. Her endurance was 16,000 miles at 10kts under trial conditions.[18]

Owing to the outbreak of war it was not possible to carry out a full programme of sea trials. Results of full power trials follow on next page.

The low rpm were accounted for by the fact that paravanes were streamed and these reduced the speed by ½ to ¾kt. The propulsive coefficient made allowance for paravanes.

A limited series of turning trials was carried out in 1943. These gave tactical diameters at 14½kts of 927yds with 35° rudder and 1106yds with 25° rudder.

Main Machinery

The machinery installation, designed to develop 100,000shp normally and 110,000shp forced, was arranged as four sets, each set working as a unit under action conditions. Each unit comprised a boiler room and an engine room in separate water-tight compartments. Cross connections were fit-

[16] An investigation in 1943 showed excessive profits on these and other ships; that on *King George V* being nearly 42%. The reason is still unclear since the estimate was based on *Nelson* of similar size. Under wartime legislation, the excess profit was taken back in tax.

[17] This means that the disc swept out by the forward propeller overlapped that swept by the after propeller by 1ft 6in. The tip clearance is small by postwar standards and one would expect considerable vibration.

[18] Fuel consumption under trials conditions was 2.4 tons/hr at 10kts; in service it was 6.5 tons/hr. The difference was due to heavy consumption by auxiliaries and steam leaks. In 1942 the USS *Washington* operated with the Home Fleet and Admiral Tovey reported that she burnt 39% less fuel at lower speeds and was still superior at higher speed. Since the US ship carried 5000 tons of oil her true endurance was double that of the British ship – a tribute to the advanced machinery introduced in the USN in the late 1930s.

[19] The time between undocking and the trial is important as fouling can grow very quickly in favourable conditions, much increasing the power needed for a given speed.

[20] There was stowage for 100 rounds per gun but only 80 were included in the Treaty 'Standard' displacement.

Ship	Date of[19] (a) undocking (b) trials	Displacement	Shp	Mean rpm	Speed (knots)	Propulsive Coeffnt	Fuel Consumption (lbs/shp/hr)	Duration of Trial (hrs)
King George V	(a) 24 Nov 1940 (b) 10 Dec 1940	41,630	111,700	230	27.8-28.0	.533	.715	2
Prince of Wales	(a) 3 Mar 1941 (b) 31 Mar 1941	42,100	111,600	228	27.6-28.0		.73	4
Duke of York	(a) 17 Oct 1941 (b) 4 Nov 1941	42,550	111,300	232	28-28.6		.823**	3
Anson	(a) 6 Jun 1941 (b) 21 Jun 1941	42,600	113,000	231	27.62*	.525	.769	4
Howe	(a) 9 Aug 1941 (b) 29 Aug 1941	42,530	112,930	231.1	27.5*		.754	4*

* measured on Brimsness measured mile
** it was thought that the fuel was of low calorific value

ted between units for routine and emergency use. Consideration was given to fitting a sound-proof bulkhead between the turbines and the gearing, but this was found to be impracticable.

Two boilers of the three-drum, small-tube type with a common stoking space were fitted in each of the four boiler rooms. The working pressure was 400lb per square inch and temperature 250°F superheat, and the boilers worked under forced draught with closed boiler rooms. In the development of the design, the uptakes were reduced in size and the boiler room air pressure increased in order to improve the protection by reducing the size of the holes in the armour deck.

Two main turbines, arranged in series and driving the shaft through double helical gears, were fitted in each engine room. An astern turbine was incorporated in the exhaust casing of the LP turbine and a cruising turbine was coupled direct to the HP turbine. The working pressure was 350lb per square inch and temperature 250°F superheat. Each set produced a quarter of the total horsepower.

After completion, as a result of experience, flexible bulkhead glands and locking gear were fitted to the shafts, steam driven fans fitted in the engine rooms and the lagging to the machinery improved. Anti-shock fittings were added to machinery securing arrangements.

Major Auxiliary Machinery

A harbour machinery room and six action machinery rooms accommodated the following auxiliary machinery:

(a) *Generators.* Six turbo and two diesel generators, each of 300kW output at 200 volts DC, supplied all the electrical power requirements for the ship. (After completion the output from the turbo generators was raised to 330kW.)

(b) *Hydraulic pumps.* Two Allens variable delivery swashplate pumps and two Weirs rotary type pumps were fitted. They were turbo driven and could deliver 3000cu ft/min at 1100lb per square inch for operation of the main armament. The fluid used was a mixture of water and Argolene.

(c) *Distillers.* Two sets of distilling machinery capable of producing 210 tons of fresh water per 24 hours were fitted; 80 to 115 tons of the water was required to make up feed water to the boilers

(d) *Air compressors.* Four in number 95hp motor driven HP air compressors, giving 128cu ft/min of free air at 4000lbs per square inch working pressure, supplied air to the armament, diesel starters etc. Two in number 26hp motor driven general service air compressors giving 75cu ft/min at 120lb per square inch supplied on air main for operating pneumatic tools, etc.

Armament

The armament, as designed, was:

10-14in guns arranged in two quadruple and one twin turret with 80 rounds per gun.[20]
16-5.25in guns arranged in eight twin HA/LA mountings with 200 rounds per gun.
32-2pdr pom-poms in four 8-barrelled mountings with 500 rounds per gun.
16-0.5in machine guns in four 4-barrelled mountings.

In addition, the ship was equipped with a D II H catapult and four aircraft; 25-250lb bombs, 30-100lb bombs and 40 or 80-40 or 20lb bombs were carried for use by the aircraft; 24 depth charges Type D or Mk VII were carried for use with the 45ft fast motor picket boats.

Arrangements were made for four Mk VII or

By 15 July 1942 Duke of York *had already received a little more radar.*

MK VII* paravanes to be carried. Torpedo armament was considered but not eventually fitted.

The 14in guns, which could elevate to 40°, were arranged in quadruple turrets forward and aft and a twin turret superposed behind the forward quadruple. The twin mounting was arranged forward to give the maximum saving in weight of barbette armour and to allow a better distribution of secondary armament. The total weight saved by adopting a twin instead of a quadruple 14in turret was 770 tons.

The grouping of the main armament forward as in *Nelson*, which resulted in that ship in an economy in protection weight, was considered but not adopted as difficulty would have been experienced in accommodating the main machinery.

Double circular bulkheads of 22½lb D quality plating were built in the ships to support the lower roller paths of the 14in quadruple turrets. These bulkheads were built upon a box structure fitted above the lower deck. The space between the two bulkheads was 1ft 11⅛in and the diameter of the roller path 35ft 6in. The revolving weight of a 14in quadruple turret was 1500 tons.

A single circular bulkhead of 40lb D quality supported the lower roller path of the 14in twin turret, whose roller path diameter was 26ft 0in. The ring bulkhead was supported on a flat fitted above the Middle Deck with arched girders fitted between the flat and the lower deck. The revolving weight of the twin turret was 825 tons.

For 14in armament control a Main Armament Director Control Tower was fitted forward and an armoured (120lb) Main Armament Director Control Tower fitted aft. 'B' Turret was fitted with a long base duplex range-finder whilst 'A' and 'Y' turrets had long base single range-finders. The DCTs in all ships of the class were originally to be fitted with 15ft base range-finders, but it was subsequently decided to fit 22ft base range-finders in the forward DCTs in *Duke of York*, *Anson* and *Howe*.

The 14in guns could be fired by either of the two main armament directors, by 'B' Turret or by local control.

The 5.25in HA/LA guns which could elevate to 70° were arranged at the four corners of the citadel in groups of four, each group consisting of a twin mounting on the upper deck level with another superimposed above it nearer amidships. This disposition was adopted in preference to four mountings each side grouped together as it gave better arcs of fire, freedom from blast, more separation for the magazines and shell rooms, and a better arrangement of ammunition supply.

Four secondary armament directors were fitted, two forward and two aft. The guns could be fired from either 5.25in director on their own side, from the main armament control or by local control.

The close range armament as designed consisted of four 8-barrelled 2pdr 'M' pom-poms Mk VI and four quadruple machine guns. One pom-pom was fitted on each of 'B' and 'Y' turrets and one port and starboard on the hangar roof. The machine guns were fitted on the hangar roof and on the boat deck aft. In 1939 the pom-pom armament was increased by two more on the hangar roof and the machine guns were removed.

In 1940 it was decided to fit rocket firing mountings to combat air attack. Three were fitted, one on 'B' and two on 'Y' turret, in place of the pom-poms. They were later removed and the pom-poms re-installed.

In 1942 two further pom-poms were approved to be fitted when aircraft were removed. They were added during refits in 1944 and 1945, bringing the total to eight M Mk VI pom-poms.

King George V general
arrangement as designed

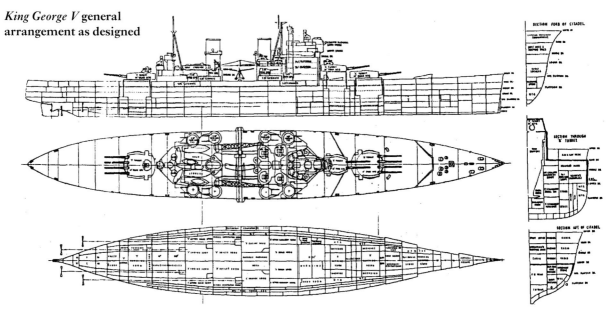

During the war six Mk VII* 4-barrelled pompoms were added to the *Duke of York* and *Howe* and four to *Anson*.

Also during the war, further changes to the close range armament were made and finally the ships were fitted as follows: two Bofors quadruple mountings to all ships of the class, also *King George V* had 4 twin Mk VI and twenty-four single Oerlikons, and two Mk III and two Mk VII single Bofors, *Anson* had eight twin Mk VI and fifteen single Oerlikons, *Duke of York* had eight twin Mk VI and thirty-nine single Oerlikons and *Howe* had four twin Mk VI Oerlikons and fourteen single Bofors. Most of these were removed at the end of hostilities.

In October 1938 the four aircraft were reduced to two and in December 1942 the remaining aircraft and the catapult were removed. The space made available was used for the additional close range armament. During the refits in 1944 and 1945 the hangars were adapted for accommodation purposes and a deckhouse was built in the flying-off space to provide further space for accommodation and amenities.

Armour and Protection

At a late stage in the design it was decided to increase the deck and side protection and to bring the underwater protection up to that required to withstand attack by a 1000lb torpedo. The reduction of the 14in armament from twelve to ten guns permitted the increased protection to be worked.

The citadel length was 414ft 0in and covered the magazines and machinery spaces. Abreast the magazines the side armour was 15in C from 14ft 9in above the 28ft 0in WL to that WL and tapered to 5½in at 8ft 6in below the 28ft 0in WL. Abreast

the machinery spaces, the side armour was 14in C tapering to 4½in at the same levels. The main deck over the magazines was of 6in NC armour, whilst over the machinery it was 5in NC. The armour of bulkheads at the ends of the citadel extended from the lower deck to the main deck and tapered from 12in C at the outboard ends to 10in at the main deck. 1½in protection was fitted from inner bottom to lower deck.

The armour extended for 40ft before and 36ft abaft the citadel. The side armour extended from the 28ft 0in WL to 8ft 6in below it, and tapered both longitudinally and vertically from 13in C near the citadel to 11in at the end of the top and from 5½in to 5in at the bottom of the belt. The lower deck forward of the citadel was 5in NC tapering to 2½in and aft of the citadel it was 5in NC tapering to 4½in. The deck aft covered the steering gear compartment and the bulkhead at the aft end, boxing in the steering gear, was of 4in NC extending from OB to the lower deck. There was no armour bulkhead at the fore end of the ship where the armour deck ended. Armour was omitted over the cable lockers.

1½in D plating was arranged around and above the magazines as splinter protection.

The ship's side armour was arranged in three tiers with butts keyed and edges tongued and grooved. A plastic composition 1in thick was worked behind it. The deck armour was arranged with plates as large as possible, butts smooth, and edges tongued and grooved. Portable plates had rabbetted edges. The armour was shaped to the round of beam.

The 14in barbette armour stood in chocks on the main deck and extended to the turret floor. It tapered from 13in C at the outboard sides to 11in at the middle line for 'A' and 'B' barbettes and from 13in C to 12in correspondingly for 'Y' turret. The front sill plate on the 14in quadruple turrets was 5in NC. This was necessary because the front of the gunhouse did not cover the barbette ring. The circular bulkheads supporting the barbette armour were 80lb NC.

The 14in turrets themselves had fronts of 13in C armour, front side plates of 9in C, rear side plates and rear plates of 7in NC and roofs of 6in NC. The protection under the tail of each turret was 3in NC.

The 5.25in turrets had roofs and sides of 1in D quality plating. The casemates had roofs of 1in D platings and sides of 1½in D plating generally. The lower casemates had 2in D plating at the ship's side. A 1in D screen plate was fitted to the roller path of each mounting.

The side underwater protection was based on the results of full scale experiments and consisted of a longitudinal protective bulkhead with three separate watertight and oiltight compartments outboard of it. The protective bulkhead within the citadel was formed of two thicknesses of plating, each 30lb D1 amidships increasing to 35lb D1 at the ends. The inner extended from the OB to the middle deck and was continued 28ft forward of the citadel between OB and the platform deck and 1ft 6in aft of the citadel between OB and the middle deck. The outer thickness extended from the OB to the lower deck. The three compartments outboard of the bulkhead extended from OB to lower deck. The inner compartment, 3ft 6in wide amidships, was built as a number of WT compartments (air spaces), the middle, also 3ft 6in wide amidships, was built as a number of oil fuel compartments, and the outer, 6ft 0in wide amidships, was again built as a number of WT compartments (air spaces). This form of protection, known as 'sandwich' protection, was expected to be effective against the explosion of 1000lb TNT in contact at half draught.[21]

21 See note 10. Also note in *Warship 1994* by Brown casting some doubt on the result of this trial.

King George V class midship section as designed

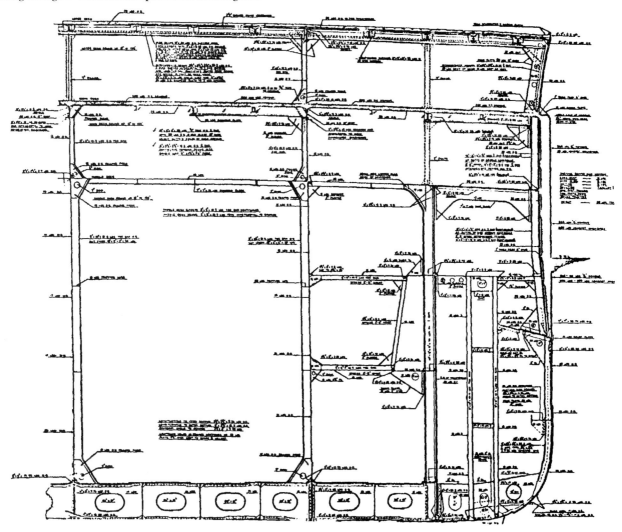

22 The light protection to RN conning towers is in contrast with the thick protection given in USN and other ships. World War I experience convinced the RN that conning towers were rarely used in action and that the true protection to the 'command' was the secondary control aft.

23 It was expected that, as in Nelson, weight savings during building would bring this down to 35,000 tons. Once the war broke out, no such attempt was made.

A conning tower was incorporated in the bridge structure and as designed the protection was 3in NC on the sides and front, 2in NC on the rear and roof and 1in NC on the floor. In 1938 this was increased to 4in NC on the sides and 3in NC on the rear. In previous battleships the conning tower was fitted as a separate structure forward of the bridge.[22] An alternative conning position was arranged on the after funnel protected by 30lb D1 HT at the floor and forward screen and by 25lb D1 HT at the after screen.

2in NC armour was originally to be fitted to the sloping sides of the funnel uptakes between the main and upper decks, but this was later reduced to 1in D quality plating. At the forward funnel the common plate to uptake and downtake was of 1½in D protection on the upper deck inside uptake protection bulkheads. Cast steel splinter protection gratings were fitted at uptake and downtake openings in the upper deck and drilled armour plate gratings to openings at the main deck.

As protection against splinters the after 14in director control tower was built of 3in NC armour and the roller path structure was protected by a 2in NC circular bulkhead 12in in diameter. The cable trunks and junction box spaces were protected by 1½ in NC armour.

The forward director control tower was of ½in D1 HT and the circular support of ¾ in D plating. Consideration was given in 1940 to providing additional protection to this director but it was not approved. Cable trunks to the forward director between main deck and junction box spaces were protected by 1½in NC and 30lb D1 HT plating.

Splinter protection was fitted on the bridge etc to positions continuously manned.

Complement

On completion of the sketch design in May 1936 the approved complement was seventy officers, 1327 men and twelve extra as a private ship, with the addition of thirty-nine officers and ninety-five men, if equipped as a Fleet Flagship. Allowing 7½% of private ship complement (ex officers) as supernumaries, it was estimated that the maximum accommodation required would be for 109 officers and 1536 men. The building drawings allowed for this.

In December 1936, instructions were received to fit *King George V* as a Fleet Flagship and the remainder of the class as Squadron Flagships. The additions to Private ship complement for a Squadron Flagship were given as sixteen officers and forty-six men for a vice admiral and eight officers and twenty-five men for a rear admiral. Revised accommodation drawings were prepared.

On completion the accommodation available in a Fleet Flagship was for 113 officers and 1582 men. The complement of *King George V* was actually 101 officers and 1472 men. The accommodation available in a Squadron Flagship was for 104 officers and 1623 men. *Prince of Wales'* complement was 85 officers and 1436 men.

In 1944 the aircraft and catapults were removed and some of the space was allocated to accommodation. The revised complements approved after this modification were 101 officers, 1684 men as a Fleet Flagship and 81 officers and 1639 men as a Squadron Flagship.

The accommodation available was estimated from drawings to be 116 officers and 1629 men (could be increased to 1700 men) as a Fleet Flagship and 88 officers and 1765 men as a Squadron Flagship.

Mess space was estimated at 20sq ft per man for senior ratings in enclosed messes and 18sq ft per man for junior ratings in broadside messes.

Weights

The following two tables show the comparison of group weights as calculated during design stages and as completed in 1940.

Standard Condition

Item	Design Weight (tons)	Design Weight + additions (tons)	Actual Weight (tons)
Hull	13,500	13,590	13,830
Equipment	1,150	1,163	1,149
Machinery	2,700	2,711	2,768
Armament	6,050	6,074	6,567
Armour and Protection	12,500	12,871	12,413
TOTAL	35,900[23]	36,409	36,727

Deep Condition

Item	Design Weight (tons)	Design Weight + additions (tons)	Actual Weight (tons)
Hull	13,500	13,590	13,830
Equipment	1,465	1,478	1,619
Machinery	2,700	2,711	2,768
Armament	6,765	6,789	7,401
Armour and Protection	12,500	12,871	12,413
Feed Water	300		255
Oil Fuel	3,700		3,720
Lub. Oil	30		30
Petrol	30		30
TOTAL	40,990		42,066

Water Protection	107
Water in Petrol Tank Compartment	54
	42,227

The increase in the hull weight was mainly due to the electric light and power circuits being 200 tons heavy.

The accepted deep displacement as inclined was 42,254 tons. It was estimated that the deep displacement had increased in 1945 to 44,460 tons. *Anson*, the heaviest ship of the class, was 900 tons in excess of this figure.

In November 1947, COs were informed that a draught of 34ft 8in was not to be exceeded. This draught represents a displacement of 45,000 tons.

Stability
In the early design stages, metacentric heights of 6ft in the standard condition and 8ft in the deep condition were decided upon and it was estimated that these could be achieved with a beam of 103ft.

Stability particulars as calculated were:

Condition	GM	Max. Righting Lever	Angle of Max. Righting Lever	Range
Standard displacement 35,900 tons	6.75ft	4.85ft	36.5°	64.5°
Deep displacement 40,990 tons	8.51ft	5.35ft	37°	72.5°

Calculations were made to ensure that the stability was satisfactory in various damaged conditions.

Actual stability data obtained from inclining experiments, etc, is given in the table following.

Longitudinal Strength
In the design stages it was decided that the maximum longitudinal bending stresses, as calculated by the standard method,[24] should not exceed 10ton per square inch tensile in the upper deck or 7ton per square in tensile in the keel. The maximum bending moments were calculated as 785,000ton/ft hogging and 729,000ton/ft sagging. After allowance had been made for modifications, the maximum inertia of section was of the order of 2½ million inches² feet². This gave stresses of the order of 8½ tons per square inch tensile and 7ton per square inch compressive in the upper deck and 6ton per square inch compressive and 6½ ton per square inch tensile in the keel.

Calculations showed that higher stresses might be expected in way of the large holes for the 5.25in mountings in the upper deck. No allowance was made for the heavy structure around the rim of the hole.

Other calculations were made to determine the effect of the armour in contributing to the strength and also the effect of the upper deck being shot away. This latter condition indicated stresses of the order of 15ton per square inch in the main deck.

Important Alterations
Radar (Radio direction finding) and degaussing arrangements (as countermeasures to the magnetic mine) were introduced during building and involved additional weight and complement. The fitting of radar resulted in an increase of sixty men. Additional splinter protection of 60lb D quality plating was fitting to the magazines. The watertight integrity was improved, damage control instituted and arrangements made to minimise the effects of shock.

It was found necessary to fit additional stiffening to the rudder to withstand the strain of the zig-zag course required during the war.

At the close of the war, alterations were directed to improvements in habitability. Apparatus for replenishment of stores, fuel, etc. at sea was later provided.

Criticisms of the Design
To meet the weight limitations imposed by Treaty, it was necessary to design the ships with the minimum depth practicable and, in order to fire 'A' turret at small angles of elevation on forward bearings, the sheer of the deck forward was kept to a minimum. The growth of weight during building still further reduced the freeboard and the class was criticised as being 'wet ships'.

War experience showed that endurance over and above that called for in the staff requirements was necessary and arrangements were made to increase the oil fuel stowage capacity.

The ventilation arrangements were in accordance with the report of the 1938 Ventilation

[24] In this standard method the ship would be considered as supported on a wave of length equal to that of the ship with a height 1/20 of the length. In the hogging condition the crest was amidships, reducing the support to the ends, for sagging there was a crest at each end and a trough amidships. Fuel and stores etc would be adjusted to give the most severe loading. It was known that this procedure exaggerated the loading on bigger ships so they were allowed to work to a somewhat higher stress.

Ship	Date Inclined	Displacement (tons)	GM	Max. Righting Lever	Angle of max. Righting Lever	Range
King George V	29 Sep 1940	36,705 (standard)	6.1ft	4.55ft	35°	62.6°
		42,245 (deep)	8.14ft	4.87ft	35.5°	70.4°
Howe	16 Aug 1942	38,015 (standard)	5.46ft	4.14ft	35°	60.5°
		43,377 (deep)	7.65ft	4.46ft	35.5°	68°
Howe	6 May 1944	39,008 (light)	4.97ft	3.6ft	33°	58.5°
		44,512 (deep)	7.25ft	3.98ft	34°	65.5°

Committee. However, under action conditions, certain compartments, viz Action Machinery Rooms, Breaker Rooms, messes on the middle decks, etc, experienced high temperatures and additional ventilation was fitted to reduce this.

War experience showed that accommodation below the middle deck could not be used freely at sea because of damage control requirements. A communal bathroom and bunk space were fitted on the middle deck.

History of Damage Suffered Due to Enemy Action
Duke of York suffered two hits on the main mast by shell when in action against *Scharnhorst* off Norway on 26 December 1943.

Prince of Wales was more unlucky. On 31 August 1940, whilst fitting out, a bomb fell about 6ft from the ship's side, between it and the wall of the basin. Damage was confined to the bulge compartments.

On 24 May 1941, when in action against *Bismarck* and *Prinz Eugen* in the Denmark Straits, *Prince of Wales* received severe shell hits mainly on the bridge and upper works. She was out of action for six weeks.

Prince of Wales was attacked by aircraft on 10 December 1941 off the Malayan Peninsula. She was struck during the first attack by two or possibly three torpedoes on the port side. In the second attack four torpedoes hit the starboard side, one bomb struck on the catapult deck and there were several near misses. She subsequently sank.

HMS *Vanguard*

Introduction
Instructions to prepare a design of an 8-15in gun battleship using 15in guns and mountings ex

Courageous and *Glorious* to expedite building, were received in February 1939. Three designs, 15/A, 15/B and 15/C, were submitted to the Board in July 1939. Other characteristics included in these designs were:

8-5.25in twin mountings
2 aircraft amidships
Displacement from 38,000 tons to 40,400 tons
Speed from 27½kts to 31kts
Armour: 14 and 15in abreast the citadel on the ship's sides.
6in over magazines and 5in over machinery on main deck, and up to 5in on lower deck before and abaft citadel.

Work on the designs was stopped at the outbreak of war.

In February 1940 instructions were received to proceed and a fourth design 15/D (based on 15/C) was prepared. This included the addition of 2/2½in splinter protection on the ship's side before and abaft the citadel from lower to middle deck and on the 5.25in armament and conning towers; a small armoured conning position aft and four UP mountings (rocket AA weapons). This design was approved on 20 May 1940 and, after a temporary suspension, work on it was re-commenced in October of that year. Assistance in the preparation of building drawings and design calculations was given by the shipbuilders Messrs John Brown, Clydebank.

While this work was being progressed, further additions were made to the design as a result of war experience; these included increases in OF stowage, close range armament and protection, and improvements in WT integrity necessitating additional trunked access to compartments. To reduce the draught the beam was increased from 105ft 6in to 108ft; docking at Portsmouth and

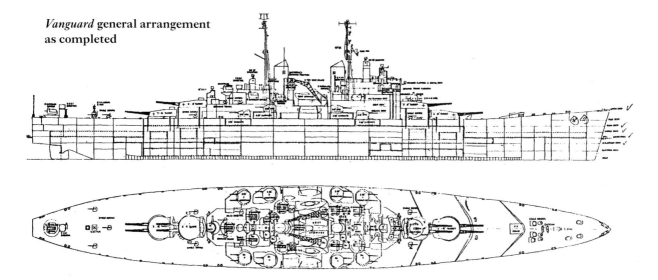

Vanguard general arrangement as completed

Rosyth thereby being sacrificed. The side armour was also reduced from 15in and 14in to 14in and 13in. A fifth design 15/E embodying these modifications was approved on 17 April 1941 and the final order for the ship was placed with the builders on 14 March 1941.

A revised legend and building drawings, omitting the aircraft and with improved close range armament, were approved by the Board in September 1942. This modified design embodied several alterations due to war experience as detailed later in this chapter.

A proposal to convert *Vanguard* to an aircraft carrier was given preliminary consideration, but not approved, on 15 July 1942.

Principal Dimensions
A comparison between the principal dimensions of the original design, the final design (September 1942 legend) and the ship as built is given opposite.

Docking
In the early designs the ship sections conformed to the batter of the dock entrances at Portsmouth and Rosyth. With the increase in beam to 106ft, docking in the United Kingdom was restricted to Devonport, Liverpool (Gladstone Dock) and Southampton (King George V Dock).

Calculations were made of pressure distribution on docking following measurement of the crush of dock blocks in No 10 Dock, Devonport.[25] No restrictions were placed on docking displacement provided trim did not exceed 3ft by the stern, and the ship was docked on blocks the spacing of which did not exceed 30in and which were doubled to 15in spacing where shown on the docking plan; bottom shores were considered unnecessary. Decks capable of accommodating *Vanguard* are shown in the list below:

Admiralty Graving Docks	Devonport, No 10
	Gibraltar, No 1
	Singapore, King George V Dock
English Private Docks	Liverpool, Gladstone Dock
	Southampton, King George V Dock
Empire Docks Africa	Durban, Prince Edward Dock
	Capetown, Sturrock Dock
Australia	Sydney, Capt Cook Dock
Canada	Esquimalt, British Columbia
	Quebec, Champlain Dock
	St John, New Brunswick

Item	Original Design 1941	Re-design (Sept 1942)	As completed (June 1945)
Length bp	760ft 0in	760ft 0in	759ft 11⅜in
Length oa	809ft 0in	813ft 0in	814ft 4⅛in over fittings
Length on wl	800ft 0in	800ft 0in	799ft 11⅛in
Breadth extreme	108ft 0in	108ft 0in	108ft 0in
Standard displacement	41,600 tons	42,300 tons	44,500 tons
Mean draught at standard displacement	29ft 6in	29ft 10in	31ft 0in
Freeboard in standard condition,			
forward	32ft 6in	36ft 8in	35ft 6in
amidships	23ft 0in	22ft 8in	21ft 6in
aft	25ft 0in	24ft 8in	23ft 6in
(Note: freeboards given for no trim)			
Deep displacement	48,000 tons	49,200 tons	51,420 tons
Mean draught at deep displacement	33ft 0in	33ft 10in	35ft 0in
Trim in deep condition	1ft 7in	1ft 6in	2ft 0in

During 1948 a thorough investigation was made of the loading and other conditions to ensure safe passage of *Vanguard* through the Panama Canal.[26] The maximum acceptable draught amidships within the canal locks was 34ft 9in (corresponding to 33ft 9in in sea water and a displacement of 49,180 tons) in December and January when the Miraflores Lake is at its highest level. At other seasons when the Miraflores Lake is at lower levels the draught amidships in the locks must not exceed 34ft 0in (corresponding to 33ft 0in in sea water and a displacement of 47,950 tons). Trim should not exceed 30in by stern.

(Note: density of water in locks is 0.99071)

All overboard discharges, refuse chutes, accommodation ladders and fittings etc had to be removed before transit. All these fittings were therefore portable.

Speed, Power and Endurance
Trials were carried out off Arran in July 1946. The machinery designed to give 120,000shp, developed 136,000shp on trials. In design calculations a propulsive coefficient of 0.505 was assured but trial results gave a coefficient of 0.602 at full speed.

The speed estimated for the final design in 1942 was:

30kts, at standard displacement of 42,300 tons
28¾kts at deep displacement of 49,100 tons

Speed obtained on trials was:

31.57kts at displacement of 45,720 tons
30.38kts at deep displacement of 51,070 tons

[25] During docking there can be a very high load on the dock blocks, particularly near the after cut up, which is most severe in short, heavy ships such as battleships and it is increased if the stern trim is great.

[26] The ship floats deeper if the water is less dense than sea water.

A series of circle trials was reported. At full speed (30.8kts) and maximum rudder angle (35°) the following were obtained:

Tactical diameter	1025 yards (= 3.84 x length of ship)
Advance	1010 yards
Time to turn 360°	4min 55sec
Rate of turn	1.23 deg/sec
Angle of drift	10.6 deg
Maximum angle of wheel	4 deg

During this turn, mean draught was 32ft 1½in, trial 41in by the stern.

The rudder was of the balanced type and 386ft² in area; 30ft of this area being forward of the stock.

On trials the maximum rudder torques recorded were approximately 500 tons ft ahead and 650 tons ft astern. The steering gear was designed to give a torque of 800 tons ft.

Vibration records were obtained by Haslar during the trials. Vibration was generally small, but when manoeuvring at speeds in excess of 180 revolutions per minute severe axial vibration of the inner shafts was experienced. As a temporary measure a restriction was imposed on the power developed by the outer shaft on the outside of the turn at speeds in excess of 180 revolutions per minute, in order to prevent propeller interaction with resultant axial vibration of the inner shaft. To obtain smooth operation at all speeds five-bladed propellers were designed for the inner shafts. As a preliminary result of speed and manoeuvring trials with these new propellers, the Commanding Officer was instructed to use not more than 10 degrees of rudder when turning at speeds in excess of 200rpm except in emergency, and that turning at 156rpm was to be avoided.

Particulars of propellers

Material	Manganese bronze	
Position	Outers	Inners
Number of Blades	3	5
Diameter	14ft 9in	14ft 9in
Pitch	14ft 6in	14ft 1in at .7R
Developed area	123sq ft	134sq ft

Tip clearances were 2.5in inner and 2ft 3in outer, the discs overlapped 2ft 3½in and had a F and A separation of 51ft 6½in. During the 1949 trials the shps were transmitted and the corresponding revolutions per minute were:

Shp	Rpm
32,575	248.3
25,500	230.0

The endurance for all the early designs including 15/H was 14,000 miles at 10kts under trial condi-

tions. In 1941 from consideration of the endurance of foreign capital ships, and the experience of the *Bismarck – Prince of Wales* action, the requirement was modified to 6000 miles at 20kts. The endurance finally achieved is given in the following table:

Speed Kts	Endurance	
	Trial Conditions	*War conditions*
10	14,100	6,720
20	7,100	5,920
28	–	3,360
Max continuous seagoing speed = 29.75kts	3,600	

Note 1. Trial conditions - clean bottom, fair weather, temperate waters.

Note 2. War conditions - figures were based on reports from sea and represented performance of ship under war conditions, six months out of dock in temperate water, allowance being made for keeping steam for full speed at ¼ hour's notice.

Note 3. Max continuous seagoing speed = speed at max horsepower which could be continuously maintained and under trial conditions.

Fuel

The original requirement for endurance was met by stowing 4100 tons of oil fuel in double bottoms and wing tanks. An additional 300 tons could be stowed in an emergency in tanks under 'A' and 'Y' barbettes. The additional fuel stowage made necessary by the demand for increased endurance in 1941 was obtained by widening the wing tanks by 2ft 3in amidships. The total fuel storage in the completed ship was 4850 tons of which 427 tons was diesel oil.

To maintain side underwater protection at all times, oil fuel was displaced by sea water, a 'Coastguard' Separating Plant being fitted for dealing with mixtures of oil and sea water.

Main Machinery

The propelling machinery consisted of a four shaft arrangement of geared turbines designed for 120,000shp; it developed 136,000shp on trials. The machinery was in four units which worked separately under action conditions but which were fitted with cross connections for routine and emergency use. One unit comprised two separate watertight compartments, engine room and boiler room.

Each engine room contained two main turbines arranged in series and driving a shaft through double helical gears at a working pressure of 350psi and temperature 700°F. The authorised output was 30,000shp at approximately 245rpm, but a maximum of 32,500shp at 250rpm was specified at the highest forcing rate. An astern turbine was incorporated in the casing of each low pressure turbine. Cruising turbines were originally to have been provided but were later omitted to save weight.

Each boiler room contained two boilers of the three-drum small-tube type with a common closed stokehold under forced draught. The working pressure was 400psi at a temperature of 250°F superheat.

Modifications were made to the main machinery at various times as follows:-

(a) Additional lagging of machinery to improve habitability of engine and boiler rooms.
(b) Improved quality boiler brickwork.
(c) Exhaust doors from boiler rooms to uptakes for ventilation on return to harbour.
(d) Additional drain cooler.
(e) Separation of domestic steam from heating range.

Major Auxiliary Machinery
Two harbour machinery rooms and ten action machinery rooms accommodated the auxiliary machinery.

In the original design electrical power was produced by 6 turbo and 32 diesel generators supplying direct current at 220 volts to a ring main. As a result of experience in Belfast when an underwater explosion caused a total loss of steam, it was decided to increase the proportion of diesel generators. The final arrangement was four diesel generators of 450kW each, two forward of the machinery spaces and two abreast the after engine rooms, and four turbo generators of 480kW each, two abreast the forward boiler rooms and two in the harbour machinery rooms between the forward engine rooms.

Four motor-driven air compressors, each of 95hp and capable of supplying 128cu ft of free air per minute at 4000psi were fitted to supply HP air to armament and for diesel starting, etc. Two motor-driven air compressors, each of 25hp and capable of supplying 75cu ft of free air per minute at 120psi were fitted to supply LP air.

Hydraulic power for the main armament was produced by four turbo pumps each delivering 95cu ft per minute at a pressure of 1000psi. These pumps were in four separate action machinery rooms.

Distilling machinery was arranged in four separate plants, as follows:

	Rated capacity
No 9 Action Machinery Room	100 tons per 24 hours
No 10 Action Machinery Room	100 tons per 24 hours
Harbour Machinery Room Std	200 tons per 24 hours
Harbour Machinery Room Port	100 tons per 24 hours
Total Rated Capacity	500 tons per 24 hours

This was an 'Aiton Plant' found to be unsatisfactory on service and later replaced by a plant similar to the others, of rated capacity 200 tons per 24 hours.

The fresh water storage capacity for the ship as designed was 390 tons; this was increased in 1947 and 1948, giving a final total capacity of 590 tons.

Armament
The armament for the three initial designs was:
    8-15in guns in four twin turrets
    16-5.25in HA/LA guns in eight twin turrets
    48-2pdr pom-poms in six 8-barrelled mounts
    1 - D.III H catapult
    2 Torpedo, spotting, reconnaissance aircraft
Designs 15/D and 15/E also included 4 UP mountings (rocket AA weapon).

By 1941 war experience had shown the need for increased close range armament and approval was given to omit the aircraft and catapult and add a number of pom-pom and Oerlikon mountings. The close range armament was further modified while the ship was being built, power operated Bofors being substituted for the pom-poms, and the final arrangement was:

8-15in guns in four turrets with 100 rounds per gun plus 9rpg practice.
16-5.25in HA/LA guns in eight twin turrets with 391 rounds per gun plus
    25rpg star shell, 25rpg practice LA and 50rpg practice HA
10 Mark VI 40mm 6-barrelled Bofors
1 (STAAG) 40mm twin Bofors
11 Mark VII 40mm single Bofors
2 15in DCTs
4 Mk 37 Directors for 5.25in Mtgs (US Fire Control System)

These directors were disposed in a 'diamond' arrangement, not the normal 'four corner' disposition.

The change from 48 pom-pom barrels in the early design to 73 Bofors barrels in the completed ship made it necessary to rearrange the magazines and convert additional spaces to magazines, but it was still impossible to stow the standard allowance of 1564 rounds per barrel. The total ammunition stowed, including RU magazines and lockers was 92,636 rounds, *ie* an average of 1269 rounds per barrel.

The four 15in turrets were those originally built for *Courageous* and *Glorious*, in which the 15in magazines were above the shell rooms. In *Vanguard*, as in *Nelson* and all later battleships, it was decided to place the shell room above the magazine in order to gain additional protection for the latter against long-range shellfire. To simplify the conversion of the mountings, the cordite

[27] Adapting these mountings to suit *Vanguard* was a major task. While it is true to say that *Vanguard* never fired her guns in anger, it is not true of her guns, which opened fire on German cruisers in 1917.

handing rooms were placed above the shell handing rooms.[27] Fixed hoists between the magazines and cordite handing rooms were armoured and fitted with flashtight doors at top and bottom. Additional flash protection was obtained by stowing the charges in cases and by transporting them in boxcloth wrappers.

Armour and Protection

The early designs 15/A - 15/D included 15in and 14in armour belts but this was later reduced to 14in and 13in in 15/E to reduce draught.

During the action between *Prince of Wales* and *Bismarck* in 1941 a shell from the latter, diving below water, pierced the former's side below the armour belt and penetrated to the protective bulkhead but did not explode. In order to prevent splinters from such a shell reaching the magazines in *Vanguard*, approval was given on 15 August 1941 to complete the protection of the longitudinal bulkheads of main and secondary armament magazines with 1½in NC armour.

The final arrangement of armour and protective plating was as follows:

*Vanguard on completion after the war. She was designed around four spare 15in turrets ex-*Courageous *and* Glorious *which had last fired in anger on November 1917. It was hoped to get an additional fast battleship into service quickly but she was delayed by more urgent construction.*

Vertical Ship's side abreast magazines 560lb C, 560–180lb C lower belt tapering vertically

Ship's side abreast machinery 520lb C, 520–180lb C tapering vertically

Ship's side before (520–180lb C)
(480–180lb C)
(440–150lb C)
and
Abaft the citadel (100lb NC)   Splinter
(80lb NC)   protection belt

Bulkheads at end of citadel 480lb C at ship's side, 440 and 400lb C at CL 60lb NC below lower deck

Bulkhead at AE of steering rear compt. 160lb NC

Barbettes 520, 480 & 440 lb C Maximum thickness on beam

Turrets front, sides, 520 C front, 360 & 280lb AQ sides and rear. 440lb AQ rear

5.25 casemates and 90lb NC shields

5.25 Hoists 80lb-240lb. Ring at main deck

Splinter bulkhead forward & aft 40lb DW

Funnel uptake protection 40lb DW

Cordite handling room 40lb NC

Magazines 60lb NC

Protection rings to Ring Bulkhead - 80lb NC

Conning Tower 120lb front & 100lb NC sides and rear

Plotting Office and Comm. Tube 80lb NC

DCT Supports and after conning tower 80lb NC

Cable trunks 80lb at main deck, 60, 40lb NC and 20 los. D1 HT at top

Superstructure splinter protection 15lb D1 HY

Protective bulkhead 2 of 30lb D1 or 2 of 35lb D1

Horizontal		
Main deck over magazines	240lb NC	
Main deck over machinery	200lb NC	
Lower deck forward at end of ship	200 to 100lb NC	
Lower deck aft at end of ship	200 to 180lb NC	
Turret roof	240lb NC	
5.25 Casemate and shield	60lb NC	
Magazines	60lb NC	
Conning Tower Roof	40lb NMMPPP 80lb NC	
Plotting Office	40lb D1 HT	
Superstructure splinter protection	20lb D1 HT	

The conning towers, main armament DCTs and important electric cables were protected against heavy splinters. Weight considerations prevented the secondary and close range armament control positions being given more than light protection.

The deck armour in the citadel was arranged on the main deck; forward and aft of the citadel the horizontal armour was on the lower deck. This deck over the magazines was thus considered proof against 15in shell inside 31,000yd and against 1000lb armour piercing bombs from 14,000ft. Over the machinery and towards the end of the ship the standard was rather lower. The belt abreast the magazines was proof against 15in shell outside 15,000yd; abreast the machinery spaces the standard was lower at the ends, below the lower deck, the lower belt of side armour was extended before and abaft the citadel to protect magazines against oblique 15in shell attack. Before and abaft the citadel a shallow 2/2½in belt was fitted, based on the lower deck, and inside it the bulkheads were increased to 1in thickness to prevent loss of waterplane area due to splinter damage from internal or external bursts.

The underwater protection was based on the results of full scale experiments and was considered to be proof against a 1000lb TNT warhead in contact at about half draught, over the greater part of the citadel. The side protection consisted of a 'sandwich' system of compartments, inboard of which was a protective bulkhead of two thicknesses of D1 quality plating 30lbs amidships and

Vanguard **midship section as designed**

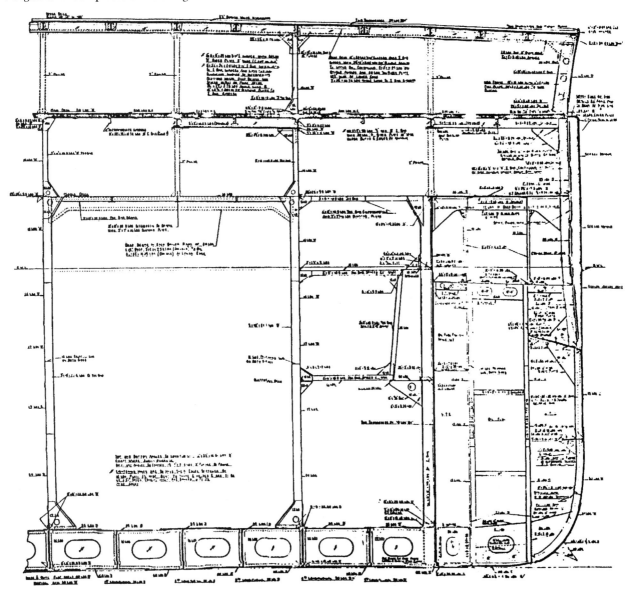

35lb at the ends. The wing compartments outboard of the protective bulkhead were 3ft 6in, 6ft 1in and 5ft 5in wide respectively amidships, the middle compartment being kept full to within 2ft of the crown with oil fuel or sea water. The Action Machinery Rooms, containing six or the eight dynamos and the four hydraulic pumps, were immediately inboard of the protective bulkhead and naturally would have been flooded if the bulkhead in the vicinity had been defeated. The units were, however, well dispersed and contained a margin of power in case some were lost.

Some protection against explosions under the bottom was provided by the 4ft double bottom, and as a result of full scale trials certain structural arrangements were embodied to localise flooding.

Complement
In the initial stages of design the complement was estimated to be seventy-six officers and 1412 men (ex supernumaries) when the ship was a Squadron Flagship. To meet the increase in close range armament and radar, the introduction of an action information organisation, the introduction of centralised messing and the decision to fit the ship as a Fleet Flagship, this estimate was revised and the war complements on completion in August 1946 were:

	Private Ship	Fleet Flagship
Admiral	-	1
Chief of Staff	-	1
Captain	1	1
Wardroom Officers	56	93
Gunroom Officers	13	13
Warrant Officers	17	19
CPSs, POs & Ratings	1793	1869
Canteen Manager	1	1
Assistants	12	12
TOTALS	1893	2010

In August 1947 DNC stated in a memorandum to DTSD that when fully converted to Fleet Flagship the war complement should not exceed 115 officers and 1860 men or overcrowding would result.

Displacement and Weight Grouping
As originally designed in accordance with the Legend approved by the Board in April 1941, the deep displacement was 48,140 tons at a mean draught of 33ft 0in. It was decided at the same time to fix the dimensions of the ship and a limit was thereby imposed on the possibilities of expansion. Later, during construction (September 1942), it was decided to dispense with the aircraft and fit additional close range armament; this resulted in an increased displacement. The deep displacement was estimated to be 49,200 tons at a mean draught of 33ft 10in.

The first inclining experiment in June 1946 showed that in the deep condition the displacement was 51,420 tons at a mean draught of 35ft.

The net increase in deep displacement of 2220 tons between 1942 and 1946 was accounted for as follows:

Increases in:

Oil fuel	100 tons
Armament	420
Equipment	150
Electric light and power	500
Radar	30
Ventilation	200
Pumping, flooding and draining	170
Navigational fittings	20
Arcticisation	90
Action information centre	50
Structure	470
Total increase =	2200 tons

The following is an analysis of weight made from Form D.464:

	Standard Condition	Deep Condition
Hull	18,657	18,657
Equipment	1,247	1,847
Armament	6,718	7,606
Armour and Protection	14,741	14,741
Machinery	3,251	3,251
Oil Fuel		4,925
Reserve Feed Water		358
Lubricating Oil		52
Water Protection		100
Total	44,614	51,537
Accepted condition as inclined June 1946	44,500	51,420

Stability
The following table gives stability data for the intact ship as estimated in 1941 and as deduced after the inclining experiment in 1946:

Condition		Displt tons	KG	GM ft	Maximum Righting Lever ft	Angle of Maximum Stability	Angle of Vanishing Stability
Deep	1941 estimate	48,140	32.30	9.90	5.96	38°	75.5°
	1946 inclining	51,420	33.72	8.2	4.7	35°	68°
Average Action	1941 estimate	46,810	33.13	9.19	5.0	37.3°	72.3°
	1946 inclining	50,145	34.50	7.48	4.44	34.5°	65.3°
Light	1941 estimate	42,220	35.37	7.91	5.49	36°	66.8°
	1946 inclining	45,116	36.22	5.89	4.25	35°	60.7°
Standard	1941 estimate	41,730	35.55	7.84	5.49	36°	66.8°
	1946 inclining	44.500	37.00	5.79	4.22	35°	60.5°

The following table gives stability data for the ship in a riddled condition, *ie* the ship open to the sea above the lower deck forward and aft and above the main (armoured) deck in the citadel:

Condition		Displt tons	GM	Maximum Righting Lever ft	Angle of Maximum Stability	Angle of Vanishing Stability
Deep	1941 estimate	48,140	8.07	1.59	14°	30.5°
	1946 inclining	51,420	6.20	0.63	10°	18°
Light	1941 estimate	42,220	5.50	1.83	20°	36°
	1946 inclining	45,116	3.62	0.92	14°	25°

Strength

Revised strength calculations were made in 1946 after the first inclining experiment and the results are summarised below:

					Deck Stress		Keel Stress	
Section No	Position	Inertia in^2 ft^2 10^6	Bending Moment ton ft	Y[28] ft	(Tension) Tons/ins^2	Y ft	(Compression) ton/in^2	
1	11ft before fore end of citadel	2,261	195,500	27.54	2.38	25.96	2.25	
2	Centre line of 'A' turret	2.436	302,500	30.74	3.82	22.76	2.83	
3	Centre line of 'B' turret	2.863	511,000	31.36	5.60	22.14	3.85	
4	Centre line of No 1 5.25in	3.601	927,000	31.46	8.10	22.04	5.67	
5	Position of max bending moment	3.894	<u>1,100,000</u>	30.90	<u>8.81</u>	22.60	<u>6.44</u>	
6	Central line of after funnel	3.879	1,076,0000	30.72	8.46	22.78	6.27	
7	Centre line of No 4 5.25in	3.403	888,000	31.06	8.10	22.44	5.86	
8	Centre line of 'X' turret	2.611	446,000	30.23	4.63	23.27	3.97	
9	Centre line of 'Y' turret	1.998	245,000	29.45	3.64	24.04	3.01	
10	3ft abaft after end of citadel	1.653	161,000	24.86	2.43	28.64	2.79	

Hogging Condition

[28] In this table, Y is the distance from the neutral axes – that about which the ship flexes – and the deck or keel.

					Deck Comp.		Keel Tensile
Section No	Position	Inertia $in^2 ft^2$ 10^6	Bending Moment ton ft	Y ft	Stress Tons/ins^2	Y ft	Stress ton/in^2
			Sagging Condition				

Section No	Position	Inertia $in^2 ft^2$ 10^6	Bending Moment ton ft	Y ft	Deck Comp. Stress Tons/ins^2	Y ft	Keel Tensile Stress ton/in^2
1	11ft before fore end of citadel	2.258	418,000	24.21	4.48	29.29	5.42
2	Centre line of 'A' turret	2.492	610,000	27.60	6.76	25.9	6.34
3	Centre line of 'B' turret	2.925	829,000	28.09	7.96	25.41	7.20
4	Centre line of No.1 5.25in	3.677	1,084,000	27.83	8.21	25.67	7.57
5	Position of max bending moment	3.967	1,140,000	27.16	7.81	26.34	7.57
6	Central line of after funnel	3.928	1,084,000	27.14	7.49	26.36	7.27
7	Centre line of No.4 5.25in	3.458	945,000	27.58	7.54	25.98	7.08
8	Centre line of 'X' turret	2.657	624,000	27.03	6.35	26.47	6.28
9	Centre line of 'Y' turret	2.022	447,000	26.45	5.85	27.05	5.98
10	3ft abaft after end of citadel	1.650	309,500	21.85	4.09	31.65	5.93

The following table shows the increase in stress caused mainly by additions of weight while building. Some of the increased stress in the sagging condition between 1942 and 1943 was caused by the increased sheer forward.

	Date	Hogging		Sagging	
		Deck Tension	Keel Comp	Deck Comp	Keel Tension
Approved for design by DNC 28.3.40	1940	10 ton/in^2 max	–	–	7 ton/in^2 max
Estimated during design	1942	8.95	5.98	7.78	6.98
	1943	8.60	6.29	8.15	7.51
Estimated after first inclining	1946	8.82	6.44	8.21	7.57

DNC considered the stresses to be higher than was desirable in a new ship and action was taken to instruct the Commanding Officer that on account of the increase in displacement over the design figure, it was necessary to place a limit of 35ft 0in on the mean draught at which the ship might proceed to sea, in order not to impose excessive strain on the ship's structure in heavy weather. Urgent operational reasons only would justify the risk entailed in exceeding this draught. Further, the Commanding Officer was informed that all proposals for alterations and additions, involving the addition of weight, were to be accompanied by proposals for the landing of equipment weight from the ship; Admiralty Departments were similarly informed.

Important Alterations

As a result of experience gained during the war, a number of important alterations and modifications were made in the design and early building states. Included were:

(i) Increased longitudinal separation of propellers.

In order to reduce the probability of two propellers being put out of action by one torpedo hit, it was decided in March 1942 to increase the longitudinal separation of the inner and outer propellers by about 18ft to 51ft 6in.

(ii) Increased proportion of diesel generators to turbo generators from 2/6 to 4/4.

(iii) Increased sheer forward.

(iv) Rearrangement of W/T office to provide a Bridge Receiving Room and Transmitter Room in the after superstructure.

(v) Omission of cruising turbines.

(vi) Substitution of electric for oil-fired ranges.

(vii) Removal of part of the sick bay to a position below armour.

(viii) Additional breakwater forward of 'A' turret.

(ix) Fittings for Arctic conditions.

As a result of the action between *Bismarck* and *Prince of Wales*, the modified design approved by the Board in 1942 incorporated the following:

(x) Additional splinter protection to the sides of the magazines.

(xi) Increased oil fuel stowage.

The loss of the *Prince of Wales* resulted in:

(xii) Closer sub-division of watertight compartments on the lower deck over the side underwater protection, and their abandonment as bathrooms.

(xiii) Substantial reduction in the number of side scuttles below the upper deck.

(xiv) Removal of 5.25in transfer positions in the supply to numbers 2 and 3 mountings from the lower to middle deck.

(xv) Trunked access to all compartments occupied in action inside the citadel as well as outside.

Centralised Messing

Centralised messing was introduced in 1944. In January 1945 it was decided to reduce dining hall space in order to increase mess space from 15 to 18sq ft per man in enclosed messes, and from 13 to 14sq ft per man in broadside messes. However, as a result of complaints of overcrowding some messes were converted to dining halls, and cabin flats to messes; at the same time team service was abandoned in favour of mess team service.

Habitability

During 1948 *Vanguard* was fitted out to the latest approved standards of amenities including the modernisation of bathrooms with stainless steel equipment and hot and cold running water; new furniture; water coolers; ice cream machine; electric deck scrubbers and polishers; electric washing machines; vacuum cleaners; barber's shop and tailor's shop. Improvements were also made to the ship's laundry by fitting modern machinery.

Action Information Organisation

The general layout of spaces for the Action Information Centre including an Air Plotting Room, Operations Room and Radar Display Room was agreed by the AIO Committee in September 1943. At that time the Director of Air Warfare and Flying Training stated that the internal layout of the Air Plot. Target indication and Operations room would be made nearer the completion date for the ship, as it was impossible to forecast the exact requirements so far ahead. A mock up was made and the layout of the admittedly small spaces agreed.

For passage through the Suez Canal, the maximum permissible draught of the *Vanguard* was limited to 34ft to conform with the minimum margin of 3ft 3in under the keel.

Cost

The cost of *Vanguard* was £11,530,503 including £3,186,868 for armament, part of which was for modernising the main armament. The initial cost of the main armament prior to taking the turrets and guns from store is not included.

Special Features

Transom Stern

Vanguard was the first British battleship to be built with a transom stern. Experiments at Haslar with models of the previous design (*Lion* – never completed) indicated that an increase of speed of the order of ⅓kt at 30 kts for the same horsepower could be obtained by this means.

Sheer Forward and Recessed Hawse Pipes

Experience with the *King George V* class had shown these ships to be wet in heavy seas and it was decided to increase the sheer in *Vanguard* forward of 'A' turret and accept an increase in the minimum elevation of guns on forward bearing.

Air Conditioning

Two steam jet plants of 500,00 BTU per hour and 10 air cooling units were installed for air conditioning the following spaces:

Vanguard decks

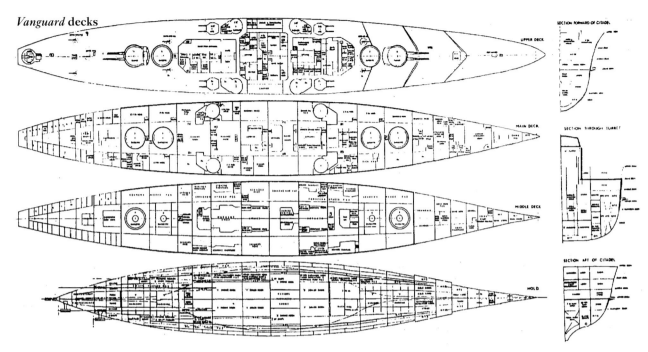

Aircraft Direction Rooms, Operations Room, Radar Display Room, Lower Steaming Position, Computer Rooms, Transmitting Station, 5.25in Magazines adjacent to Boiler Rooms, Damage Control Headquarters, Switchboard Room, Lower Sick Bay, Electronics Maintenance Room, DCHQ(2), Lower Receiving Room, Lower Transmitting Room.

Tropical and Arctic Conditions

The ship was fitted for service in tropical and Arctic conditions. Sprayed limpet asbestos was fitted to exposed ship's side, decks and bulkheads. For Arctic conditions steam heating was fitted to many ship fittings, armament, exposed navigational controls and look-out positions, ventilation to Officers' and Crew's accommodation, seacocks, etc. Some of these services had to be supplied by superheated steam because fitting for Arctic Service was not catered for in the original design and there was not sufficient saturated steam available.

Type 960 Radar (WA Set)

Vanguard was the first ship to be fitted with this general warning set to give advance information of a possible target at great range and height.

Chronology

The following dates are reiterated for convenience of reference:

19 Mar 1940 Information received stated that a 15in battleship would be ordered in the 1940 Programme.

14 Mar 1941 An order for the ship was placed with Messrs John Brown & Co, Clydebank.

24 Mar 1941 Advance Building Drawings were forwarded to Messrs John Brown & Co.

26 Mar 1941 Building Drawings stamped by the Board.

2 Oct 1941 First keel plate laid.

3 Nov 1941 Messrs John Brown & Co were informed that the ship was to be named *Vanguard*.

4 Sep 1942 Revised Building Drawings were received by Messrs John Brown & Co.

30 Nov 1944 *Vanguard* launched, by Princess Elizabeth.

June 1945 Sea trials off Arran.

9 Aug 1946 *Vanguard* handed over at Portsmouth.

CHAPTER 2

Monitors

Editorial Note

The most comprehensive treatment of these ships is that given by Buxton[1] which covers their operational history as well as that of the design.

During the 1914-18 war monitors were designed and built for the bombardment of Belgian ports. No monitors were built after 1918 but, soon after the beginning of the war in 1939, it was realised that monitors would again be required. The possibility of refitting the old 15in monitor *Marshal Soult* was considered, but it was eventually decided to build a new ship.

Roberts – 1939 Programme

The design of this vessel was started in November 1939, and completion of the ship was required in twelve months. To avoid long delays in the approval of drawings, the latter were sent direct to DNC, who consulted the other Admiralty Departments as necessary. The constructor in charge of the work made fortnightly trips to Clydebank, taking back drawings and settling doubtful points.

Specifications were not prepared, but the builders were given a Statement of Requirements.

In an attempt to keep the cost of the vessel down, the sections were moulded[2] to eliminate curvature in the bottom plating and frames as much as possible.

Armament

The main armament consisted of the 15in twin turret from the old *Marshal Soult*, reconditioned at Portsmouth by Messrs Vickers-Armstrong Ltd.

No reliable drawings of *Marshal Soult* were available; very careful measurements had therefore to be made at the ship to ensure the turret fitting correctly into the new ship. Further details of the armament are given in Appendix I.

Protection

The armour protection of *Roberts* consisted of a sloped side belt of non-cemented armour extending from the Deep WL to the main deck - 200lb abreast the main magazines and 160lb forward and aft. This belt was closed at the after end by a 60lb non-cemented armour bulkhead. No armour bulkhead was fitted forward.

On the main deck 160lb non-cemented armour was fitted for protection to main magazines, and 120lb over machinery spaces, tapering to 80lb forward. On lower deck aft over steering gear 120lb non-cemented armour was fitted.

[1] I L Buxton, *Big Gun Monitors* (Tynemouth 1978).

[2] The word moulded refers to the 'mould loft' where the shape of each part of the ship was drawn out full size and wooden patterns made from which frames and plates were cut and bent to shape.

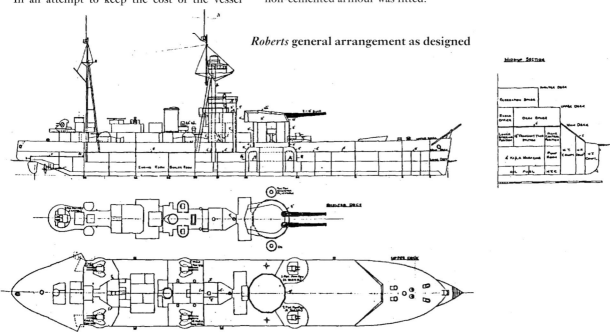

Roberts **general arrangement as designed**

[3] The word 'considered' has been inserted in manuscript on the original typescript at this point, showing some reduction in confidence in the bulge.

The barbette armour was 320lb cemented and 60lb non-cemented armour was fitted to the deck and sides of the 15in magazine and 160lb on the crown of the magazine.

The conning tower was of 80lb non-cemented armour on front, rear and crown, 120lb on the sides and 60lb on the deck with an 80lb cast steel communication tube to the lower steering position.

Bulges 17ft in width were fitted, which were[3] more than good enough to keep out a 1000lb contact torpedo, but the extra beam was necessary to provide buoyancy in order to keep the shallow draught of 12ft 0in. The bulge spaces were divided up into watertight compartments, using the bulges (internal) of *King George V* as a guide. The bulge compartments were fitted with elaborate flooding and pumping arrangements to enable heel and trim to be rapidly corrected.

In addition the ship's side proper constituted the protection to the vitals of the ship against mines and torpedoes. This plating, two thicknesses of 30lb D1 quality steel, extended about three quarters the length of the ship.

Speed and form
Staff requirements were not received at the commencement of the design, and so DNC laid down that the maximum draught was not to exceed 12ft 0in and the speed was to be 12kts deep. The form was based on the lines of the old monitor *Terror*.

At about this time reports were coming in from sea that HMS *Erebus* was very difficult to manoeuvre, and it was decided that the new monitor must have good manoeuvring qualities – a necessity when bombarding off shore under enemy gunfire. Model steering trials were carried out at Haslar with both single and twin rudders and it was finally decided to fit twin rudders. It was rather difficult to get the twin steering gear fitted in under the armour deck, but Messrs Hasties managed to produce a suitable design of steam hydraulic gear. The twin rudders were fitted as nearly as possible behind the screws, this resulted in a long cut-up which, however, still further helped the ship to answer the helm readily.

A trial was also carried out at Haslar to see if spray caused by waves breaking on the bulge was swept across the upper deck. This was proved not to be the case.

Machinery
A set of sloop machinery, *Black Swan* type, was used as it was immediately available. This consisted of twin screw steam turbines developing 4800shp at 250 revolutions and arranged in two engine rooms. There were two oil-burning boilers fitted in separate boiler rooms.

Two 200kW steam-turbine driven dynamos and two 60kW oil-driven dynamos were fitted for supply of electrical energy.

The distilling machinery included one evaporator of 60 tons per day normal capacity.

Four 550 tons per hour salvage pumps were provided for pumping out damaged or leaking compartments and for flooding, if necessary, the 15in magazine which was situated above the waterline.

Cooling machinery was provided as follows:
(a) For food rooms - two 20,000 BTU/hour automatic methyl-chloride plants.
(b) For magazine air cooling - one 30,000 BTU/hour automatic Freon plant.

Accommodation
The mess space accommodation was arranged to meet the initial 'Scheme of Complement' of 428. Later it was found necessary to accommodate an additional 50 ratings. This naturally resulted in the accommodation becoming cramped, and necessitated a new mess space being provided on the lower deck.

Additions after Completion
HMS *Roberts* completed in October 1941.

Additions to complement made it necessary to increase the fresh water supply, two DB compartments were therefore converted into fresh water tanks and two additional 10 tons per day evaporators were installed.

The funnel was subsequently increased in height by 12ft to reduce smoke interference on the bridge.

Cost of *Roberts* was £1,100,000.

Abercrombie – 1941 Programme

In April 1941 an order was placed with Messrs Vickers-Armstrong Ltd, Walker-on-Tyne, for the monitor *Abercrombie* which was to be, with minor modifications, a repeat of *Roberts*.

The most important modifications were:
(1) Substitution of 160lb armour for 100lb on the main deck over machinery spaces.
(2) Increase in dynamo power, involving slight modification to the watertight sub-division in the hold, to meet the increased demands of remote power control to the 4in HA/LA mountings and 2pdr pom-poms. Two 150kW oil-driven dynamos were fitted instead of two 60kW machines.
(3) Shelter deck extended to ship's side and the 4in HA/LA twin mountings fitted on shelter deck.

Abercrombie, *the second monitor built in World War II, seen in June 1946. Note the additional superstructure compared with the plan of* Roberts. *She took part in many landings.*

(4) The refrigerated stowage was increased and the cooling machinery consisted of two 25,000 BTU/hour automatic methyl-chloride plants.

(5) The fresh water stowage was increased and additional distilling plant of 25 tons per day output was fitted.

The accommodation arrangements were originally arranged for a complement equal to that of *Roberts* at the time of the latter vessel's completion. Subsequent increases in complement resulted in overcrowding on the mess decks and necessitated an additional mess being built on the shelter deck.

Abercrombie was completed in May 1943.

Cost of *Abercrombie* was £1,563,000.

Additions after Completion

It was found during the sea trials of *Roberts* and subsequently on service that the ship answered the helm very readily, but once she started to turn it was difficult to stop her. This was attributed to lack of deadwood and it was therefore approved to fit a deadwood in both *Roberts* and *Abercrombie* but this work was not undertaken in either ship up to the time of their being placed 'in reserve' shortly after the end of the war.

APPENDIX I

Name	Roberts	Abercrombie
Where Built	John Brown	Vickers–Armstrong
Engines	John Brown	Parsons
Laid down	30 Apr 1940	26 May 1941
Launched	1 Feb 1941	31 Mar 1942
Completed	27 Oct 1941	5 May 1943

Dimensions, etc

	Roberts	Abercrombie
Length between perpendiculars	354ft 0in	354ft 0in
Length overall	373ft 0in	373ft 0in
Breadth extreme (over rubbers)	89ft 8in	89ft 8in
Displacement in tons to 12ft 0in WL	8123	8123
Depth of ship – forward USK to upper dk	30ft 6in	30ft 6in
beam at middle – amidships	27ft 6in	27ft 6in
– aft	27ft 6in	27ft 6in
Deep load draught (mean BP)	13ft 5½in	14ft 3¾in
Height of turret guns from 12ft 0in WL	36ft 9in	34ft 1in
Shaft horse power of engines	4800	4800
Speed at deep load draught (kts)	12¼	12¼
Oil fuel stowage (tons)	549	554
Complement of officers and men	428	494

Armament

		Roberts	Abercrombie
15in BL Mark I (guns) Mtg Mk 1/N	Number	2	2
	Rounds per gun	110	110
QF 4in HA/LA Mk VI* (guns) Mtg Twin XIX	Number	8	8
	Rounds per gun	400	400
QF 2-pdr Mk VIII HV (guns) Mtg Mk VII*	Number of equipments	2	2
	Rounds per barrel	1800	1800
QF 2-pdr Mk VIII HV (guns) Mtg Mk VIA* (8 barrel)	Number of equipments	2	2
	Rounds per barrel	1800	1800

Close range armament included also Oerlikons, later replaced by Bofors.

Stability

	Roberts	Abercrombie
Metacentric height in deep condition	18.1ft	14.0ft
Range of stability in deep condition	69½°	68°

Weights

	Tons	Tons
General equipment	538	656
Armament 1516	1552	
Machinery 275	298	
Reserve feed water	41	41
Oil fuel 549	554	
Hull, armour and protective plating 5645	6030	
Water protection	586	586
Deep displacement	9150	9717

CHAPTER 3

Fleet Carriers

Editorial Note

The development of British carrier aviation, both ships and aircraft, is well covered by Friedman.[1] The ships described in this chapter all derive from the work of two men: Henderson who, as Rear Admiral Aircraft Carriers had developed an unusual understanding of air power at sea and as Controller was to initiate the armoured hangar concept; and W A D Forbes, who spent much of his career as a naval constructor in carrier design.

All the ships described are of 'closed hangar' design; that is the the ship's side was carried up to the flight deck which thus became the strength deck, carrying the principal loads imposed on the ship. The closed hangar helped greatly in containing a fire but, conversely, it meant that engines could not be run in the hangar either for test or to warm up before a flight. The closed hangar would normally be smaller than an open hangar which led to the double hangar in many British ships. The hangar of Ark Royal (and of earlier ships) was unarmoured, though she

had heavy cruiser protection below, but the later ships had protection to the hangar as well. It is worth noting that the protection on the side of the hangar was gradually reduced in thickness in later classes eventually becoming little more than splinter protection.

During the war the concept of a permanent deck park of 20-25 aircraft was accepted. However, aircraft fuel stowage was already limited compared with the provision in USN carriers, partly because of a different concept of operations but also because of the elaborate fire protection given to petrol in British ships. Though this policy, together with the closed hangar, helped the RN to avoid devastating fires, it meant that replenishment was needed frequently.

It is also interesting to note the increase in complement during the war which made life on board very unpleasant in the Pacific Fleet.

[1] N Friedman, *British Carrier Aviation* (London 1988).

[2] The text is not quite correct at this point. The wires fitted in *Argus* were longitudinal rather than transverse and intended to stop the planes falling over the edge of the deck. *Argus* was the world's first true aircraft carrier and the only one operational in World War I. Her designers identified and solved most of the problems of a carrier. For some interesting background see I Johnston, *Beardmore Built.* (Glasgow 1993).

[3] A wood and canvas mock-up island had been tried on *Argus* in 1918.

[4] British carrier designers were very early users of wind tunnels to study air flow over the flight deck. See D K Brown, 'Early Aircraft Carrier Projects', *Warship* 35 (1985). Great attention was paid to the round down and to the shape of the island. The USN relied on strong and powerful aircraft which were less sensitive to eddies.

[5] The designers referred to them as 'Funnel' carriers rather than 'Island' as their island contained only the funnel and a small steering position.

History of Fleet Carriers Between the Two World Wars

During the First World War, ships converted for the carriage of aircraft proved beyond doubt that this form of warfare was of strategic value to the Fleet, that the aeroplane was definitely superior to the seaplane and that larger and faster carriers were necessary to maintain station with other units of the Fleet.

In August 1915 the *Argus*, a passenger and cargo ship, was purchased and converted to a carrier, the work being completed by September 1918.

The ship was used to try out various proposals under consideration to improve landing conditions in aircraft carriers under construction or conversion. One of these was the new arresting device, the purpose of which was to rapidly decelerate the aircraft after it had landed on the deck.[2]

In mid-1917 the order for *Hermes* was placed. This was the first ship to be designed as an aircraft carrier. Later in the same year the *Eagle*, a battleship being built for the Chilean government at Messrs Armstrongs, was purchased and converted. Both these vessels were completed by dockyards in 1924. They had full length flight decks

with an 'island'[3] on the starboard side, through which passed the funnel uptakes and mast and from which navigation was effected. The flight deck was carried to the after end of the ship and gently curved downwards to obviate eddying[4] and the danger of the undercarriage of an aircraft fouling the transverse edge of the deck.

Early in 1917 it was also decided to convert the light cruiser *Furious*. This vessel, after a series of conversions, was finally completed in 1925.

There being some doubt as to the effect of an island, it was removed in the *Furious* and she became the first British carrier with two-storied hangars and with flying deck not carried to the fore end. The upper hangar deck was carried to the fore end and a slight downward slope given to it to form a subsidiary flying-off deck.

The experience gained with the flush deck of *Furious* led to a change of opinion and later the *Courageous* and *Glorious* were designed with an island.[5] This, as a result of investigation into contemporary opinion, was placed on the starboard side. It was appreciated that if the island was short and reasonably streamlined there was little or no interference with air currents abaft the island. Apart from the discomfort of the long horizontal smoke stacks in *Furious*, the hot gases rising at the after end caused air disturbances which increased the difficulties of landing.

The design of carriers during the inter-war years, as for other warships, was kept in check by the limitations of the Washington and London Naval Treaties.

The Washington Treaty of 1922 defined an aircraft carrier as a vessel of war with a standard displacement in excess of 10,000 tons but not exceeding 27,000 tons, designed for the specific and exclusive purpose of carrying aircraft. It had to be so constructed that aircraft could be landed thereon and launched therefrom, and not designed and constructed for carrying a gun in excess of 8in. The number of guns not exceeding 5in was not limited. It also provided for all carriers in existence or building on 12 November 1921 to be considered as experimental and for these carriers to be replaced within the tonnage limit without regard to age[6].

The London Naval Treaty of 1930 limited the maximum calibre of guns in aircraft carriers of standard displacement of 10,000 tons or less to 6.1in.

In Article V of the London Naval Treaty 1936, the standard displacement of an aircraft carrier was limited to 23,000 tons, and the maximum gun 6.1in. If the armament of any carrier included guns exceeding 5.25in the total number of guns carried which exceeded that calibre should not be more than ten in number.

The power and speed of these earlier carriers was generally fixed by their design characteristics. Experience proved, however, that high speed in a carrier was an essential feature to enable the ship to keep station, operate aircraft (which might necessitate changing course to turn into wind) and to meet other tactical considerations.

As the armament of the carrier was primarily for self-defence, the small and medium calibre of AA guns were generally used and the 8in guns allowed by treaty limits were not considered.[7]

Many arrangements and fittings found in carriers are not found in ordinary warships and much thought and attention has had to be given to them. As a result of experience and experiment, considerable improvement has been made in modern carriers in comparison with earlier carriers.

With the ever-increasing landing weight and speeds of aircraft, the arresting gear and the safety barriers have called for special attention.[8] In order not to impose a deceleration greater than the aircraft is designed to withstand, much experimental work and pioneer effort has been involved in developing this gear. Similarly, considerable advances have been made in the method of catapulting aircraft off the ship.

[6] Signatories were allowed two conversions of up to 33,000 tons. The USN took advantage of an ambiguous clause to increase *Lexington* and *Saratoga* to 36,000 tons.

[7] This passage is not entirely correct. Studies for *Courageous* and *Glorious* with 8in guns were produced and rejected after consideration.

[8] See D K Brown, 'Ship Assisted Landing and Take Off', *Flight Deck* (1985), (partially reproduced in *Warship* 49).

Ship	Date of Completion	Length ft	Beam ft	Dispt. ton	Speed kts	Shp	Armament	Approx. no. of Aircraft
Argus	1918	567	75	14,450	20	20,000	6–4in AA	15
Hermes	1924	600	70	10,850	25	40,000	6–6in LA 3–4in AA	21
Eagle	1924	667	105	22,600	24	50,000	9–6in LA	21
Furious	1925	786	90	22,450	31	90,000	10–5.5in 3–4in AA	35
Courageous	1928	786	90	22,500	30½	90,000	16–4.7in AA	50
Glorious	1930	786	90	22,500	30½	90,000	16–4.7in AA	50

Ark Royal *as completed in 1938. Note the short funnel, soon raised, and the empty pom-pom sponsons. DNC and the builders, Cammell Laird, had worked together to develop the use of welding and she had more such work than any previous British ship, saving 500 tons.*

Ark Royal general arrangement as designed

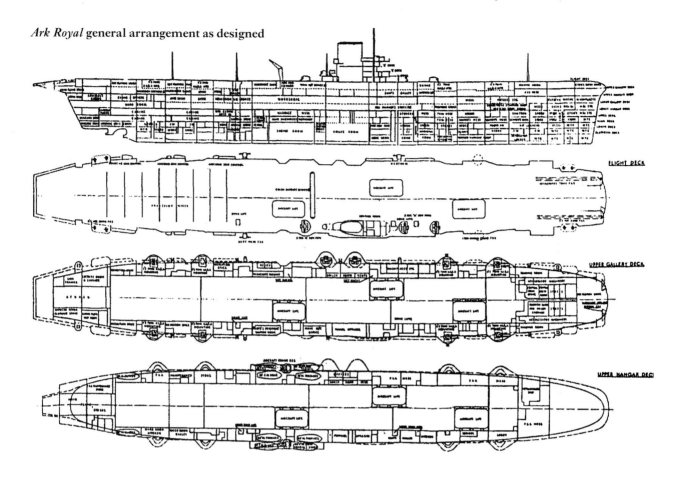

Ark Royal lower decks as designed

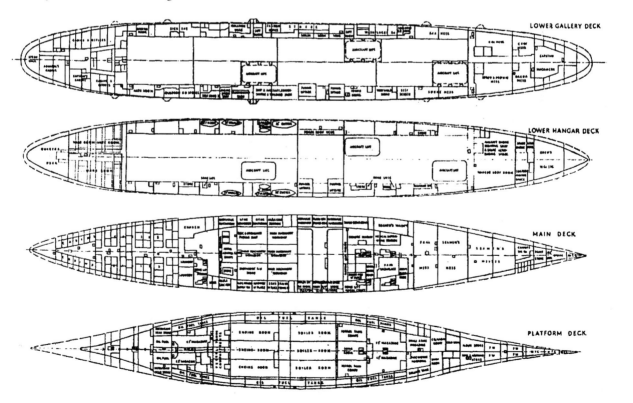

Ark Royal (1934)

In 1933 there were six aircraft carriers in service, viz *Argus*, *Hermes*, *Eagle*, *Courageous*, *Glorious* and *Furious*. Of these the last three only were suitable for fleet operations on a major scale. It was decided in 1933 to design a new aircraft carrier embodying all the lessons learned and experience gained during the preceding ten years.

The aircraft carrier, at that particular time, was limited by Treaty to a standard displacement of 27,000 tons, so a number of preliminary designs were prepared covering a range of displacements from 12,000 to 24,000 tons. These designs demonstrated that a small ship, owing to its limited aircraft carrying capacity, was very costly and that our major requirements for an aircraft carrier could be generally satisfied on a standard displacement of about 22,400 tons. Based on this, staff requirements were drawn up for a vessel to carry and operate seventy-two aircraft on a flight deck length of 900ft; maximum speed in the standard condition to be 30kts; protection required to all magazines, shell rooms and machinery spaces, etc. Petrol stowage was required for 100,000gall and oil stowage for 4000gall. It was found that the requirement for the 900ft flight deck could not be met on the 22,000 tons displacement, but that by adopting the waterline length of 725ft it was possible to work a deck 800ft in length and still meet the other main requirements.

Before building commenced the behaviour of the proposed new design under helm was thoroughly investigated at the Admiralty Experiment Works, Haslar, and as a result it was decided to fit a rudder rather larger than that fitted in *Courageous*. This, together with a partly cut-away deadwood and centre line propeller, resulted in quicker turning and better manoeuvring qualities; further, it facilitated the control of the ship in high winds while at low speeds - a great advantage in restricted anchorages.

The sketch design was approved by the Board in June 1934. Shortly after, it was decided to replace the 4.7in armament by HA/LA guns of 4.5in calibre and so bring the design in line with the rest of the ships under construction at the time. As a result of this change in policy a new set of building drawings was prepared early in 1935. *Ark Royal* was laid down at Cammell Laird's in September 1935 and the general particulars as built were:

Length overall	800ft 0in
Length on waterline	725ft 0in
Length between perps	685ft 0in
Breadth on waterline	94ft 9⅛in
Breadth extreme	112ft 0in
Depth of ship	83ft 6in
Standard displacement	22,000 tons
Deep displacement	27,700 tons
Draughts, deep - FP	26ft 7¼ in
- AP	28ft 0½ in
- Mean	27ft 4in
Shp	102,000
Speed (deep)	31kts
Endurance at 12kts (6 months out of dock)	4300 miles
Oil fuel	4443 tons
Petrol	100,000gall
Complement	151 officers; 1630 men

Group Weights

Hull	13,651
Protection	2,854
Machinery	2,468
Armament	1,042
Aircraft equipment	1,629
General equipment	1,382
Reserve feed water	252
Oil fuel	4,443
Deep displacement	27,721 tons

Structure

The ship was designed for the extensive adoption of welding.[9] About 65% of the structure was welded, including the whole of the first 100ft from forward; the estimated approximate saving in weight as compared with rivetting being 500 tons.

The two hangars in this design were of the closed type and the flight deck (30lb) was worked structurally.

Aircraft Arrangements

The effective length of the flight deck was 797ft with a minimum width of 50ft at the stern. The minimum width of flight deck abreast the island structure was 74ft 0in while the maximum width was 96ft just abaft the island.

The hangar dimensions were 568ft x 60ft for the upper hangar and 452ft x 60ft for the lower; each had a clear height of 16ft. The total hangar area was 61,200sq ft and stowage was arranged for seventy-two aircraft each 40ft x 18ft x 13ft 16in as stowed, although it was eventually decided to provide for sixty only.

Three lifts were fitted, one forward, one aft and the other amidships;[10] the forward lift was 46ft x 25ft while the other two were slightly smaller being 45ft x 22ft. The safety barrier and the eight

[9] *Ark Royal* was the first large RN ship to use welding extensively. Cammel Laird was one of the few commercial shipbuilders prepared to use welding.

[10] The lifts had two platforms and moved only through a single deck height. In consequence, moving a plane from the lower hangar to the flight deck involved three operations, which was slow and labour intensive.

11 The torpedo protection was tested full size on a large pontoon, Job 74. There seem to have been some problems with the welds on the thick bulkhead: see D K Brown, 'Attack and Defence', *Warship* 24 (1982).

arresting wires (spaced 24ft apart) were designed to take a landing load of 800lb at 66kts, while the two accelerators fitted forward were designed for a maximum of 12,000lb at 56kts.

A parking space with a hydraulically operated wind breaker was arranged on the flight deck forward.

Armament

The final arrangement was settled as:

16-4.5in HA/LA guns in eight twin UD
   mountings
6 8-barrel 2pdr pom-pom mountings
8 4-barrel machine gun mountings

The main armament was controlled by four HADTs, two on the starboard side (one at upper gallery deck level and one abreast the island at 'A' deck level), and two on the port side at upper gallery deck level.

The supply to the 4.5in guns was by electrically driven chain hoists in two stages, from handing room to upper deck, and upper deck to gun position.

Protection

In this ship the hangars and flight deck were not protected; the vitals of the ship were, however, given protection of heavy cruiser standard.

side belt	- 180lb C
top of citadel	- 140lb NC
citadel bulkheads	- 100lb NC
magazine crowns	- 140lb NC
magazine sides	- 100lb NC

The steering gear was also protected by 140lb and 100lb NC armour.

The underwater side protection system was designed to withstand a contact charge of 750lb TNT and consisted of an air-liquid-air sandwich space bounded inboard by the main protective bulkhead.[11]

The sandwich space was 13ft in total width and consisted of a 2ft 6in air space inboard, 3ft outboard and a central liquid space of 7ft 6in.

The main protective bulkhead was worked in 60lb D quality plating in one thickness and extended from station 56 to station 134 on the port and starboard sides (ie about 312ft); the protective bulkhead was generally continuous from the outer bottom to main deck.

Machinery

Machinery consisted of a three-shaft arrangement of geared turbines fitted in three engine rooms arranged abreast. Each shaft was driven by a HP and a LP turbine connected in series and the

transmission of power was through single reduction double helical gearing. The shp was 34,000 on each shaft giving a total of 102,000 at 230rpm.

The boilers, six each of 17,000shp, were paired off into three boiler rooms arranged abreast. The working pressure at the boilers was 350lb/sq in with 230°F superheated steam at full power.

The machinery was arranged on the 'unit' system and was controlled from a control room situated between the centre boiler room and centre engine room.

Propeller particulars	Outers	Centre
No of blades	3	3
Diameter	15ft	15ft
Pitch	16ft 6in	15ft 3in
Developed blade area	125sq ft	135sq ft

Generators

Six turbo-generators each of 400kW capacity were fitted in the ship, one in each engine room and three behind armour on the main deck, port side. They supplied direct current to the ring main at 220 volts.

The LP supply was obtained from separate motor generators. The steering gear was of electric-hydraulic type and designed to give a maximum torque on the rudder head of 500ton ft.

Stability

From the inclining experiment carried out in November 1938, the following stability particulars were obtained, assuming free flooding of the hangar:

	Deep Condition	Light Condition
Metacentric height	6.37ft (fl)	3.56ft
Max GZ	4.08ft	2.9ft
Angle of max GZ	33½°	31¼°
Range (hangars free flooding)	59.4°	48.4°
Displacement	28,481 tons	22,691 tons

Strength

The strengths of the ship were obtained from the standard longitudinal strength calculations and the following results were obtained:

	Hogging	Sagging
Max bending moment	660,000ft ton	555,000ft ton
Stress in flight deck	7.6ton/sq in	5.6ton/sq in
Stress in keel	4.0ton/sq in	3.8ton/sq in
Displacement	24,710 tons	24,260 tons

Stress at 6½ ord. 4.2ton/in².

In calculating the moduli of the sections, the armour was omitted in both tension and compression. Although welding was extensively adopted the material contributing most to longitudinal strength, viz. flight deck and bottom plating, was riveted; thus the usual 2/11 reduction from material in tension was used.

Complement for ship as a flagship was 1600. This was made up of a ship's company of forty-nine officers and 809 men, and a Fleet Air Arm complement of a hundred officers and 642 men. Provision was made in the design for 7½% of this total as supernumaries, in addition.

The complement was later increased to 151 officers and 1630 men.

General

The *Ark Royal* gave satisfactory service, especially during the early part of the war. In November 1941 while returning to Gibraltar she was torpedoed and sunk; many lessons were learned as a result of this incident.

Cost

Vote 8 cost of this ship was £3,500,000.

Illustrious Class

In 1935/6 when the political situation was causing some anxiety, careful thought was given to the part that an aircraft carrier would play in a future war. The aircraft, it was realised, would be the 'eyes' of the Fleet as well as being both attackers and defenders in an engagement, and consideration was therefore given to the protection of the aircraft themselves.

Staff requirements[12] were drawn up for a carrier to be built within the Treaty displacement limit of 23,000 tons, and to carry thirty-six aircraft in a protected hangar; flight deck to be not less than 3in NC armour.

A design was produced by DNC and approved by the Board in 1936: the first two ships of the class, viz *Illustrious* and *Victorious* were included in the 1936 new construction programme, and laid down in April 1937.

General particulars for the class were:

Length overall	740ft 0in
Length on waterline	710ft 0in
Length between perps	673ft 0in
Extreme breadth	106ft 9in
Depth of ship	67ft 9in
Displacement (standard)	23,207 tons
Displacement (deep)	28,619 tons
Draughts (deep) - FP	27ft 5in
- AP	28ft 10in
- Mean	28ft 2in
Shp of engines	111,000
Speed (deep)	30kts
Endurance at 10kts	
(6 months out of dock)	14,000 miles
Oil fuel	4854 tons
Petrol	50,660gall

Group Weights (from Book of Calculations)

Hull	12,724 tons
Protection	4,941 tons
Machinery	2,464 tons
Armament	997 tons
Aircraft equipment	1,186 tons
General equipment	1,266 tons
Reserve feed	187 tons
Oil fuel	4,854 tons
Deep displacement	28,619 tons

Aircraft Arrangements

The length of the flight deck was 740ft with a minimum width of 62ft 6in between gun recesses; the maximum width of the flight deck was 95ft 9in.

[12] The armoured hangar concept was due entirely to the Controller, Admiral Henderson, and the preliminary design was completed by Forbes before the requirement. Note the comment by Sir Rowland Baker, RCNC, that the requirement is to the design as the chicken is to the egg.

Victorious in 1943 whilst operating with the USN in the south west Pacific (New Georgia and New Hebrides). Her airgroup carried USN markings at this time but saw no action.

13 The lifts were outside the armoured volume of the ship. They were designed to operate even if the structure round them was distorted which proved its value when *Indomitable* was bombed.

14 This number of Oerlikons was not fitted on completion.

The hangar was 456ft x 62ft x 16ft clear height, with a clear deck area of 28,500ft to take thirty-six aircraft each 36ft x 18ft x 13ft 6in x 9000lb (as stowed). Later, it was decided to carry thirty-three aircraft of Albacore type.

Two lifts were fitted in this design, one at the forward and the other at the after end of the hangar.[13] Each lift was 45ft x 22ft and was designed to take a working load of 6 tons with a time cycle of 30 seconds (*ie* a down journey loaded and an up journey unloaded). An accelerator at the forward end of the flight deck was embodied in the approved design. Consideration was given to the fitting of two sets of assisted take off gear, but only one set was finally fitted. This gear was designed to take 11,000lb aircraft with a maximum launching speed off 66kts – mean acceleration of 1.5g.

The arresting gear consisted of six wires (three units) and was tested to 11,000lb at 60kts max.

The crash barrier was designed to take aircraft up to 10,000lb at 40kts in a distance of 25ft.

Armament on completion[14] consisted of:

16-4.5in HA/LA in twin mountings
6 8-barrel 2pdr pom-poms
18 twin Oerlikons
14 single Oerlikons

Control of the main armament was achieved by four HADTs – one at middle line of island, one forward and one aft at flight deck level on port side, and one aft at flight deck level on starboard side.

6400 rounds of 4.5in ammunition was carried in each ship of this class. The bombs carried varied from 500lb to 20lb and the total weight was 180 tons. The supply to the 4.5in guns on the upper gallery deck was by eight electrically driven endless chain hoists from magazines to upper deck. Here, horizontal conveyers passed the ammunition to the loading positions of the upper chain hoists. Main supply for the multiple pompoms was by the bomb lifts to the flight deck. Forty-five 18in aircraft torpedoes were carried.

These ships were not fitted with Asdics.

Protection

This was the first aircraft carrier to be designed with full protection for the aircraft carried.

The flight deck consisted of structurally worked 120lb NC armour, which was considered proof against 6in plunging fire (100lb projectiles) below 23,000yds and 500lb SAP bombs dropped from 7000ft. For protection against 6in gun fire at ranges greater than 7000yds the protection to the hangar sides was 180lb C - while the hangar bulkheads were of 80lb NC plating.

The armour protection to the magazines was included in the main protection which consisted of 180lb C on the ship's side and 120 and 100lb NC on the hangar deck.

The side protection system was designed to withstand a 750lb TNT contact charge and consisted of an air-liquid-air 'sandwich' system with a 60lb D1 quality main protective bulkhead extending between stations 61 to 121, *ie* 240ft port and starboard, and continuous from outer bottom to

Illustrious in 1945 with a much enhanced radar fit and a number of modern American built aircraft.

9in above the main deck. The width of the 'sandwich' protection as 14ft 0in. To balance the asymmetric moment due to the weight of the island structure, the liquid space of the 'sandwich' protection on the port side was designed to carry a greater weight of fuel than that on the starboard side. The balance of the asymmetric moment was completed by 400 tons of ballast carried in the side protection on the port side.

Machinery
The boilers consisted of six three-drum small tube type each of 18,500shp, two in each of the three boiler rooms arranged abreast. The working pressure at boilers was 400lb/in², with steam superheated 240°F at full power. Turbine pressure gave 350lb/in². The propelling machinery consisted of a three-shaft arrangement of geared turbines fitted in three engine rooms arranged abreast. The turbine power was transmitted to the propeller shafts through single reduction double helical gearing.

The total shp was 111,000 (37,000 on each shaft) at 230rpm.

The engine rooms and boiler rooms were positioned 36ft apart to give the ship protection from underwater attack, and the machinery was arranged on the 'unit' system to further decrease the vulnerability.

The control room for the machinery was situated forward of the centre engine room.

Propeller particulars: three 3-bladed, manganese bronze propellers.

	Outers	Centre
Diameter	15ft 6in	15ft 6in
Pitch	16ft 2in	15ft 3in
Developed blade area	132ft²	144ft²

Auxiliary Machinery
Six turbo generators (each 400kW capacity) were fitted, one in each of the wing engine rooms and the remainder on the main deck, *ie* under armour. An additional four 60kW diesel generators were fitted later.

Steering gear was of electric-hydraulic type with two electrically driven pumps, one in each steering compartment, and a steam-driven pump in the centre engine room. With any one of the main pumps in use, the steering operating gear was capable of exerting a maximum torque of 500ton ft.

The gear was controlled by hydraulic telemotor systems.

The original rudder (area 28sq ft) was modified to reduce the torque, and on trials with the modified rudder of area 27sq ft a tactical diameter of

944yds and advance 918yds were measured for a speed of 27kts.

Radar fitted in 1945/6 included Types 960, 242H, 293P and 285(P).

Stability Particulars
The inclining of the first of the class, *Illustrious*, in April 1940 gave the following:

	Light Condition	Deep Condition
Metacentric height	5.02ft	7.73ft (fl)
Max GZ	3.45ft	4.32ft
Angle of max GZ	32°	32½°
Range	53°	90°
Displacement	22,260 tons	28,210 tons

These figures compare with a metacentric height and max GZ of 8.26ft and 4.99ft respectively, for the designed deep condition of 28,619 tons.

Subsequently, in 1946, another inclining showed that the displacement had increased 2980 tons due to added equipment.

The standard longitudinal strength calculation gave the following stresses:

	Hogging	Sagging
Maximum bending moment	710,250ton ft	528,000ton ft
Stress in flight deck	4.7ton/in²	2.8ton/in²
Stress in keel	4.5ton/in²	4.1ton/in²

In obtaining these figures, the modulus of the strength section was calculated in the normal way, but the side armour was omitted in both tension and in compression. The flight deck armour was arranged to form part of the structural strength of the ship, and full allowance was made for this in calculating the inertia of the section.

Complement
For the ship as designed the total war complement as a flagship was 1276. This was made up of fifty-three officers and 789 men for ship's staff, *ie* 842; and sixty-eight officers and 366 men of the Fleet Air Arm, *ie* 434. As experience was gained during the war, however, and improvements made to ship's equipment, this complement was increased considerably. This led to space difficulties and an adverse effect on habitability.

General
In all, three ships were built to this design, viz *Illustrious*, *Victorious* and *Formidable*. A fourth vessel, *Indomitable*, was ordered in the 1937 programme, and while she had the same hull and machinery as the first three ships, a number of the

[15] Only *Illustrious* had
Czech armour (see
forthcoming article by
Brown in *Warship
International*).

features of the *Implacable* and *Indefatigable* design
were introduced into her and resulted in redesign.

The *Illustrious* class served satisfactorily
throughout the war, the main modifications being
those for handling aircraft and improvements in
associated equipment. Action Information
Organisation, Radar, etc modifications were carried out as opportunity offered and as experience
was gained.

Illustrious Class

Ship	Builder	Laid Down	Launched	Completed
1936 Programme				
Illustrious	Vickers-Armstrong	27 Apr 1937	5 Apr 1939	25 May 1940
Victorious	Vickers-Armstrong	4 May 1937	14 Sep 1939	15 May 1941
1937 Programme				
Formidable	Harland & Wolff	17 Jun 1937	17 Aug 1939	24 Nov 1940

Indomitable

The *Indomitable* was originally built as one of the
Illustrious class, as included in the 1937 building
programme. At this time the design of the
Implacable and *Indefatigable* was in hand, and the
Board decided where practicable to incorporate a
number of the improved features of the new
design in the carriers still under construction. It
was only possible to do this in *Indomitable*.

Difficulty in the supply of armour from
Czechoslovakia also resulted in a redistribution in
the hangar protection.[15]

The *Indomitable*, as redesigned, was similar to
Illustrious in that she remained unaltered from
keel to upper deck, but two hangars were
arranged with an increase of 6ft in the total depth
of the ship; to save weight, a reduced thickness of
hangar side armour was accepted. To accommodate this hangar arrangement the forward lift was
moved aft 16ft and the after lift was moved forward 24ft; to maintain distance between the forward arresting wire and the crash barrier, the
arresting wires were spaced 20ft apart instead of
24ft.

In this ship, extra petrol, bombs and aircraft
equipment had to be carried and stowed, as well as
accommodation found for the increased FAA
complement. The extra gallery deck built into
this design covered these extra requirements and
also gave more space for accommodation.

The general particulars for *Indomitable* as
redesigned were:

Length overall	753ft 11in
Length on waterline	710ft 0in
Length between perps	673ft 0in
Extreme breadth	116ft 3in
Depth	73ft 9in
Displacement (standard)	23,080 tons
Displacement (deep)	28,216 tons
Draughts (deep) - FP	26ft 11in
- AP	28ft 8in
- Mean	27ft 9½in
Shp of engines	111,000
Maximum speed (deep)	30kts

Indomitable general arrangement as designed

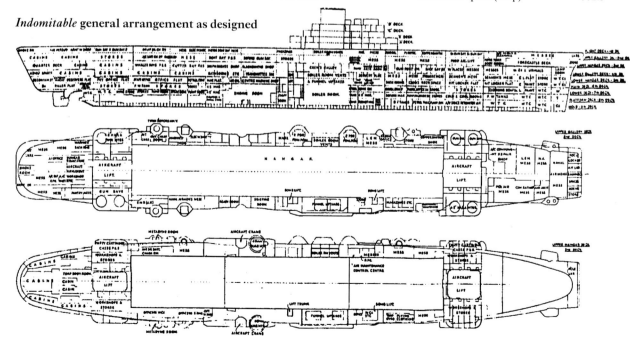

Indomitable *at Rosyth in 1944 prior to Far East deployment. Note the cruiser* Emerald *and a* Royal Sovereign *class battleship behind. The original negative of this photo is cracked.*

Endurance at 10kts (6 months out of dock)	4517 tons
Petrol	70,000gall
Legend Group Weights	
Hull	12,969 tons
Protection	4,299 tons
Machinery	2,471 tons
Armament	997 tons
Aircraft equipment	1,448 tons
General equipment	1,328 tons
Reserve feed water	187 tons
Oil fuel	4,517 tons
	28,216 tons

Aircraft Arrangements

The effective length of the flight deck was 751ft 3in with a minimum width abreast the island of 69ft 0in; deck parking for twenty aircraft was arranged.

The upper hangar was 416ft x 62ft x 14ft clear height-area 25,792sq ft, and accommodated thirty aircraft each of 20,000lb. The lower hangar was 208ft x 62ft x 16ft clear height and stowed fifteen aircraft.

The ship as designed therefore carried sixty-five aircraft - forty-five in the hangars and twenty in the park on the flight deck.[16]

Two electrically driven single platform type lifts were fitted 45ft x 33ft forward and 45ft x 22ft aft, each being capable of a 14,000lb working load. The after lift served both hangars, the forward lift served the upper hangar only. The lifts were eventually balanced for 20,000lb loads.

The time cycles obtained for the forward and after lifts were 26 and 43 seconds respectively.

One BH III catapult was fitted; this was designed to give a take-off speed of 70kts, with a 14,000lb aircraft and 66kts with a 20,000lb aircraft. The flight deck was fitted with ten arresting wires to take 20,000lb aircraft at 60-52kts, and three safety barriers for 20,000lb aircraft at 60/40kts.

Armament

This was the same as for *Illustrious* and class except that the total allowance for aircraft bombs and ammunition were for the forty-five aircraft carried instead of the thirty-three carried in *Illustrious* and class.

Protection

The protection of *Indomitable* was much the same as that for *Illustrious* and class except that the hangar side protection was reduced from 4½in C to 1½in C - this incidentally helped the situation as regards supply of armour. The flight deck remained at 3in NC.

[16] Note that petrol stowage was increased over *Illustrious* in the ratio of the number of aircraft carried in the hangar. The extra 20 in the deck park exacerbated the limited petrol supply. Similar remarks apply to aircraft weapon stowage; complement was ncreased but not the space for accommodation.

Machinery and Propeller particulars were the same as for *Illustrious* and class.

Stability

From the first inclining the following results were obtained:

	Light Condition	Deep Condition
Metacentric height	3.79ft	6.72ft
Max GZ		
(hangar intact)	3.10ft	4.67ft
Angle of max GZ	33½°	40½°
Range	64½°	over 90°
Displacement	23,526 tons	29,084 tons

These figures showed an increase of about 860 tons for the deep condition with a corresponding decrease in GM of about 12in. The increase in weight was accounted for and was due mainly to improved equipment, modifications to structure, etc., during building, and permanent ballast.

The standard longitudinal strength calculation gave the following stresses:

	Hogging	Sagging
Maximum bending moment	710,250ton ft	584,000ton ft
Stress in flight deck	5.07ton/in²	2.95ton/in²
Stress in keel	4.06ton/in²	3.96ton/in²

In obtaining the modulus of the strength section the side armour and hangar side armour was neglected in both tension and compression.

Complement

The redesigning of the *Indomitable* resulted in more spaces for accommodation especially towards the ends of the ship. This was largely offset by the increase in complement which in 1938 was given as 136 officers plus 1256 men (FAA ninety-four officers plus 433 men) and in October 1941 as 142 officers plus 1450 men. The complement increased still further and in 1946 the war complement was given as 215 officers plus 1731 men.

Implacable on completion on 14 June 1944. Note the irregular outline of the flight deck, cut away to give arcs of fire to guns and directors, but making aircraft operation more difficult than in US carriers.

1937 Programme

Ship	Builders	Laid down	Launched	Completed
Indomitable	Vickers-Armstrong	10 Nov 1937	26 Mar 1940	10 Oct 1941

Implacable and *Indefatigable*

In 1937, during the rearmament period, it was decided to build two more aircraft carriers on the lines of *Illustrious* and class, but with improved speed. Consideration was at first given to forcing the machinery to give 126,000-135,000shp but with the small improvement in speed resulting from this forcing, and the troubles expected from fitting larger propellers to meet this greater power, it was decided to adopt a four shaft arrangement of machinery. This decision meant, of course, that the *Illustrious*' lines would not be suitable and consequently a new design was started. Other requirements for the design were (i) increase in the number of aircraft carried to improve the attacking power and (ii) increase in anti-aircraft fire for defence purposes.

To satisfy these requirements and keep within the Treaty limitation of a standard displacement of 23,000 tons, it was necessary to save weight wherever possible. One item carefully considered was hangar protection and in view of the fact that a projectile would have to pass through at least one deck or the shipside before reaching the hangar, it was decided to save weight by reducing the side armour of the hangar to 60lb NC.

Another important item which was fully discussed during the design of *Implacable* was the requirements as regard the heights of the hangars. In this particular design it was found that by saving weight on the hangar side armour and elsewhere, it was practicable to stow thirty-three aircraft in the upper hangar and incorporate a lower hangar for the stowage of fifteen aircraft. A hangar height of 14ft clear was considered sufficient for

aircraft in use, or being designed at that time, and this height was fixed for the upper hangar. The air staff, however, wanted 16ft clear height in the lower hangar in order to be able to accommodate seaplanes or any other aircraft likely to be received aboard. The ship was therefore designed with a 14ft upper hangar and a 16ft lower hangar.

In 1939 there was a change in policy and it was agreed that the lower hangar should be reduced to 14ft in height.

Only one ship, *Implacable*, was included in the 1938 programme. The other ship of this class, *Indefatigable*, was included in the New Construction programme for the following year. General particulars of the class were to be:

Length overall	766ft 2in
Length on waterline	730ft 0in
Length between perps	690ft 0in
Extreme breadth	141ft 5in
Depth	70ft 11½in
Displacement (standard)	23,460 tons
Displacement (deep)	28,968 tons
Draughts, deep - FP	25ft 11½in
- AP	27ft 3¾in
- Mean	26ft 7½in
Shaft horse power	148,000
Max. speed (deep)	32-32.5kts
Endurance at 14kts	11,300mls
Oil fuel	4693 tons
Petrol	96,230gall

Legend Weights	
Hull	13,235 tons
Protection	3,645 tons
Machinery	3,128 tons
Armament	1,074 tons
Aircraft equipment	1,503 tons
General equipment	1,428 tons
Reserve feed	262 tons
Oil fuel	4,693 tons
Displacement (deep)	28,968 tons

The design was subsequently modified by raising the flight deck aft, enlarging the forward lift, extending the flight deck in way of the forward lift, increasing the splinter protection, modifying the bow and fitting diesel generators, etc. These modifications resulted in an increase in displacement of about 540 tons, and gave a new deep displacement of 29,512 tons at a mean draught of 27ft 0¾in.

Aircraft Arrangements
The dimensions of the flight deck were 760ft effective length by a minimum width at the stern of 58ft 9in; the width abreast the island structure was 88ft 6in and the width abaft the island 102ft 0in.

The two hangars were a clear 62ft wide and had a clear height of 14ft; thirty-three aircraft were stowed in the upper hangar which was 456ft in length and fifteen in the lower, 208ft in length. Arrangements were made on the flight deck for a park for twenty-four aircraft.

The middle line lifts fitted were of the same type as those in *Indomitable*, ie 45ft x 33ft forward and 45ft x 22ft aft, and were designed to take a 20,000lb working load; one BH III catapult was also fitted. The arresting gear consisted of eight arresting wires designed for 20,000lb at 60/52kts and three safety barriers tested to 20,000lb at 40kts.

The dual purpose cranes fitted port and starboard for the lifting of boats and aircraft had a working load of 7 tons at 44ft radius and 9 tons at 39ft radius.

Armament
This was generally as for *Illustrious* and class:

16-4.5in QF HA/LA guns in twin BD mountings; 400rpb
6 8-barrel, 2pdr pom-pom; 1800rpb
4-2pdr sub calibre L/A (for 4.5in guns); 135rpb
1 4-barrel, 2pdr pom-pom; 1800rpb
14-20mm Oerlikon guns in twin powered mountings; 24000rpb
2-20mm single Oerlikons; 2400rpb

Indefatigable *in January 1944. Note the rows of Oerlikons on the side of the island.*

The 4.5in guns were grouped at positions abreast at the forward and after ends of the upper hangar thus leaving the amidships portion of the flight deck available for parking aircraft free from excessive gun blast. The 4.5in magazines were arranged under the guns and supply of ammunition was direct; no horizontal conveyor belts were needed as in *Illustrious* etc. Four multiple pompom mountings were on the starboard side and the other two on the port side; the latter were arranged not to project above the level of the flight deck.

Four Directors were fitted for the main armament and one Director for each of the multiple pom-pom mountings.

With experience in the war and the need for still further improvement in close range armament, a number of modifications were made to the armament of this ship while she was still building.

With the end of hostilities in 1945 the armament fitted consisted of:

16-4.5in QF HA/LA guns
5 8-barrel, 2pdr pom-poms
3 4-barrel, 2pdr pom-poms
4-40mm single Bofors
34-20mm Oerlikons in twin powered mountings
17-single 20mm Oerlikons

Protection

The protection was, in general, the same as for *Illustrious* and class, in that flight deck consisted of 120lb NC; main side belt 180lb C. A saving in weight was made by limiting the hangar side and end protection to 60lb NC, while the lower hangar deck (top of citadel) was 100lb or 60lb NC armour. Bulkheads were of 80lb NC.

Protection to steering gear was 120lb NC and the magazine protection, which was included in the main protection, consisted of 180lb C on side and 120lb and 80lb NC on the crowns.

Underwater protection was the same as *Illustrious*, *ie* designed to withstand a 750lb contact charge of TNT over the length of the citadel. As a result of the trials on Job 74 a protective bulkhead of 55lb was fitted in lieu of the 60lb protective bulkhead in the previous classes.

Machinery

A major requirement for this design was that it should be capable of speeds up to 31kts in the deep condition. To meet this requirement four units of machinery were installed, each unit being the same as in *Illustrious*, *viz* two three-drum small-tube type boilers working at 400lb/sq in and geared turbines giving 37,000shp at 230rpm.

The total shp was 148,000, *ie* 37,000shp on each of the four shafts at 230rpm.

On trials the *Implacable* developed 149,000shp at 226rpm and gave 31.89kts on a displacement of 31,240 tons

The machinery was installed in four units with cross connections from boiler rooms to engine rooms for use in the event of damage. The boiler rooms and engine rooms were not separated longitudinally as in the three-unit aircraft carriers where the machinery spaces were three abreast, but being wing compartments were separated, where the beam of the ship permitted, by a middle line auxiliary machinery compartment 20-14ft in width.

The control room for the machinery was situated just forward of the engine rooms at platform deck level.

Propeller particulars were:
Four 3-bladed manganese bronze propellers.
Diam.   15ft 0in
Pitch   17ft 6in
Dev. blade area   132sq ft

Auxiliary Machinery

Seven turbo-generators each 400kW capacity were fitted in this ship - all under armour protection.

The steering gear was of electric hydraulic type as fitted in *Illustrious* and class.

Stability Particulars

In January 1944 an inclining experiment for the first of this class, *viz Indefatigable*, gave the following particulars:

	Deep Condition	Light Condition
Metacentric height	6.91ft	4.06ft
Max GZ (hangar intact)	4.82ft	3.27ft
Angle of max GZ (hangar intact)	$57\frac{1}{2}°$	$34\frac{1}{2}°$
Range	more than $90°$	$77°$
Max GZ (hangar free flooding)	3.52ft	3.08ft
Angle of Max GZ (hangar free flooding)	$32\frac{1}{2}°$	$32\frac{1}{2}°$
Displacement	32,101 tons	26,125 tons

The stability particulars for the deep condition in the original design were:

Metacentric height   7.65ft (FL)
Max GZ (hangar intact)   5.43ft
Angle of max GZ (hangar intact) $45\frac{1}{2}°$
Displacement   28,968 tons

The standard longitudinal strength calculation gave the following stresses:

	Hogging	Sagging
Maximum bending moment	746,500ton ft	643,000ton ft
Stresses in flight deck	5.38ton/in²	3.34ton/in²
Stresses in keel	5.26ton/in²	5ton/in²
Displacement	24,359 tons	26,676 tons

In these calculations the ship's side armour was neglected both in tension and compression.

Cost
£5,400,000 per vessel (on guns, aircraft, etc).

Complement
In the original design allowances were made for a complement of 1390 officers and men; this included 550 officers and men of the Fleet Air Arm. By the end of hostilities, due to increases in the aircraft complement and the need for more men on maintenance etc, the complement had increased to a total of 1925, *ie* 180 officers and 1745 men.

Ship	Builder	Laid Down	Launched	Completed
1938 Programme				
Implacable	Fairfields	21 Feb 1939	10 Dec 1942	28 Aug 1944
1939 Programme				
Indefatigable	J Brown	3 Nov 1939	8 Dec 1942	3 May 1944

Ark Royal Class

In 1940 consideration was given to a repeat *Implacable* modified as necessary in the light of war experience. The important modifications envisaged were:
(i)   improvement in the protection afforded by the flight deck;
(ii) increases in the number of aircraft carried;

general aircraft equipment and stores, etc. and also in the flying complement of officers and men;
(iii) increases in the sizes of the flight deck and forward lift;
(iv) increase in the clear height of the hangars by at least 6in;
(v) improved protection to magazines.

In order to produce a rapid design to meet, as far as possible, the above requirements, it was decided that *Implacable*'s underwater form and arrangements were to be remain unaltered; this also would have enabled drawings and specifications to be issued without delay.

With the minimum standard metacentric height of 4-6ft laid down by the DNC it was not found possible to incorporate a thicker flight deck in the repeat design, but the requirement for more aircraft was met by stowing the aircraft four abreast instead of three, and the increased hangar height was provided by reducing the depths of the flight deck and upper hangar deck beams by 6in. This latter modification to the *Implacable* design was agreed to after a thorough examination of the deck structural arrangements had proved that the strength and stiffness of these decks were quite inadequate [*sic*, but sense is clearly 'adequate'], and that the 6in reduction in depth could be accepted without serious effect.

On these lines the design gave a standard displacement of 23,900 tons with a GM of 4.75ft.

In February 1941, however, it was decided that the redesign should include only such modifications as had been introduced during the building of *Implacable*, and those additional requirements of outstanding importance. These included the concentration of HADTs on the island, extension of flight deck on the port side, enlargement of the forward lift and increase in the thickness of armour on the crowns of magazines. Further it was recommended that the flight deck should remain the same thickness as that in *Implacable*, but the depth of the hangar beams should be

Eagle as completed in January 1952 may be seen as representing the ultimate British carrier design of World War II. She has a very good radar fit and rows of Bofors replacing the now obsolete pom-poms and Oerlikons.

reduced 6in and the length of the lower hangar should be reduced from 208ft to 150ft.

The following month DNC began the revision of drawings from *Implacable* on the lines stated, and approval was submitted to place an order accordingly.

All the foregoing requirements and decisions were largely influenced by the understanding that the carrier of the 1940 Supplementary Programme would be ordered in the spring of 1941, and that it was essential in order to avoid delay that the carrier should be essentially a repeat *Implacable*. However, no order was placed and in the light of war experience, especially the loss of the 1934 *Ark Royal*, it became quite evident that further modifications were desirable to improve the ship generally and also her ability to withstand severe underwater damage. The important modifications considered necessary included:

(i)   greater diesel dynamo power;
(ii) improved watertight subdivision of machinery spaces;
(iii) increase in the beam to improve stability.

Meanwhile design studies were prepared for the additional tonnage involved in incorporating these latest modifications and in accordance with Controller's instructions. Three designs were submitted for consideration by the Naval staff.

(a) *Carrier with 4in Armoured Flight Deck*
Beam   100ft
Standard displacement 25,300 tons
Speed (deep)   31½kts
Overall depth as *Implacable*
Lift arrangement as *Implacable*

(b) *Carrier with 4in Armoured Flight Deck and Double Hangars*
Double hangars considered the only satisfactory solution for a requirement for the forward lift to serve both hangars.
Beam   104ft 6in
Standard displacement 27,000 tons
Speed (deep)   30½kts
Overall depth   80ft

(c) *Carrier with 3in Armoured Flight Deck as* Implacable *and Double Hangars*
Beam   100ft
Standard displacement 25,000 tons
Speed (deep)   31½kts

These designs were considered and as a result DNC was asked to investigate increasing the armour on the citadels compensated by reducing the flight deck armour, for a double hangar ship.

Two further designs were produced, but it was finally decided that (b) above most nearly met the general requirements. It was therefore decided in October 1941 to drop the 'repeat' *Implacable* design included in the 1940 programme and proceed with this new design which became the basis for the 1942 Programme Aircraft Carriers.

The staff requirements were then formulated, and in approving them ACNS(W) remarked that: 'In view of the long time taken to complete, it seems desirable for these Staff Requirements to be reviewed annually in the light of war experience and development, so that any practicable minor amendments may be made if desirable.'

The general requirements were for a carrier:

Displacement (standard) 27,000 tons
Beam   104ft
Speed (deep and dirty) 29½kts
Endurance   6000mls at 24kts
Petrol   115,000gall
Aircraft requirements   72 aircraft (folded)

with operational requirements for sixty.

Two full-length hangars with two lifts serving both the upper and lower hangars.

Armament   16-4.5 HA/LA guns
           4 HADTs
           8 8-barrelled pom-poms with predictors
Protection 4in NC armour flight deck
           4½in NC side armour
           1½ and 2in NC hangar sides

Based on these requirements, seven designs were worked out, and design 9 was submitted and approved by the Board in March 1942. The design was then worked out in detail and the Legend of particulars was submitted and approved in September 1942.

There were considerable differences between the approved design and the staff requirements, mainly due to improvements in the separation and subdivision of the machinery spaces, and the improved protection from an explosion under the bottom.

The main features of the approved design were:

Length overall   790ft
Length between perps   720ft
Breadth   108ft 8½in
Displacement (standard) 31,600 tons
Shp   152,000
Speed (deep)   31½kts
Endurance at 24kts   6000mls
Oil fuel   7000 tons
Petrol   115,000gall
Armament   16-4.5in HA/LA guns
                        8 8-barrelled pom-poms

The incomplete Ark Royal being manouevred into the Gladstone Dock, Liverpool in May 1954 for fitting out. Because her completion was so protracted, various modifications could be incorporated into the design, the most visible being the US-style deck-edge lift (seen here in the down position) on the port side amidships.

Aircraft   69-44ft x 13ft 6in
x 13ft 6in
or 57-44ft x 18ft 0in
x 13ft 6in

Steering Gear   This design was prepared with a single self-centring rudder which necessitated a considerable increase in the power of the steering gear compared with that in earlier ships.

Compared with *Implacable*, it was considered that this new design had many advantages, the more important ones being:

(i)   improved underwater protection

(ii)   improved disposition of the machinery spaces

(iii) separate funnel uptakes and air intakes to each boiler room

(iv) large side openings raised to avoid flooding in a damaged condition and their number reduced

(v)   more powerful electric generating machinery of which half were diesel driven

(vi) larger hangar space enabling a greater complement of aircraft

(vii) larger lifts, each serving both hangars, and more extensive arresting and catapulting arrangements

(viii) improved close range defence with more elaborate control arrangements

Four ships were ordered to this design, *Ark Royal*, *Audacious*, *Eagle* and *Africa*. Work on *Africa* and *Eagle* was eventually suspended, the *Audacious* later being renamed *Eagle*.

Limitations of the Design

In September 1942, in accordance with Controller's instructions, DNC prepared a statement of the limitations of the design in the light of experience, probably developments of weapons etc. The following points were covered in DNC's statement:

(a) the staff requirements in themselves implied certain limitations.

(b) the necessarily greater beam than *Implacable* afforded better protection, but limited docking.

(c) the RU ammunition stowed in exposed positions near petrol supply points constituted a fire risk.

(d) the aircraft lifts were outside the armoured flight deck and were unprotected. The sizes of the lifts, which served both hangars, involved extensive cuts through the structure of the ship and although this was allowed for in the design of the structure in the vicinity, there was an inevitable discontinuity of strength. This was particularly undesirable in view of the possibility of underwater explosion in the neighbourhood.

(e) the underwater protection was based on full-scale trials. The shape and breadth of the ship at the ends, however, did not permit working underwater protection other than close subdivision. No complete protection against explosion under the bottom had been devised, but the inner bottom had been made 1in thick and was connected to the transverse and longitudinal bulkheads. This localised the flooding between intact bulkheads.

(f) concentration of controls in the island which was only protected against splinters.

(g) propulsion and steering - like all existing ships the design was vulnerable to a hit aft near the rudder and propellers. To meet this danger to some extent, the propellers were separated as far as possible and each of the twin rudders had a separate steering gear in its own WT compartment. In addition an auxiliary bow rudder was provided.[17]

(h) the large armoured doors at ends of hangars could possibly jam and prevent operation of aircraft from the hangars.

(i) the citadel was relatively short.

The increase in height of the hangar had now become a further staff requirement and was based on very recent experience showing that our carriers might be required to carry American aircraft. Also the necessity for removing this particular limitation would facilitate the development of aircraft of higher performance.

It was evident that a clear height of 17ft 6in was necessary in the hangars to take account of these extra requirements, and the various methods of doing this were reviewed.

DNC decided to keep the flight deck thickness of 4in and increase the beam 4ft to 112ft 8½in to compensate for the increase in top weight. This method was approved by the Board in December 1942, and a new sheer draught and general arrangement and structural drawings were prepared.

In order to minimise delay:

(i) the main longitudinal protective bulkhead was retained in its original position.

(ii) increased width taken up in OF tanks, the air spaces outside main protective bulkhead remaining the same on the port side, ie 4ft, but increased to 5ft 3in on the starboard side.

(iii) main transverse bulkheads at same stations as before.

(iv) layout of ship below the lower hangar deck was not greatly changed.

(v) above the lower hangar deck the hangar bulkheads were straightened to give a clear width of hangar of 67ft, in lieu of the original 62ft.

(vi) deep beam under the upper hangar deck increased from 2ft 6in to 2ft 9in in depth due to increase in the width of the hangar.

(vii) flight deck plating under the armour was reduced from 60lb to 40lb to save weight.

The main machinery arrangements remained unchanged, but the centre of the outer propellers was lowered 3in order to give satisfactory tip clearance. Then refairing the lines for the new body the width at the transom was reduced as much as possible as recommended by Haslar for improving steering qualities and EHP. There was a small loss in design speed due to change of form. The resultant displacement was about 32,400 tons standard.

In accordance with the instructions issued by ACNS(W), the staff requirements for the design were reviewed in November 1942 and the following amendments were made:

(1) Standard displacement approximately 32,500 tons with a beam of 112ft 8½in overall on the waterline.

(2) Ship should be fitted as a carrier flagship but consideration should be given to fitting as a fleet flagship.

(3) Estimated design speed with clean bottom about 31¼kts; 29¼ six months out of dock in tropical waters.

(4) Consideration to be given to fitting a small retractable rudder forward to maintain steerage in the event of the main steering gear being put out of action.

(5) Hangar space for at least sixty-nine aircraft of 13ft 6in width x 17ft 0in height. The space provided also to be capable of accommodating at least fifty-seven aircraft of 40ft x 18ft x 17ft. The operational number of aircraft to be regarded as sixty.

(6) Both hangars to have a clear height of 17ft 6in under the beams.

(7) A minimum clear width of 62ft in the hangars.

(8) Working load of lifts to be increased to 30,000lb.

(9) Side transporters to be fitted in hangars.

(10) Approximately 115,000gall petrol and 7760gall oil.

(11) Increase in size of bomb lifts to take 2000lb, AP bomb. Revision of scale of bomb stowage.

(12) Provision of two fixed masts.

(13) Modifications in communication rooms arrangements and communication equipment and RDF equipment.

The second annual amendment to the staff requirements included the following revisions:

(1) Aircraft complement: 42 TBR + 36 FF
or 24 TBR + 54 FF
and acceptable for a proportion of the aircraft complement to be permanently parked on the flight deck, ie Introduction of the Deck Park Policy.

(2) Arresting gear and safety barrier gear to deal with 30,000lb aircraft at 75kts, maximum deceleration 2g.

(3) Two cranes 25,000lb, working load.

(4) Bridge offices and action information organisation revised.

(5) Further revision of bomb outfit based on 42 TBR + 18 FF.

(6) 8 8-barrelled pom-poms or alternatively 8 8-barrelled Bofors.

Numerous other changes were made to the design during building and in September 1945 Deputy Controller proposed to consider the changes necessary to bring the ships up-to-date. Long discussions followed, the results of which were found completely unsatisfactory by the First Lord. A comprehensive statement of changes to date and a new legend were prepared by DNC in 1946.

DNC's statement pointed out that most of the proposed modernisation items had already been approved piecemeal, and that the differences between the design to date and the design originally submitted were mainly accounted for by large alterations which took place in 1942 and 1943. These large changes brought about an increase in dimensions and displacement with a corresponding reduction in speed.

General particulars of the design to the 1946 Legend were:

Length between perpendiculars	720ft 0in
Length overall	803ft 9in
Length on waterline	750ft 0in
Breadth on waterline	112ft 8½in
Breadth extreme	135ft 0in

Depth of ship USK to flight deck	86ft 2in
Deep displacement	45,720 tons
Standard displacement	36,970 tons
Draughts (deep) - F	31ft 1½in
- A	34ft 5½in
- Mean	32ft 9½in
Shp	152,000
Speed (deep)	30½kts
Speed (standard)	31½kts
Endurance at 24kts	5000mls
Oil fuel	6510 tons
Petrol	103,000gall
Aircraft diesel oil (ASF)	279,000gall

Legend Weights

Hull	20,680 tons
Machinery	3,560 tons
Armament	1,390 tons
Armour and protection	6,320 tons
Equipment	2,510 tons
Aircraft equipment	3,510 tons
Oil fuel	5,820 tons
Reserve feed water	270 tons
Lubricating oil	30 tons
ASF	440 tons
Displacement (deep)	1,190 tons
	45,720 tons

Aircraft Arrangements

The ship was designed to operate aircraft up to 40,000lb weight but, as aircraft of this weight were not likely to be in service for some years, the lifts were balanced to 35,000lb only. The limitations on dimensions of British naval aircraft were:

Length	48ft
Span	60ft
Span folded	27ft
Height	17ft

All these dimensions could be exceeded in *Eagle* and *Ark Royal*.

The effective length of the flight deck was 797ft 6in and the width (abaft the island) 112ft. The widths of the flight deck at the bow and stern were 68ft and 91ft 6in respectively.

There were two main hangars and one hangar extension. The dimensions of the upper hangar were 364ft x 67ft x 17ft 6in giving a clear area of 24,390sq ft; the lower hangar's dimensions were the same but the clear area was 23,760sq ft. The upper hangar extension was 52ft x 64ft x 17ft 6in with a clear area of 3,270sq ft.

The hangars were each divided into three sections by fire curtains while the lift openings could

be sealed off by hydraulically operated armour
doors. The time to open and close was about three
seconds.

Two electrically driven lifts were provided, one
at each end of the hangars. Each lift served both
hangars and had a running time from lower
hangar to flight deck of 18.3 seconds, and upper
hangar to flight deck of 11.5 seconds. The dimensions of the lifts were 54ft x 44ft and 54ft x 33ft,

forward and aft respectively, and both were
designed for a working load of 35,000lb.

Two BH5 catapults were fitted at the bow. They
were designed to take 30,000lb at 75kts or
14,000lb, at 85kts. The total length of trolley track
was 140ft 9in, with maximum accommodation for
$3\frac{1}{4}$g. The rate of launch per catapult was one aircraft every forty seconds with three pumps working, or one aircraft every sixty seconds with two

pumps. Automatic roller-type aircraft positioners were fitted to centre the aircraft in the catapult loading position.

Arresting gear Mark 10 was fitted. This consisted of sixteen wires rigged in pairs to eight self-contained units mounted vertically against the hangar bulkheads port and starboard, HP air of hydraulic power was only required for recharging the system. The gear was designed to a capacity of 30,000lb, with a maximum entry speed of 75kts, or 20,000lb, with a corresponding maximum entry speed of 91kts. The maximum pull-out was 172ft.

Six safety barriers were fitted and operated from three units similar to the arresting units. The barrier stanchions were operated by vertical hydraulic rams situated under the flight deck. From aft the barriers were:

No 1 Net for jet aircraft
No 2 Three wire barrier for single propeller aircraft
No 3 Three wire barrier for single propeller aircraft
No 4 Net for Sea Hornet aircraft
No 5 Net for jet aircraft
No 6 Three wire barrier

Two aircraft cranes were installed, one port and one starboard, each with a working load of 25,000lb at 27ft radius and 14,000lb at 41ft radius. The mobile equipment included one 20,000lb mobile crane, two 15,000lb fork lift trucks with 2ft 3in outreach, two Olding Mk II tractors and six Clarkat tractors.

Aircraft Ammunition

Stowage was provided in the main and ready use magazines for ten loads of gun ammunition for seventy-five aircraft, based on an average of 640 rounds per aircraft. Provision was made in the bomb rooms for nine loads of bombs for thirty-six strike aircraft, based on a load of one 2000lb, or two 1000lb, or four 500lb, bombs per load.

Three hydraulically operated bomb lifts were fitted. Torpedoes were stowed in adjustable racks which were capable of stowing weapons from 10½in to 30in in diameter. A total of sixty 18in torpedoes could be stowed in the torpedo rooms.

Structural Arrangements

Welding was used to a greater extent in this design than in previous aircraft carriers. The principal items which were welded included:

(i) butts of outer bottom plating below the lower hangar deck
(ii) double bottom structure
(iii) main transverse bulkheads
(iv) longitudinal bulkheads, except the main protective bulkheads

(v) outer bottom plating above the lower hangar deck
(vi) flight and other deck plating, fore and forward of 33 station

(The Unionmelt welding process was used wherever possible.)[18]

Riveted items included:

(i) seams of outer bottom plating below the hangar deck
(ii) connection of vertical keel to flat keel and gutter strake
(iii) structure in way of gun supports and shaft brackets
(iv) main longitudinal protective bulkhead

As there had been evidences of weakness in the fore end structure of previous carriers, the fore ends of these ships were strengthened by reducing the frame spacing forward of the citadel from 4ft to 3ft. Attention was also given to the shape of the bow in order to reduce the possibility of damage from seas slamming the areas under the overhang of the flight deck.

The flight deck was designed to handle 40,000lb aircraft and to take a mobile crane loaded with 30,000lb.

An essential feature of the design was the subdivision of the ship into as large a number of watertight compartments as was practicable. This subdivision was obtained by:

(i) Main transverse bulkheads which were watertight up to the underside of the upper hangar deck. Below the main deck these bulkheads were only pierced for essential services and in such instances watertight valves and glands were provided at the bulkheads.
(ii) Longitudinal bulkheads which were watertight up to the lower hangar deck.
(iii) All decks up to and including the lower gallery deck were watertight.

Excluding the bottom plating and the island structure, there were ten watertight decks. Of these, the top seven decks were continuous except where broken by hangars and lift wells; and the bottom three decks were only broken in way of machinery spaces, deep compartments forward and aft, and in way of petrol stowages. In addition to the normal subdivision by transverse bulkheads, the ship was specially subdivided along its length into seven self-contained sections. Each of these sections had a self-contained salvage pumping system for damage control.

To restrict flooding resulting from underwater explosion damage, the main transverse bulkheads

[18] 'Unionmelt' was a proprietary automatic welding process.

were carried intact to the outer bottom and particular attention paid to the welded connection with the inner bottom.

Armament

16–4.5in guns in twin mountings
8 6-barrelled 40mm Bofors mountings
2 twin-barrelled Bofors
12 single mountings

The main 4.5in armament was mounted in four batteries each with its own Mk 37 long-range control director, two to port and two to starboard. All turrets were flush with the flight deck, as were the port side directors.

The 4.5in gun armament was expected to function efficiently up to approximately 20° of heel, provided of course that electric power was maintained.

A total outfit of 6600 rounds of separate ammunition was stowed in two magazines forward and two aft, shell lines and bottle racks being fitted in each magazine. Ammunition supply to the main armament was by Inclined Duplex Endless chain hoists - one for each mounting; each hoist was capable of delivering ammunition at the rate of thirty rounds per minute direct from the magazine to the gun bay.

The secondary armament consisted of eight 6-barrel 40mm Bofors each with its own CRBF director, two twin Bofors with simple tachymetric directors and single Bofors. Total ammunition stowage was 32,080 rounds, while a minimum of 288 rounds per barrel was stowed adjacent to each mounting.

Protection

Ship sides	180lb NC lower strake 180lb NC (special)
Flight deck	160lb C (lightly cemented)
Hangar sides and ends	60lb NC
Magazine sides	180lb C
Magazine deck (over)	160lb NC
Protection over shafts etc.	100lb NC on lower deck

Above water there were two main systems of armour protection. The first of these was intended to protect the hangars and restrict damage to the flight deck, besides giving general protection to the inside of the ship. This upper system consisted of a 4in armoured flight deck and 1in structural plating extending over the hangars, with $1\frac{1}{2}$in vertical splinter protection over the sides and ends of the hangars. The second system, the citadel, was complementary to the first and was

Eagle *in March 1952. As completed, the ship was relatively well equipped with radar and other electronics.*

intended to provide similar protection to the magazines, machinery and other vital spaces. It consisted of 4½in side protection with 2½in 'roof', where not protected by the hangar decks.

Vital compartments outside this citadel were boxed in with armour, *eg* steering gear 4in armour on the deck over and 2in and 4½in on the forward and after ends respectively.

The boiler uptakes and downtakes, hangar access lobbies, bomb lifts and electric cables trunks were also armoured. Splinter protection was fitted in way of the 4.5in mountings, island structure and Bofors platforms.

Underwater Protection
The side protection was of the sandwich type with an air-liquid-air system outboard of the main protective bulkhead. The main longitudinal bulkhead comprised two thicknesses of 'D' quality plating up to the middle deck with the inner plate continued to the main deck. The bulkhead was sloped at an angle of 5° from the vertical with the top end nearer the ship side and was approximately 19ft 6in from the ship side at 20ft above the keel.

The oil fuel in the wing tanks was displaced by water, so that the air-liquid-air system was not affected when using oil from these tanks. The mean width of the side protection was about 20ft and consisted of a 4ft inboard air space, an 11ft fuel space and an outboard air space of 5ft approximately. The structure was all riveted.

To provide some measure of protection against explosions under the bottom, the inner bottom was made 40lb DW plating, *ie* 10lb heavier than the outer bottom.

Machinery
The main propelling machinery consisted of four self-contained, independent units giving the four shafts a total of 152,000shp at full power. Each unit consisted of a boiler room, engine room, gearing room, turbo generator room, diesel generator rooms and evaporator room etc.

The forward units driving the two outer shafts were divided into two boiler rooms in tandem; immediately abaft were two engine rooms abreast and then two gearing rooms abreast. The two inner shafts were operated by a similar arrangement of machinery spaces situated abaft the forward units.

Each boiler room contained two Admiralty three-drum type boilers side by side, with working pressures of 400lb/in².

Malesco superheaters were fitted to raise the steam in the boilers to 250°F superheat; the temperature of the steam at the turbines was 700°F. Foster Wheeler Economisers were also fitted and the exhaust gas temperatures were reduced to 450°F at full power.

The main engines consisted of the usual arrangement of impulse reaction HP and LP turbines driving the shafts through single reduction gearing. No cruising turbines were fitted but there was an impulse type cruising stage at the forward end of each HP turbine.

The machinery was controlled from the starboard forward engine room, and a complete set of instruments and controls were fitted in the damage control secondary headquarters.

Propeller particulars:
Four 3-bladed propellers
Diam	15ft 0in
Pitch	17ft 2in
Developed blade area	125sq ft
Propeller shaft	21in external diameter
	16½in internal diameter

Trial Results
On trials in April 1951, *Eagle* at full power made 30.53kts at 44,250 tons displacement with 156,630shp and 228.2rpm. The corresponding propulsive coefficient was 0.51. This result gave an estimated maximum speed of 29.6kts (deep and clean) with the deep displacement of 49,950 tons and the same propulsive coefficient. The corresponding endurance from these results gave 4500mls, at 24kts, six months out of dock and on an average action condition of 48,700 tons.

The ship was fitted with twin stern rudders and an emergency bow rudder which was retractable. The two main steering gears were designed to exert a torque of 550ton ft at amidships and work to 35° P and S, time from hard over to hard over being thirty seconds. The bow rudder was driven by electric hydraulic gear capable of exerting 125ton ft at 35°.

The twin stern rudders each had an area of 170sq ft, with 17.6% balance. The bow rudder was 56sq ft in area with 20% balance.

The turning trials demonstrated that the ship handled well and easily with main rudders even in strong winds. The turning qualities were favourable and the tactical diameter at 30kts and 35° rudder angle was 847yds, and at 15kts 802yds. The maximum angle of heel at full power was 5.3° and the average rate of steady turn 1.4 degrees/sec.

Electric Generating Machinery
A total of 4000kW was provided by four turbo generators and four diesel generators each of 500kW capacity; these supplied a 220v ring main situated on the middle deck. The ring main was designed to operate in four separate units under

action conditions, each unit being powered by one turbo and one diesel generator. Each turbo-generator was situated in its own compartment, but the diesel generators were in each engine room. 220v HP radar supplies were provided by two 35 kVA-60 cycle motor alternators; LP supplies were provided from duplicate sets in separate groups of LP rooms.

Hydraulic Machinery

Three hydraulic units were fitted to pump 8cu ft per minute at 1250lb/in². The following services were supplied from the hydraulic ring main: bomb lifts, hangar door operating gear, wireless mast raising and lowering gear, barrier stanchion operating gear, initial filling and topping up of arresting and safety barrier units.

The hydraulic gear was designed so that each pump was capable of operating one bomb lift plus the W/T mast system.

Pumping, Flooding and Draining Arrangements

The firemain consisted of a 6in ring main maintained at 75lb/in² by eight 75ton/hr hull and fire pumps, eight 75ton/hr turbo-driven fire and bilge pumps and four 75ton/hr electrically driven fire and bilge pumps.

The fire and bilge pumps, although intended primarily for fire fighting, were connected to the salvage pump system and could be used for routine pumping of machinery spaces.

A salvage pumping system was fitted in this ship and consisted of twelve 350 ton/hr salvage pumps; two pumps, one port and one starboard, in each main watertight subdivision of the ship. In addition one 1000ton/hr salvage pump was fitted in each boiler room and engine room.

The hangar spray system consisted of a ring main under the lower hangar deck maintained at 90lb/in² by four 150ton/hr hangar spray pumps.

The ships also carried eighteen portable pumps with a total pumping capacity of 1200ton/hr.

The following air compressors were fitted:

> Four 128cu ft/min (free air) at 4000lb/in²
> Two 50cu ft/min (free air) at 4000lb/in²

Radar

Fitted included types 960, 293Q, 982, 983 and 961.

The PPIs fitted on the compass platform, chart house and admiral's bridge were fed from types 293Q or 982.

Stability Particulars

As a result of the first inclining of the ship the stability particulars were quoted as:

	Deep Condition	Light Condition
Metacentric height	7.08ft	2.85ft
Max GZ (hangar intact)	6.52ft	4.3ft
Angle of max GZ (hangar intact)	42°	47°
Range	79°	61.6°
Max GZ (hangar free flooding)	5.8ft	4.2ft
Angle of Max GZ	37°	40°
Range	64.2°	59.5°
Displacement	49,950 tons	39,500 tons

These figures compared with the designed metacentric height of 8.6ft in the deep condition of 45,720 tons. A thorough investigation into the reasons for the increase in weight during building showed that approximately 1400 tons was accounted for in hull incidentals; 1100 tons in general fittings including pumping, flooding and draining arrangements, W/T and radar; armament and ammunition 400 tons, and permanent ballast 600 tons etc.

The standard longitudinal strength calculation gave the following stresses for hogging and sagging:

	Hogging	Sagging
Bending moment amidships	11.64 x 10⁵ton ft	8.79 x 10⁵ton ft
Stress in flight deck	7.15 (a) ton/in² 7.16 (b) ton/in²	5.0 (a) ton/in² 4.9 (b) ton/in²
Stress in keel	5.0 (a) ton/in² 4.9 (b) ton/in²	4.05 (a) ton/in² 3.34 (b) ton/in²
Displacement	43,702 tons	42,265 tons

The inertias of sections had been worked out, (a) neglecting altogether armour not worked structurally, (b) assuming this armour effective in compression only. In both cases armour worked structurally was included as fully effective in both tension and compression.

Complement etc.

The estimated war complement as a flagship based on eighty-four aircraft with 50% overbearing of aircrews was 2739. This was made up of a ship complement of 1562 including 132 officers and an air complement of 1177 including 151 officers. Accommodation was provided for 2843 total. The peace complement as a private ship was 2275.

Two important innovations were introduced to improve the standard of accommodation. Firstly, the adoption of centralised messing, in which all meals were eaten in special dining halls and not in individual messes, which then became virtually sleeping and recreation spaces. Secondly, the provision of air conditioning to the mess spaces on the main deck.

The following standards of accommodation were obtained in messes:

CPO & 18sq ft/man (kit lockers in the mess)
PO   16sq ft/man (kit lockers outside the mess)
Ratings 16sq ft/man (kit lockers in the mess)
       14sq ft/man (kit lockers outside the mess)

Seats were provided for 70% of the complement.

The crew's galley was situated on the upper gallery deck forward, and catered for 1760 ratings; the layout of the galley was suitable for team service or self service, from either side. The CPOs' and POs' galley was on similar lines and could cater for 880 men, while the officers' galley (for 440 men) was for both ward room and gun room officers. Other galleys fitted included the admiral's galley on the upper gallery deck aft, the admiral's bridge galley and two bridge galleys for officers. All galleys were electric.

Cost
Vote 8 cost of *Eagle* was £16,500,000.

General
Great care was taken in designing the ventilation arrangements for these ships and the ventilation finally fitted was arranged to suit both tropical and Arctic conditions.

Two stage HE screw fans were used where large quantities of air were needed low in the ship and, to avoid 'short circuiting', the exhausts and intakes were sited as below:

(a) All ship and machinery exhausts under the flight deck.
(b) All intake under the upper gallery deck.
(c) Hangar and petrol compartment exhausts under the upper hangar.

Air conditioning arrangements were fitted to all vital action compartments, all living and working spaces low down in the ship and all spaces containing perishable goods. The machinery for air conditioning comprised three steam jet cooling plants each of capacity 1,000,000 BTU per hour. A calorifier was fitted with each plant for alternative heating under cold weather conditions.

For service in Arctic conditions the ships were lagged with limpet asbestos lagging[19] and steam heating was fitted to FW tanks, exposed control positions, scuppers, accelerators and other exposed mechanisms.

Fuelling at sea - arrangements were provided for receiving furnace fuel oil at sea, and for replenishing escorts. Sufficient equipment was provided for replenishing two escorts simultaneously - one abeam and one astern.

Stowage for provisions was arranged as follows:

Dry provisions, flour and canteen stores - stowage for ninety days' stores for the full war complement
Fresh and frozen provisions - forty-five days' stores
Sea victualling reserve - thirty-four days' stores
Potatoes - thirty days' requirements based on the full war complement

Ark Royal Class

Ship	Builder	Laid Down	Launched	Completed
1942 Programme				
Eagle	Harland & Wolff	24 Oct 1942	19 Mar 1946	1 Mar 1952
1940 Supplementary Programme				
Ark Royal	Cammell Laird	3 May 1943	3 May 1950	–

19 The hazards of asbestos were then unknown and many shipyard and dockyard men died as a result of working with this material.

CHAPTER 4

Light Fleet Carriers

Editorial Note

The light fleet aircraft carriers described in this chapter may be seen as amongst the most successful warship designs of all time, some of them remaining in service in other navies in 1995. The designs were developed by Vickers' chief naval architect, J S Redshaw, from preliminary studies by A Mitchell, RCNC. It should, however, be noted that none suffered action damage and few were involved in fighting where their limitations of speed, armament and protection might have been apparent.

The later Hermes class were clearly much superior warships to the Colossus class but it is by no means clear that the additional building time and use of scarce resources was justified in wartime. Hermes, herself, was referred to during the Falklands war as 'like a •••• great steel fort'.

By mid-1941 our experience in the war at sea had shown that there was a great need for more fighter support ships. At that time there were a number of fleet carriers building and projected, but the urgency of the situation demanded an even greater number of aircraft carriers and as quickly as possible.

The Naval staff considered that the general requirements would be met by a ship with a flight deck 450ft x 60ft hangar to accommodate and service fifteen fighter aircraft, and speed of 25kts; no protection would be needed. DNC was requested to investigate the possibility of meeting these requirements by either:

   (i)   the conversion of a *Hawkins* class cruiser
   (ii) conversion of a liner of the *Winchester Castle* type
or (iii) designing and building a new cheap unprotected carrier - 'Woolworth' carrier.[1]

On DNC's advice it was decided to proceed with (iii) and on 30 December 1941 instructions were given for sketch designs to be prepared. In order to simplify the design and accelerate the production of these ships it was suggested that merchant ship practice should be adopted except in regard to the main propelling machinery.[2] They were to have little armament and no protection.

As DNC department was more than fully occupied with other design work at the time, it was proposed by DNC that the design should be undertaken by a shipbuilding firm to requirements laid down by the Admiralty. The Controller agreed to this proposal and suggested that the main machinery of *Bellerophon* - a *Fiji* class cruiser on which work had been suspended - should be used in the first ships of the class, while a measure of underwater protection should be provided by filling the hold spaces with buoyancy drums.[3] As soon as DNC had investigated the whole scheme

and had decided that it was practicable, Messrs Vickers-Armstrongs, whose staff were well versed in both warship and merchant ship practices, were selected to undertake the design to the following draft staff requirements prepared by DNC:

Flight deck	600ft x 75ft
Hangar height	14ft 6in
Ship to accommodate fifteen fighters and fifteen TSRs	
Two lifts 45ft x 34ft to take 15,000lb	
Petrol	40,000gall
Armament:	2-4in HA/LA guns aft
	2-4in HA/LA guns forward
	4 4-barrel pom-poms
	8 Oerlikons
Generators:	3-300kW turbo generators
	2-150kW diesel generators
Endurance	6000 miles at 20kts

The first sketch design was received and discussed with the Controller on 14 January 1942; as a result of the discussions it was decided to develop the design and incorporate the following improvements:

   (i)   provide assisted take-off gear
   (ii) move the lifts
   (iii) increase the length of the flight deck by 20ft to enable a Typhoon aircraft to take off without using the ATOG
   (iv) arrange separate boiler rooms and fit extra small boilers
   (v) move engine room aft to reduce the length of the propeller shafts
   (vi) fit two crash barriers
   (vii) increase the number of aircraft carried to eighteen fighters or TSRs in the hangar, six aircraft on the flight deck and four aircraft stripped
  (viii) increase in petrol stowage to 75,000gall

---

[1] It is interesting that these ships were the original 'Woolworth' carriers, a nickname more usually associated with escort carriers.

[2] This seems to be the origin of the persistent and incorrect story that they were designed for easy conversion to liners after the war.

[3] The use of empty drums as torpedo protection had proved very effective in armed merchant cruisers, see chapter XXV.

Colossus class general arrangement as completed

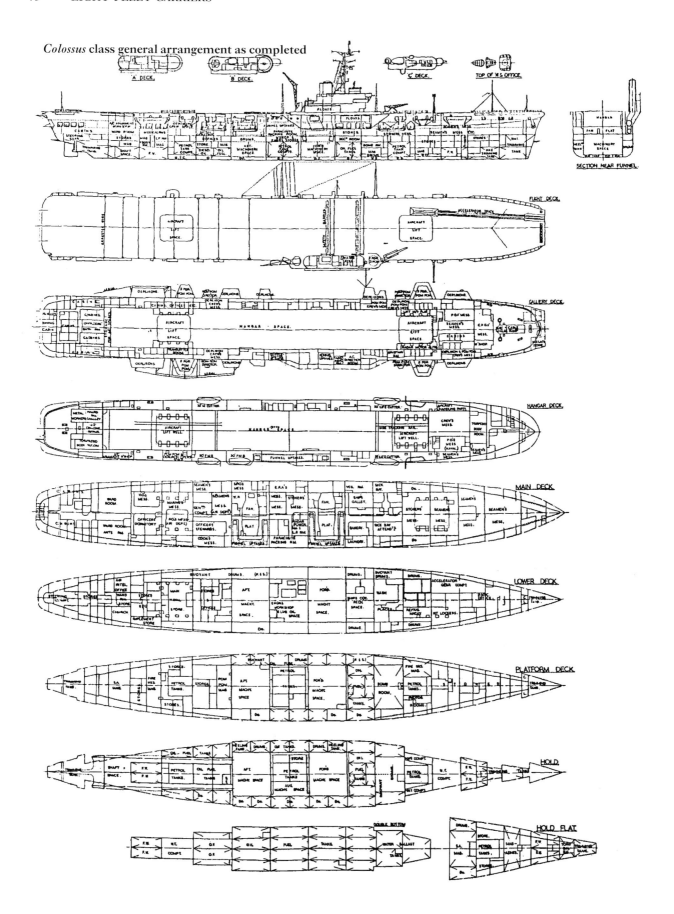

4 *Ocean* completed in 1945 at a cost of £2,362,000 taking 20,772 man months of shipyard work.

These improvements were incorporated in a new sketch design which was produced by Vickers-Armstrongs and examined by Controller, ACNS(W) and DNC on 23 January 1942. The building time for this new sketch design was estimated to be twenty-four months - an increase of three months.

Further additions were still required by the staff and another, but more elaborate, design was prepared for consideration. Included were:

(i)   increase in the clear height of the hangar to 16ft 6in
(ii) revision and increase in the armament
(iii) petrol stowage increased to 100,000gall
(iv) increased electrical power
(v)   more spaces to be allocated for the stowage of buoyant drums
(vi) protective plating to be fitted around the bridge, etc.

This final sketch design of the intermediate carrier was submitted to the Board in February 1942, and the submission included a statement to the effect that the estimated cost was of the order of £1.8m and the time to build twenty-seven months.[4]

In approving the ordering of three intermediate carriers the First Lord minuted to the effect that he was concerned with the increase in time to build and in view of the fact that the ships were to be unarmoured and therefore vulnerable it was not wise to be continuously adding to the design and delaying production when what was needed was temporary reinforcements pending completion of the armoured carriers included in the long-term programmes. He then stated that the maximum period of construction was to be twenty-one months and that everything which was not vital was to be omitted to ensure that this building time was not exceeded. The building time was later modified to twenty-four months, but there was an all-round reduction in requirements including a reduction in armament.

Colossus Class

The general particulars of the design as approved were:

LBP	630ft
Length on waterline	650ft
Length overall	682ft 0in
Extreme breadth	80ft 0in
Displacement (standard)	14,000 tons
Mean draught (standard)	19ft 0in
Mean draught (deep)	23ft 0in
Shp	40,000 (2 shafts)

Speed (deep)	25kts
Endurance at 20kts	8500 miles
Petrol	96,000gall
Aircraft lubricating oil	7000gall
Complement (inc 7½% supernumaries)	1054

The first contracts were placed in March 1942, two ships with Vickers-Armstrongs and one with Harland & Wolff; further contracts were placed in August of the same year.

With the placing of the contracts Messrs Vickers-Armstrongs were made responsible for the development of the approved design and for forwarding all the necessary information to the other builders. A demarcation of drawing work was arranged between the builders, who in turn, were made responsible for submitting all structural drawings and those not requiring special Admiralty approval, to Vickers-Armstrongs for approval. The building firms were given a free hand to amend structural plans etc, to suit their own particular practice and facilities, providing of course that the departures from the structural arrangements did not reduce the strength of the design or unduly increase the weight. Further, they were encouraged to forward any suggestions they had which would lead to reduction in the times for building.

Towards the end of 1942 proposals were put forward to increase the length of the flight deck of these ships, by extending the deck further aft; this was approved in March 1943. To allow for the extension of the flight deck the two 4in twin mountings on the quarter deck were removed and two quadruple Oerlikons fitted in lieu.

In the light of experience in *Illustrious* and *Victorious* in the operation of large deck parks of aircraft, it was decided in January 1944 to work a deck park and so provide the intermediate carriers (or light fleet carriers as they were to became called) with an establishment of aircraft to enable them to be equipped at any time with the maximum numbers which the occasion demanded. For this class - *Colossus* class - the total establishment became twenty-four TBRs and thirty-four fighters, to provide for twenty-four Barracuda aircraft and twenty-four Seafires, or eighteen Barracuda aircraft and thirty-four Seafires.

The increase in aircraft establishment resulted in additional complement, which rose to 120 officers and 1216 men, and extra demand for stowage for small arms, ammunition, aircraft equipment and spares, etc. No increases were made for torpedo and bomb stowages.

The final particulars for *Colossus* class as built were:

Length overall	695ft 0in
Length on the waterline	650ft 0in
Length between perps	630ft 0in
Extreme breadth on WL	80ft
Breadth over gun sponsons	112ft 6in
Depth of ship	62ft 6in
Displacement (deep)	18,040 tons
Displacement (standard)	13,190 tons
Mean draught (deep)	23ft 5in
shp of machinery	40,000
Speed (deep)	25kts
Endurance at 20kts	8500 miles
Oil fuel	3190 tons
Petrol	80,000gall

Summary of Weights

An estimate of group weights made during build-ing gave the following figures:

Hull and general fittings	9,240 tons
Machinery	1,180 tons
Armament	215 tons
Aircraft equipment etc	1,240 tons
Stores and equipment	1,440 tons
RFW	128 tons
Oil fuel and diesel oil	3,315 tons
Water protection to petrol tanks	830 tons
Board margin	300 tons
Deep displacement	17,888 tons

Aircraft Arrangements

The effective length of the flight deck was 690ft 0in with a minimum width of 45ft at the bow; the width abreast the island structure was 75ft 0in.

The hangar dimensions were 342ft x 52ft clear width x 17ft 6in clear height which gave a hangar clear area of 17,450sq ft. The hangar was fitted with spraying arrangements and four fire cur-tains.

Two lifts were fitted, each 45ft x 34ft and designed to take a 15,000lb working load. The time cycle for these lifts (ie a down journey loaded and an up journey unloaded) was about thirty-six seconds. In an effort to simplify this design to keep to the stipulated building time of twenty-four months, only one set of lift operating machinery was fitted per lift instead of the usual two sets.

Eight arrester wires with four Mark 8 units were fitted. These were rated to arrest a 15,000lb aircraft at 60kts. Experience with the first ships to complete showed that additional wires would be an advantage and an additional unit and two extra wires were fitted as opportunity offered. Two safety barriers tested to take 15,000lb aircraft at 40kts were also fitted.

Each ship was fitted with one BH III catapult designed to launch a 20,000lb aircraft at 66kts.

Armament

The class was originally designed with two twin 4in mountings aft. In order to increase the length of the flight deck the 4in mountings were sacri-ficed and approval obtained for the fitting of Oerlikons in two quadruple mountings in lieu.

The final approved armament was:

> 24–2pdr pom-poms in quadruple mountings
> 44 Oerlikons in quadruple mountings
> 20 Oerlikons in twin hand-worked mount-ings

In the first few ships to complete twin Oerlikons were fitted in place of the quadruple mountings, until the latter became available.[5]

Ammunition stowage was arranged on the basis of 1800 rounds per barrel for the pom-poms and 2400 rounds per barrel for the Oerlikons. The stowage arrangements for aircraft armament was

[5] The quadruple Oerlikon never entered service.

Triumph, a light fleet carrier, one of the great designs of all time, designed by J S Redshaw of Vickers-Armstrong. Few of these completed during the war but they were to form the backbone of postwar fleets and performed well in the Korean war. Some even remain in service in 1995.

based on the requirements for eighteen TBRs and thirty-four fighters which consisted broadly of:

36-2000lb AP bombs
216-500lb SAP bombs
72-500lb MC bombs
216-100lb A/S bombs, etc
and approximately 1½ million rounds of aircraft gun ammunition.

Torpedo body and parting spaces forward and aft with combined stowage for thirty-three aircraft torpedoes, were also arranged.

Protection

These ships were not designed with any form of underwater protection but to improve their resistance to underwater damage the wing spaces in the vicinity of the waterline were fitted out for the stowage of watertight buoyancy drums.

The actual spaces allocated for the buoyancy drums extended from station 55 to station 168, *ie* about 340ft, and were abreast magazines, machinery spaces and bomb rooms.

Machinery

The first ship was fitted with machinery which had been designed for the *Fiji* class cruisers, while the rest of the class had similar machinery built by contractors to the same general specification.

The propelling machinery consisted of a two-shaft arrangement of geared turbines, each shaft being driven by two main turbines arranged in series and coupled by pinions to a gear wheel on the propeller shaft. The working pressure and temperature of the steam at the turbine was 350lb/sq in and 700°F respectively, and the shp 20,000 on each shaft at 230rpm.

Four main water tube boilers were installed, two to each set of main engines. The boilers were worked at 40lb/sq in under a system of forced draught with closed main machinery compartments. The boilers were fitted with superheaters to give a superheat of 250°F at full power. Air preheaters were not fitted.

The machinery was arranged in two large machinery spaces separated by two main watertight subdivisions of the ship, each 24ft long, containing auxiliary machinery and petrol tanks etc. Each machinery space contained two boilers and a set of main engines, together with all the necessary auxiliaries for the unit.

Propeller particulars:
Two three-bladed manganese bronze
  propellers
Diameter   14ft
Pitch   14ft 3in
Developed blade area 90sq ft

Auxiliary Machinery

The auxiliary machinery included two 200kW diesel generators situated in middle line compartments on the main deck, and two 500kW turbogenerators, one in each of the main machinery compartments.

Experience in this class showed that the electric power provided was not really sufficient, and in due course an additional 180kW diesel generator was fitted in the later ships.

Radar fitted included types 941, 293, 253, 277Q and 281B, etc.

Stability Particulars

The inclining experiment carried out on *Colossus* in November 1944 gave the following stability particulars:

	Deep Condition	Light Condition
Metacentric height	8.6ft (fl)	4.9ft
Maximum GZ (hangars free flooding)	5.65ft	2.84ft
Angle of maximum GZ	36½°	36°
Range	74°	58°
Maximum GZ (hangars intact)	5.65ft	2.84ft
Angle of maximum GZ	37½°	36°
Range	more than 90°	59½°
Displacement	18,040 tons	12,320 tons

A longitudinal strength calculation made by Vickers-Armstrongs gave the following figures:

	Hogging Condition	Sagging Condition
Maximum bending movement	470,700ton ft	376,500ton ft
Stress in flight deck	7.54ton/sq in	5.29ton/sq in
Stress in keel	6.04ton/sq in	5.52ton/sq in
Displacement	17,300 tons	17,300 tons

In calculating the moments of inertia, the 2/11 correction was made for the items in tension. Further, the calculations were made on a displacement of 17,300 tons with a depth to flight deck at side of 61ft 0in moulded instead of the 61ft 9in as built.

Contracts were placed for fourteen ships of the *Colossus* class; the last six ships were eventually modernised during building and became known as the *Majestic* class.

The aircraft arrangements of the *Colossus* class light fleet carriers were generally popular although there were a number of complaints re the inadaequacy of stores etc for the aircraft.

The habitability of these ships was, however, a cause of continual complaint; messes, bathrooms, cabins, etc were all criticised.

Cost

Mean Vote 8 cost of each vessel was £2,500,000.

Ship	Builder	Laid Down	Launched	Completed
Colossus	Vickers-Armstrong	1 Jun 1942	5 Apr 1939	16 Dec 1944
Vengeance	Swan Hunter	16 Nov 1942	23 Feb 1944	15 Jan 1945
Venerable	Cammell Laird	3 Dec 1942	30 Dec 1943	17 Jan 1945
Glory	Harland & Wolff	27 Aug 1942	27 Nov 1943	2 Apr 1945
Ocean	Alex Stephen	8 Nov 1942	8 Jul 1944	8 Aug 1945
Theseus	Fairfields	6 Jan 1943	6 Jul 1944	9 Feb 1946
Warrior	Harland & Wolff	12 Dec 1942	20 May 1944	14 Mar 1946
Triumph	Hawthorn Leslie	27 Jan 1943	2 Oct 1944	9 May 1946

Majestic Class

In September 1945 it became necessary to consider the alterations to the designs of the aircraft carriers building to ensure that they would be up-to-date, and capable of operating the naval aircraft then coming into service. The light fleet carriers principally concerned were the last six of the *Colossus* class which were still under construction; the remainder of the class were either completed or far too advanced for drastic alteration. These six ships, *Hercules*, *Leviathan*, *Majestic*, *Magnificent*, *Powerful* and *Terrible*, were already a little different from the remainder of the class in that they were designed for centralised messing of the crew, and incorporated a number of improvements as a result of war experience. In view of the fact that these six ships would be, when completed, somewhat different to the others of the *Colossus* class, it was decided to rename them *Majestic* class. With the cessation of hostilities it as finally decided to approve in principle the details of the modernisation of the *Majestic* class, but only progress the actual modernisation, and then only on the first three ships. The last of the class, *Leviathan*, *Powerful* and *Hercules*, were to be completed to the towing stage and then laid up for an indefinite period; the completion of these ships, when resumed, would be to the approved modernised design.

The extent of the modernisation approved by the Board was arrived at after very careful consideration by the departments concerned and consisted mainly of the following items:

(1) Stiffening of flight and hangar decks to take 20,000lb aircraft.
(2) Improving performance of the accelerator whilst retaining the existing machinery.
(3) Fitting Bofors and directors in lieu of the pom-poms.
(4) Fitting the following warning radar equipment type 277Q, type 960 and type 293 with associated spaces etc.
(5) Replacement of W/T equipment
(6) Increasing the generator capacity.
(7) Fitting up-to-date replenishment-at-sea arrangements.
(8) Rearrangement of a number of offices etc, and improvements in accommodation.

The second part of the modernisation which was to be done when the equipment became available consisted of

The Canadian Magnificent *showing the original configuration of the* Majestic *class. Three other ships of this class were transferred to Commonwealth navies, two to Australia and one to India.*

(9) Enlarging the lifts to 50ft x 34ft and modifying the machinery to deal with 20,000lb aircraft.
(10) Fitting new arresting gear to deal with 20,000lb aircraft entering at 75/80kts.
(11) Fitting a third crash barrier.
(12) Modifying aircraft crane to deal with the heavier load.

Eventually work on *Majestic* was temporarily suspended. *Terrible* (renamed *Sydney*) was handed over to the Royal Australian Navy on completion, and *Magnificent* to the Royal Canadian Navy.

Ship	Builder	Laid Down	Launched
1942 Programme			
Hercules	Vickers-Armstrongs	14 Oc 1943	22 Sept 1945
Leviathan	Swan Hunters	18 Oct 1943	7 Jun 1945
Majestic	Vickers-Armstrongs	15 Apr 1943	23 Feb 1945
Magnificent	Harland & Wolff	29 Jul 1943	11 Nov 1944
Powerful	Harland & Wolff	27 Nov 1943	27 Feb 1945
Terrible	Devonport	19 Apr 1943	30 Sep 1944

1943 Programme – *Hermes* Class

The 1943 new construction programme included eight light fleet carriers which were originally to have been improved repeats of the 1942 design *Colossus* class. However, it was realised that the 1943 programme carriers would be scheduled to complete from early 1946 onwards and would thus be contemporary with the *Ark Royal* class fleet carriers. This resulted in an obvious operational requirement that the new light fleets, or at least a proportion of them, should be capable of carrying the same types of aircraft as the *Ark Royals*, even though the aircraft would be too large for normal operation in the light fleet carriers. Another important point which was borne in mind was the advisability of ensuring that our new carriers could operate US aircraft.

It was decided to prepare a design for a new light fleet carrier; a simple type of construction, such as that used in building *Colossus* class, was still required, but an increase in the time for building was to be accepted in order to incorporate essential improvements.

The draft staff requirements prepared in March called for a carrier to handle 30,000lb aircraft and to have a minimum operational speed of 25kts with an endurance of 6000 miles at 20kts (6 months out of dock).

Hangar space was required for eighteen TBRs and clear hangar height was fixed at 17ft 6in. Two lifts each 54ft x 44ft and capable of lifting 30,000lb loads were to be fitted. Arresting gear, barriers and accelerator were to be designed for 30,000lb loads at 75kts.

The main armament of the ship was to be four twin 4.5in HA/LA mountings with two 6-barrelled Bofors (or 8-barrelled pom-poms), ten twin 40mm *Busters*, eleven quadruple Oerlikons and up to twelve twin Oerlikons. Protection was to be confined mainly to splinter protection for the bridge personnel etc but consideration was to be given to providing horizontal protection over the machinery spaces, magazines and bulk petrol stowage. The underwater protection was to be as in *Colossus* class.

A sketch design to these broad requirements was produced and submitted to the Board in June 1943.

The general particulars on the legend were:

LBP	650ft 0in
LOA	736ft 9in
Breadth	90ft
Depth of ship	70ft 7in
Standard displacement	28,310 tons
Draught (Standard)	20ft
Deep displacement	23,800 tons
Deep draught	24ft 8in
Shp (2 shafts)	76,000
Deep speed	29kts
Endurance (6 months out of dock)	6000mls at 20kts

Aircraft complement to be twenty-four TBRs and sixteen fighters or forty-eight fighters.

It was anticipated that it would take two years nine months to build this design.

The Board drew attention to the increases which were taking place in the size, complement and period of construction of these carriers and stated that the ships were in the nature of a makeshift supplement to the armoured carriers which would form the nucleus of a post-war fleet. Against this, however, was the fact that the ships had to be designed to operate the aircraft expected to be in service when they completed. The First Lord said that he did not feel satisfied that the case for the 1943 design had been established and that he was not prepared to agree to it without Cabinet approval. He proposed that the sketch

design should be considered further and resubmitted.

In accordance with instructions from the Controller the development of the design was proceeded with as though the necessary approval had been obtained. Board approval of the sketch design was eventually promulgated in February 1944 and final approval of the design and legend in the following month.

With the end of the war in 1945 the contracts for four out of the eight ships ordered were cancelled, and because of the low priority afforded the remainder, their progress became very slow indeed. As a result of the number and extent of improvements and additional requirements incorporated in the class during building a revised design was prepared in 1947. Included in the revised design were centralised messing arrangements, improvements in accommodation arrangements and numerous additions which were the result of the reintroduction of many of the peacetime amenities.[6] The major structural items included in the revised design were the fitting of a second accelerator, the omission of the 4.5in gun armament and the fitting of an action information centre in the island structure.

Actual progress on the ships remained slow for a number of years, and it was eventually decided

to further modify one ship, *Hermes* itself, and fit the most up-to-date arresting gear and steam catapults. This particular modernised design became known as the *Hermes* class modernised.

The remaining three ships, *Albion*, *Centaur* and *Bulwark*, were built to the revised 1947 design (with further improvements). Following are the main features of the *Hermes* class design as built.

General Particulars:

Length between perps	650ft 0in
Length on waterline	686ft 9in
Length overall	736ft 0in
Breadth on waterline	90ft 0in
Breadth extreme	120ft 6in
Depth of ship (USK to underside of flight deck)	70ft 7in
Displacement (standard)	22,471 tons
Displacement (deep)	27,015 tons
Draughts deep mean	27ft 2½in
Shp	76,000
Maximum speed (deep) (clean bottom)	28.5kts
Endurance at 20kts deep and 6 months out of dock	6000mls
Oil fuel	4083 tons
Complement (peace)	227 officers; 1596 men as flagship

Centaur in 1954, the first of the Hermes *class to complete. A number of modifications were made during construction, and the ship even had an interim angled deck when she entered service.*

[6] The original cost was estimated at £2,800,000 which rose due to inflation and the long delays to £10,530,000 for *Centaur* in 1953. The man months needed were 65,941, some three times that for *Ocean*.

Group Weights

Hull and protection etc.	12,402 tons
General fittings	2,514 tons
Machinery	2,109 tons
Armament and ammunition	358 tons
General equipment	1,583 tons
Aircraft equipment	2,352 tons
Oil fuel and lub oil	4,133 tons
Avgas and water	573 tons
Avcat	666 tons
RFW	175 tons
Permanent ballast	150 tons
Deep displacement	27,015 tons

Aircraft Arrangements

These ships as completed to the revised design were capable of operating the same aircraft as the *Eagle*, the equipment for handling the aircraft being designed and rated for aircraft up to 30,000lb in weight. Aircraft up to 40,000lb could be flown off the deck - aircraft complement in 1952 was thirty-six including sixteen Sea Hawks.

There was one hangar 381ft x 62ft giving a clear floor area of 23,522sq ft while the hangar height was 17ft 6in clear. Four fire curtains were fitted in the hangar.

Flight deck dimensions were length 732ft 9in, mean width 90ft and minimum width at the fore end 84ft.

Two electrically driven middle line lifts were provided each 54ft x 44ft. These lifts were originally designed for a 30,000lb working load with a running time cycle of twenty-five seconds, but they were actually balanced for a load of 35,000lb.

Arresting gear Mark 11 was installed. This consisted of twelve wires rigged in pairs to six units. The gear was designed to a capacity of 30,000lb with a maximum entry speed of 75kts or 20,000lb

with a corresponding maximum entry speed of 91kts. The maximum pull out was 162ft.

Four safety barriers were fitted, Nos 1 and 3 barriers were for jet aircraft while No 2 and 4 barriers were the conventional three-wire type.

Two BH5 catapults were fitted at the fore end; these were designed to give a 30,000lb aircraft a launching speed of 75kts. When working on three pumps one aircraft was launched every forty seconds from each catapult.

The aircraft crane was rated for lifting 30,000lb, while a mobile crane was provided for lifting 20,000lb.

Ammunition Stowage for the aircraft's machine guns was sufficient for ten loads for fifty aircraft and consisted of 316,000 rounds of 20mm Hispano ammunition. 2000-3in rocket projectiles were also carried in the magazines.

Two bomb rooms situated one above the other on the hold and platform decks were served by a bomb lift which was designed for transporting 4000lb loads up to the hangar or flight deck in two stages. Speed of bomb lift was such that sixteen aircraft could be bombed up in forty minutes. Bomb room stowage was sufficient for nine loads for twenty-six strike aircraft; each load being 2-1000lb bombs or 4-500lb bombs. Thirty-two 18in aircraft torpedoes were also carried.

Structural Arrangements

The hull was designed to a certain extent using merchant ship practice, *eg* the transverse framing was of bulb angle. With the exception of the flight deck, longitudinal protective bulkhead, middle deck over machinery spaces and lower decks over petrol compartments etc. the hull was entirely of mild steel plating. These special items were of DW quality plating while the island structure and

Hermes, the last of the wartime light fleet carriers to complete. She is seen in May 1966 with the side lift, which was a great technical feat in a closed hangar design but removed fairly rapidly. The 1943 light fleets were much more capable than the earlier ships but were far more demanding in resources for their construction.

protection to gun mountings in spansons was of DKM or UXW HT steels.

As the hulls of these ships were progressed during the latter years of the war, welding was adopted to the greatest practicable extent.

Armament

The armament of this class consisted of:

12-40mm Bofors in two [6-barrel] mountings
16-40mm Bofors in twin mountings
4-40mm single power Bofors

Ten CRBF directors were fitted for this armament.

Protection

80lb NC armour was provided over the magazines and bomb rooms. Remaining protection was limited to splinter-proof protection to island, gun sponsons, etc.

The ships had no sandwich protection, merely wing fuel or watertight compartments outside the longitudinal bulkhead abreast machinery spaces. The subdivision of the ship was essentially transverse.

Machinery

The machinery in this class was the same as that installed in *Ark Royal* and *Eagle*, except that only two units were fitted instead of four. Each unit consisted of a boiler room containing two Admiralty three-drum type boilers side by side, engine room and a gearing room.

Propeller particulars:

Two three-bladed manganese bronze propellers at 235rpm

Diameter	15ft 6in
Pitch	15ft
Developed blade area	136sq ft

Auxiliary Machinery included eight generators, four diesel generators and four turbo generators, each 400kW. The diesel generators were situated in separate compartments, two forward and two aft, while the turbo generators were at lower or platform deck level, one in 'A' engine room, one in a separate WT compartment in 'A' engine room, one in 'B' engine room and the other in 'B' boiler room.

Radar fitted included Types 982, 983, 960, 293, 974 and 961.

Stability Particulars

Stability Particulars for the ship with hangar free flooding were:

	Light condition	Deep condition
Metacentric height	3.7ft	7.07ft (fl)
Maximum GZ	3.33ft	5.62ft
Angle of maximum GZ	38°	40°
Range	60½°	74½°
Displacement	20,029 tons	27,015 tons

Strength

The standard longitudinal strength calculation was carried out on this design, and the moduli were calculated with the usual 2/11 reduction for material in tension. This probably over-estimated the loss of material area in tension.

Results were

	Hogging	Sagging
Maximum bending movement	738,000ton ft	480,000ton ft
Stress in upper deck	8.32ton/sq in	4.78ton/sq in
Stress in keel	5.9ton/sq in	4.31ton/sq in
Displacement	22,030 tons	23,309 tons

General

In these ships the officers were accommodated in single, double, three or four berthed cabins, but the accommodation provided for the crew was unique in that it included bunks in lieu of the time-honoured hammocks.

Centralised messing was worked with separate dining halls for CPOs, POs and junior ratings. The junior ratings' dining hall seated about 420, necessitating feeding in three sittings.

All ratings were provided with an 'S' type or 'NS' type (modified) kit locker.

Ship	Builder	Laid Down	Launched
1943 Programme			
Albion	Swan Hunter	23 Mar 1944	6 May 1947
Centaur	Harland & Wolff	30 May 1944	22 Apr 1947
Hermes	Vickers Armstrong	21 Jun 1944	[16 Feb 1953]
Bulwark	Harland & Wolff	10 May 1945	22 Jun 1948

CHAPTER 5

Escort Carriers

Editorial Note
It is often not realised that well before the war the Admiralty had quite detailed plans for escort carriers which could not be implemented at the outbreak of war due to shortage of merchant shipping. The few that were built or converted in the UK fell well short of the ideal, Type A, ships described below.

The vast majority of RN escort carriers were built in the United States and very good ships they were too. The first group had a number of detailed problems which were soon corrected in later ships. Even so, there remained a difference in philosophy between the RN and USN, particularly over the vulnerability of the ammunition stowage and petrol stowage. Eventually, the USN adopted RN views on bomb stowage and went a considerable way to improving the safety of petrol stowage. The points are covered in the text, and amplified in the footnotes.[1] The changes seen as necessary by the RN involved 6 weeks' work at Vancouver which together with a 6 weeks' work up and passage to the UK meant that these ships only entered service some 20-27 weeks after leaving the shipyard. This led to considerable USN criticism at the time but their own times for the Bogues *to enter service were little different.*

In the cold waters of the Arctic, the British built ships were preferred as cracking in the hull plating which was common in steels of the day would be stopped at a rivetted seam but might spread uncontrollably in a welded hull.

Costs are difficult to compare but Activity *cost £850,000 and* Campania *£1,520,000 compared with $11,000,000 for the* Commencement Bay.

Escort Carriers

As far back as 1926 proposals were put forward by the Admiralty to the Air Ministry that armed merchant cruisers should, where possible, be equipped for carrying one or two aircraft, the method of launching being dependent on the type of vessel selected. In 1931, when the strategic problems affecting merchant convoy arrangements were under discussion, it was suggested that consideration should be given to fitting some merchant ships with a catapult and a landing-on deck; the requirements being for a catapult capable of being loaded with an launching aircraft up to 7000lb in weight, and a landing-on deck fitted with arresting gear, abaft the funnel.

By 1934, outline arrangements had been prepared for the fitting of launching and landing-on arrangements for a series of ships ranging in size from 14,000 to 20,000 gross tons, and in speed from 15 to 20kts. In these arrangements, a hangar and an aircraft lift were provided, and the landing decks which were fitted with three arresting wires varied in size from 285ft x 65ft to 300ft x 80ft according to the size of the vessel. The time necessary to carry out such conversions was estimated to be nine to twelve months.

After further consideration it was decided that the presence of funnels and bridge structure on the centre line ahead of the landing decks was undesirable and the investigations were re-contin-ued on diesel-driven ships where it would be easier to side the exhausts and so enable conversion to a flush deck or island type of carrier to be carried out more readily.

In 1935, firm requirements were formulated for the type of ship needed for conversion to Trade Protection Carriers, they were:
  (i)   Gross tonnage between 10,000 and 20,000 tons.
  (ii) Machinery to be diesels, to give as high a ship speed as possible.
  (iii) Endurance of at least 6000 miles at 14kts.
  (iv) An overall flying deck, not less than 70ft in width, fitted with arrester gear and aircraft lifts.
  (v)   Hangar stowage for twelve to eighteen aircraft.
  (vi) HA/LA armament of 4.7in guns and close range weapons.

By 1936, outline arrangements embodying the above requirements were available for two typical ships:

MV *Winchester Castle*, a twin screw, diesel-driven vessel, 20,000 gross tons, and 631ft overall.

MV *Waipawa*, a twin screw, diesel-driven vessel, 12,500 gross tons, and 516ft overall.

The time for conversion in each case was estimated to be twelve months.

At this stage, DNC suggested that approval should be sought for the earmarking of merchant ships considered suitable for conversion to aircraft

[1] D K Brown, ' The Development of the British Escort Carrier'. *Warship* 25 (1983).

Requirement	Type A	Type B	Type C
Max Speed	20kts	18kts	16½kts
Endurance	15,000mls	15,000mls	as high as possible
No of aircraft	25	15	10
Hangar accommodation	16	12	4
Aircraft lifts	Two 45ft x 34ft x 15,000lb	One 45ft x 34ft x 15,000lb	One 42ft x 20ft x 10,000lb
Flight deck	not less than 550ft x 75ft	not less than 500ft x 70ft	not less than 450ft x 60ft
Island bridge	To be fitted	To be fitted	To be fitted
Accelerator	To be fitted	To be fitted	To be fitted if practicable
Arrester gear	six wires and two barriers	six wires and two barriers	a minimum of four wires, one safety wire and one barrier
Crane	To be fitted	To be fitted	To be fitted if practicable practicable
Petrol	75,000 galls minimum	50,000 galls minimum	33,000 galls minimum
Armament	2-4in twin HA/LA 4-'H' pom-poms and Oerlikons	As for type A	1-4in twin HA/LA 4-'H' pom-poms and Oerlikons
Asdics	To be fitted	To be fitted	To be fitted

carriers to the above requirements, and that structural plans of the ships selected should be obtained so that the whole question of conversion could be thoroughly investigated by the technical staff. This would allow the necessary building drawings and specifications to be prepared and ready for issue to the shipyards in the event of emergency. General approval was given to these proposals, providing staff was available, and in 1937 five ships were selected as being suitable for rapid conversion, viz *Winchester Castle, Warwick Castle, Dunvegan Castle, Dunottar Castle* and *Reina del Pacifico*. Details of the conversions of these ships were not worked out due to the shortage of staff, however, and no further work was done on this project until after the outbreak of war.

In 1940 the need for more ships carrying aircraft became acute in view of the heavy merchant ship losses by enemy U-boat and aircraft attack. Staff requirements for such ships were cut to the bare essentials and an ex-German motor vessel *Hanover* was taken in hand for conversion.

Later, staff requirements were prepared for three types of carrier conversions designated 'A', 'B' and 'C' conversions.

The main points of the requirements are listed in the table above.

The above general requirements, of course, were rather elastic since the details of the conversions varied with the characteristics of the ships concerned.

The following ships were requisitioned and converted to escort carriers in the United Kingdom: *Audacity, Activity, Pretoria Castle, Nairana, Vindex* and *Campania*.

Audacity

This ship (ex *Hanover*)[2] was captured from the Germans earlier in the war and was the first merchant ship to be converted to an aircraft carrier.

Due to urgency, the modifications were restricted to bare essentials: superstructure, masts, derricks, etc above the shelter deck were removed and a flight deck constructed. This flight deck, which was approximately 60ft above the keel, was supported by deep beams and girders, pillared to the shelter deck; as this was the strength deck it was necessary to fit three expansion joints in the flight deck. The ship side above the shelter deck was plated up with openings arranged for working boats and embarking stores etc. An island was not fitted in this ship; the engine exhaust was led out through the starboard side and navigation and signalling etc were carried out from platforms built port and starboard forward and about 4ft 6in below the level of the flight deck.

[2] This ship was originally known as *Empire Audacity*. It is interesting to note from the diary of Sir Stanley Goodall, DNC, that he took a very close personal interest in this ship which he saw as an important step forward.

General particulars of the ship were:

Length between perps	434ft 9in
Length overall	467ft 3in
Breadth (moulded)	56ft 0in
Depth to flight deck	59ft 9in
Displacement (deep)	10,230 tons
Mean draught (deep)	21ft 7in
Maximum speed	14½kts
Endurance	12,000 miles at 14½kts
Oil fuel	649 tons (diesel)
Petrol	10,000gall
Complement	210 officers and men

Aircraft Arrangements

The flight deck dimensions were 453ft 0in x 60ft 0in and arresting gear consisted of two arrester wires designed for 9000lb aircraft at 55kts, with a pull-out of 120ft, one safety wire and a barrier. There was no hangar, accelerator, crane or lift in this conversion, and the six aircraft carried were parked on the flight deck.

Armament - consisted of:
  1-4in single mounting
  4-single Oerlikons
  4-2pdr single pom-poms

Machinery

One diesel engine of 5200ihp giving a maximum ship speed of 14½kts. Four 220kW diesel generators were fitted.

Protection

Splinter protection was fitted to exposed positions but magazines, machinery spaces etc. were unprotected.

Asdics, Radar, etc - no asdics were fitted, and only a type 79M radar set.

Stability Particulars

	Light Condition	Deep Condition
Metacentric height	2.7ft	3.3ft
Max GZ	4.1ft	4.2ft
Angle of max GZ	49.5°	48.5°
Range	over 90°	over 90°
Displacement	8600 tons	10,200 tons

To realise these figures it was necessary to stow 3000 tons of permanent ballast.

Audacity was taken in hand by the Blyth Shipbuilding Company in January 1941, and the conversion was completed within six months.

Activity

This ship was nearing completion at the Caledon Shipbuilding Company as the cargo liner *Telemachus* when she was taken over in January 1942 for conversion to an escort carrier.

The ship was converted generally in accordance with staff requirements for Type C escort carriers. The structural modifications were on similar lines to those for *Audacity* but with the addition of a small island, hangar and aircraft lift; decks below the upper deck were made watertight.

Aircraft Arrangements

The flight deck was 498ft x 66ft and was completed with two arrester wires with 145ft pull-out designed for 15,000lb at 60kts and two wires with 120ft pull-out for the same load at 55kts; a safety wire and crash barriers were also fitted. This ship was constructed with a hangar 87ft x 59ft and an aircraft lift 42ft x 20ft of 10,000lb capacity. Six aircraft were stowed in the hangar. Ten 18in aircraft torpedoes were carried.

Armament
  1-4in twin mounting
  4 single-barrel Oerlikons
  10 twin-barrel Oerlikons

Machinery

Two diesel engines with two shafts, giving a total of 12,000bhp to give the ship a maximum speed of 18kts. Four 200kW diesel generators were fitted.

Activity general arrangement as designed

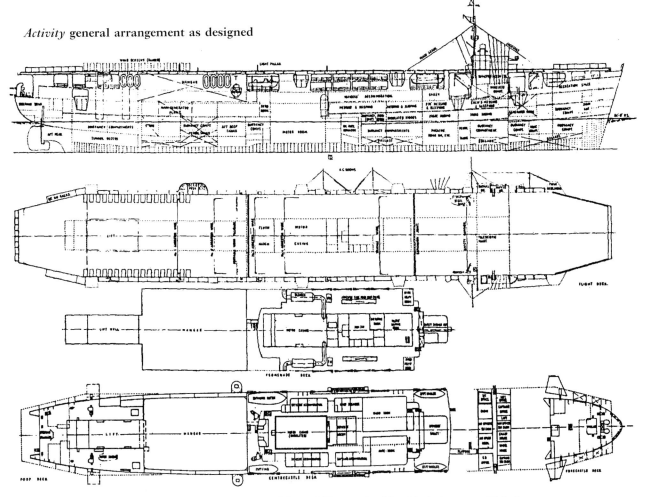

General Particulars

Length between perps	475ft 0in
Length overall	513ft 0in
Breadth (moulded)	66ft 0in
Depth to flight deck	64ft 0in
Displacement (deep)	14,250 tons
Mean draught (deep)	25ft 2in
Maximum speed	18kts
Endurance	15,000 miles at 16kts
Oil fuel	2015 tons (diesel)
Petrol	20,000gall
Complement	50 officers, 325 men

Protection was limited to splinter protection around exposed positions.

Asdics and Radar - Type 132 asdics and types 79M and 272 radar.

Stability Particulars

	Light Condition	Deep Condition
Metacentric height	3.9ft	4.3ft
Max GZ	3.8ft	3.4ft
Angle of max GZ	43.5°	39.5°
Range	76°	77.5°
Displacement	10,870 tons	14,250 tons

The stability standard for this design was a GM of 3ft under any intact condition and to achieve this it was necessary to fit 1600 tons of permanent ballast.

Accommodation

Usual standards of accommodation were provided for officers and RN ratings, but a proportion of the crew comprising victualling and engineering staffs and certain tradesmen were merchant navy personnel serving under special agreement by which they were allowed merchant standards of accommodation. Bed berths and separate messes were accordingly provided and similar standards were allowed for RN, CPOs and POs.

Work on this conversion was commenced in January 1942 by the Caledon Shipbuilding Company, Dundee, and completed in October 1942.

Ship	Activity
Builder	Caledon S.B. Co
Laid Down	1 Feb 1940
Launched	30 May 1942
Completed	14 Oct 1942

Pretoria Castle

This ship was fitted out at the commencement of the war as an AMC but was taken in hand for conversion to an escort carrier at Swan Hunter's in July 1942.[3] The conversion was generally in accordance with the requirements for Type B escort carriers and consisted mainly of stripping down the superstructure, completing 'C' deck to form a continuous hangar deck and building up the hanger and flight deck. Expansion joints were fitted to hangar bulkheads and the flight deck.

General Particulars

Length between perps	560ft 0in
Length overall	594ft 7in
Breadth (moulded)	76ft 0in
Depth to flight deck	78ft 0in
Displacement (deep)	23,450 tons
Mean draught (deep)	29ft 1in
Maximum speed	18kts
Endurance	16,000 miles at 16kts
Oil fuel	2430 tons (diesel)
Petrol	74,000gall
Complement	86 officers and 580 men

Aircraft Arrangements

Flight deck dimensions were 560ft 0in x 76ft 0in and it was fitted with six arrester wires to take 15,500lb at 60kts, with a maximum pull-out of 145ft. Two barriers were fitted to take the same load at 40kts. One accelerator, Type CII (cordite) was fitted forward and fifteen aircraft were accommodated in the hangar which was 354ft x 46ft with a clear height of 17ft 6in. A lift was fitted forward; its dimensions were 45ft x 39ft and it was designed to take a working load of 15,000lb. Stowage was arranged aboard for twenty-one 18in aircraft torpedoes.

A crane for lifting aircraft up to 15,000lb in weight was fitted on the starboard side abaft the island.

Armament

2–4in twin mountings
2 4-barrelled pom-poms
10 twin Oerlikon mountings

Machinery

Two diesel engines gave a total of 16,000bhp on two shafts. Four 450kW, two 200kW and one 50kW diesel generators were fitted.

Pretoria Castle **general arrangement as completed**

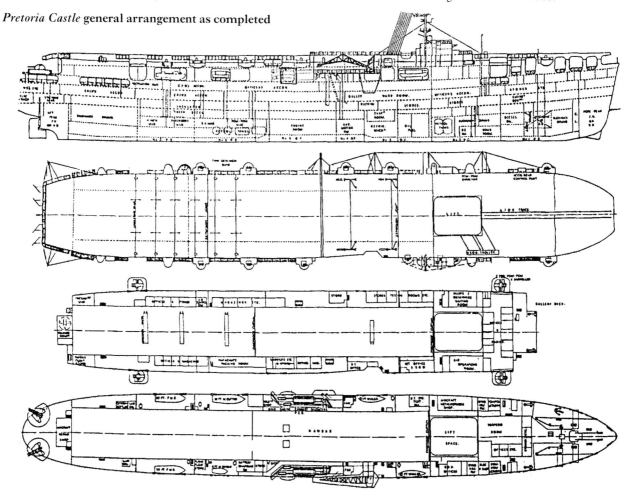

Protection provided in this conversion consisted of 40lb plating fitted over the bomb room and magazines together with 40lb side protection; 40lb plating was also fitted around the steering gear compartment. Splinter protection was provided at exposed positions.

Accommodation

A combination of RN and Merchant Navy standards of accommodation was provided as in *Activity*.

Pretoria Castle was taken in hand for conversion in July 1942 and was completed in July 1943.

Stability Particulars

	Light Condition	Deep Condition
Metacentric height	1.97ft	3.8ft
Max GZ	4.54ft	5.4ft
Angle of max GZ	47°	48°
Range	over 90°	88°
Displacement	19,900 tons	23,450 tons

2500 tons of permanent ballast was fitted.

Asdics and Radar were fitted - Type 132 asdics and Types 281H, 272 radar

Nairana and *Vindex*

These sister ships were requisitioned in the early building stages for conversion from cargo liners to escort carriers. In general, the original merchant ship design was followed for the ship up to the upper deck level, except that the shell plating scantlings were reduced in the vicinity of the upper and 2nd decks, decks were made watertight and additional transverse bulkheads were introduced at the fore and after ends to improve the watertight subdivision.

The gallery and flight decks were constructed above the upper deck and the shell plating carried up to the flight deck. The whole of the main structural work was completed while the ship was on the slip and the hangar and flight decks were incorporated as strength decks - no expansion joints were fitted.

In order to obtain maximum space for stowing aircraft etc, the hangar extended the full width of the ship; fore and aft access being arranged at the upper deck with embarkation openings amidships. A small island was constructed well forward on the starboard side.

General Particulars

Length between perps	498ft 0in
Length overall	528ft 6in
Breadth (moulded)	68ft 0in
Depth to flight deck	72ft 7in
Displacement (deep)	17,200 tons
Mean draught (deep)	25ft 8in
Maximum speed	16kts
Endurance	13,200 miles at 16kts
Oil fuel	1655 tons (diesel)
Petrol	52,000gall
Complement	85 officers and 554 men

Aircraft Arrangements

Flight deck dimensions were 502ft x 66ft, while the hangar floor clear area was 231ft x 61ft with a clear height of 17ft 6in, and accommodated fifteen aircraft. In *Nairana* eight arrester wires were fitted to land 15,500lb aircraft at a maximum speed of 60kts; the maximum pull-out was 145ft; two barriers were also fitted. *Vindex* was fitted with six arrester wires and one safety barrier. One lift, 45ft x 34ft, to take 1500lb, was fitted at the after end of the flight deck.

Stowage was provided for twenty-one 18in aircraft torpedoes.

No crane was fitted but there was a derrick on the starboard side aft to lift 12,000lb.

Armament

1-4in twin mounting
4 4-barrelled pom-poms
8 twin Oerlikon mountings

Machinery

Two diesel engines giving a total of 100,700bhp on two shafts. Auxiliary machinery included four 245kW and one 200kW diesel generators.

Propeller particulars

Two 4-bladed propellers	
Diameter	17ft 0in
Pitch	15ft 9in (adjustable 14ft 9in to 16ft 9in)
Developed blade area	98sq ft

Protection

40lb MS plating was used for protection on the sides of the 4in magazines and the bomb rooms. Splinter protection was fitted at exposed positions. Buoyant drums were also fitted.

Asdics and Radar - Type 132V asdics were fitted and Types 281H, 277 and 293 radar.

Stability Particulars for *Nairana* were:

	Light Condition	Deep Condition
Metacentric height	2.75ft	4.8ft
Max GZ	4.38ft	5.8ft
Angle of max GZ	53½°	57°
Range	over 90°	over 90°
Displacement	14,500 tons	17,200 tons

The figures for *Vindex* were very slightly better than these.

To obtain a metacentric height of at least 3ft in any intact condition, it was necessary to stow approx 3000 tons of permanent ballast.

The large complement of these ships precluded merchant navy standards of accommodation being provided for the special agreement personnel. By maintaining RN standards throughout however, it was possible to accommodate all personnel on 2nd deck and above, thus giving a minimum distance of 9ft above deep waterline for all living spaces.

Ship	*Nairana*	*Vindex*
Firm	John Brown	Swan Hunter
Laid Down	6 Nov 1941	1 Jul 1942
Launched	20 May 1943	4 May 1943
Converted	3 Jul 1942	24 Oct 1942
Completed	12 Dec 1943	3 Dec 1943

Campania

This ship was also requisitioned in the early stages of building, and the conversion carried out was on very similar lines to that of *Nairana* and *Vindex*.

General Particulars

Length between perps	512ft 0in
Length overall	538ft 0in
Breadth (moulded)	70ft 0in
Depth to flight deck	68ft 0in
Displacement (deep)	15,970 tons
Mean draught (deep)	22ft 10in
Maximum speed	18kts
Endurance	17,000 miles at 17kts
Oil fuel	2229 tons (diesel)
Petrol	52,000gall
Complement	85 officers and 554 men

Aircraft Arrangements

The dimensions of the flight deck were 515ft x 70ft 6in, and hangar 198ft x 63ft 6in with an extension 25ft 6in x 47ft. The clear height in the hangar, which accommodated fifteen aircraft, was 17ft 6in. One lift, 45ft x 34ft, fitted aft was designed for a 15,000lb working load. Four arrester wires, one safety wire and a barrier, designed for 15,500lb aircraft at 60kts, were fitted on the flight deck.

Machinery

Two diesel engines giving a total of 13,250bhp on two shafts. Five 300kW diesel generators were fitted.

Propeller Particulars

Two 3-bladed manganese bronze propellers	
Diameter	19ft 0in
Pitch	21ft 3in – 17ft 9in (varying)
Developed blade area	97sq ft

Armament, Protection, Asdics, Radar etc were as for *Nairana* and *Vindex*.

Stability Particulars

	Light Condition	Deep Condition
Metacentric height	3.85ft	4.95ft
Max GZ	4.62ft	5.62ft
Angle of max GZ	45°	46½°
Range	81°	over 90°
Displacement	13,000 tons	16,000 tons

1620 tons of permanent ballast was stowed.

Campania, a UK built escort carrier, cheaper and simpler than the US ships. This class were preferred for Arctic convoys as cracks in their hull plating were less likely to spread across riveted joints.

Ship	*Campania*
Firm	Harland & Wolff
Laid Down	12 Aug 1941
Launched	17 Jun 1943
Converted	1 Aug 1942
Completed	7 Mar 1944

Many lessons were learned as a result of the conversion of these merchant ships to RN escort carriers etc.

Anchor and cable equipment: it was necessary in the majority of these conversions to fit heavier anchors and to insert additional lengths of cable to the existing merchant type equipment.[4] It was not possible however to replace the cable windlasses by more powerful ones, and this resulted in overloading, with consequential deterioration and breakdowns requiring overhauls and repairs.

Arrester gear: operational experience showed that four arrester wires, one safety wire and a safety barrier were not sufficient to give adequate standards of safety and efficiency. Additional arrester equipment was fitted where possible.

Ventilation arrangements: experience in this type of ship showed that for living spaces in the vicinity of the hangar forced exhaust was necessary. Further, all supplies should be taken from port side and exhausts led out through starboard side.

[4] The additional windage of the hangar and flight deck led to the need for bigger anchors.

Athene and *Engadine* – Seaplane Carriers /Aircraft Transports

In 1939 consideration was given to converting merchant ships of the *Clan* type to seaplane carriers. However, as there appeared to be no urgent or intermediate requirement for such ships, no action was taken until June 1940. About this time the need for ships of this type was demonstrated in such operations as those being conducted in Norway and Iceland. With the loss of *Glorious* and its consequential loss of Fleet Air Arm mobility, and with the considerable accession of merchant navy tonnage resulting from the Allies taking over ships from Norway, Holland etc, and from captures from Italy, proposals were again made to convert a number of merchant ships to seaplane carriers.

The general requirements for seaplane carriers were:

(i)   to operate at least nine aircraft.
(ii) endurance of about 12,000 miles at 12kts
(iii) hangar stowage for one spread aircraft.
(iv) good hoisting arrangements for handling the aircraft.
(v)   workshop facilities etc
(vi) a catapult, if available for installation and subject to no delay in the completion of the ship.

In July 1940 it was decided to take over two *Clan* cargo liners then under construction and convert them to seaplane carriers to the above requirements. The two ships concerned were renamed *Athene* and *Engadine*.

Engadine, a mercantile conversion designed as a seaplane carrier but used as an aircraft transport.

Work on conversion was commenced, but in April 1941 it was decided that although *Athene* and *Engadine* were to complete eventually as seaplane carriers, they would serve a more urgent service if they were made ready for use as aircraft transports at the earliest possible date. The work of conversion to seaplane carriers was to proceed, where possible, concurrently with their preparation as transports, but was not allowed to delay their completion.

Following are the particulars of the ships as completed:

General Particulars

Length between perps	457ft 0in
Length overall	487ft 0½in
Breadth extreme	63ft 0in
Depth to upper deck	40ft 9in
Deep displacement	10,890 tons
Mean draught (deep)	20ft 3in
Maximum speed	16.5kts
Power	8300ihp
Endurance	5840 miles at 16kts
Oil fuel	1000 tons
Petrol	32,000gall
RN Complement	116

Aircraft Arrangements

Stowage arrangements made for forty Hurricanes, and two cranes were fitted, each of four tons lifting capacity. The hangars, one on the weather deck and two in the hold, were capable of carrying twelve Walrus.

Armament

1-4.7in LA gun
1-4in HA gun
4-2pdr pom-poms (single)

Machinery consisted of two sets of triple expansion engines with forced draught boilers driving two shafts.

Propeller Particulars

Two 4-bladed bronze propellers
Diameter	17ft 0in
Pitch	18ft 1½in
Developed blade area	100sq ft

Stability Particulars

	Light Condition	Deep Condition
Metacentric height	3.3ft	4.15ft
Angle of max GZ	50°	51°
Range	88°	over 90°
Displacement	8590 tons	10,890 tons

Approximately 1300 tons of permanent ballast was fitted.

After the war, these ships were reconverted and taken back into the merchant fleet.

American Escort Carriers – *Avenger*, *Tracker* and *Smiter* Classes

Avenger Class

In mid-1941 negotiations were already under way in the United States for the procuring of a number of auxiliary aircraft carriers. The Admiralty's requirements were for ships of the general type of HMS *Audacity*, a conversion which had been carried out early in 1941.

The US had well in hand at this time the conversion of the USS *Long Island* on a Maritime Commission C-3 type hull, and further conversions of this type in early stages. Arrangements were made for the first ship to be turned over to the Admiralty, but in view of the advanced stage of the structural work the ship was completed to the original plans. Concurrently, the design was discussed with the US authorities with a view to making such changes as were possible to make the subsequent ships more nearly meet British requirements.

The first ship became HMS *Archer*.

The following three ships of the class, *Biter*, *Dasher* and *Avenger*, showed marked development over the original conception as a result of continual discussion with the Navy Department and experience with earlier ships. *Avenger* class - as the ships came to be called - were built to the best US commercial marine construction practice.

The leading particulars of *Avenger*, the fourth and last of these ships, were:

Length on waterline	492ft 0in	
Length between perps	465ft 0in	
Beam (moulded)	69ft 6in	
Depth (moulded)	42ft 6in	
Power (diesel machinery)	8500ihp	
Displacement (deep)	13,305 tons	on
Mean draught (deep)	22ft 10in	arrival
Metacentric height	1.67ft (fl)	in UK

Machinery etc consisted of two diesel engines (Sun Doxford) connected to the shaft by electro magnetic couplings and single reduction gears. The shaft horse power of 8000 was sufficient to give a maximum speed of 16½kts on a mean draught of 27ft 3in.

Fuel stowage was arranged as 1660 tons for the ship and 1700 tons as cargo. Arrangements were made for fuelling destroyers at sea.

Fencer, *an early US built escort carrier of the* Tracker *class, in 1944.*

Armament

2-4in LA guns forward P & S
1-4in LA gun aft
6-0.5in short range weapons (sided)
10 Oerlikons
No directors were fitted

Protection

Ships were not armoured but splinter protection was provided for guns, bridge wings, lookouts, pilot house, aviators ready room etc, and radio rooms.

Stability

On arrival in this country the four ships of this class were found to have insufficient stability as a margin against damage. They had originally been designed as two-compartment ships and, while this was satisfactory from a buoyancy point of view, the ships rapidly became unstable.

Approximately 1000 tons of ballast was fitted with a corresponding increase in metacentric height from 1.67ft (fl) to 3.02ft (fl). In addition to putting in this ballast, buoyancy drums were fitted over the ballast in the wing deep tanks, with the object of preventing a large angle of heel should the ship be damaged.

Aircraft Arrangements

Accommodation was provided for nine TBRs and six fighters.

The flight deck, which was wood-faced, had dimensions of 442ft in length x 69ft 6in constant breadth. One lift (42ft x 34ft) was fitted in the centre of the after end of the flight deck; working load 12,000lb. The lift served the hangar whose dimensions were 190ft in length x 47ft minimum width x 16ft minimum clear height.

The catapult (American HII) was of fixed type fitted parallel to the middle line on the port side forward. Capacity of catapult was 7000lb at 60kts.

The arrester gear consisted of nine wires, three barriers, designed (*Avenger* only) to take 16,000lb at 85mph.

Magazines were provided for the alternative stowages of bombs, depth charges and ammunition; stowage and upkeep space was also provided for 15 torpedoes.

There was no island structure in *Archer*.

General

After *Avenger*'s initial difficulties in operating Hurricane aircraft, proposals were made to extend the flight deck aft and incorporate a round down. The flight deck, as originally constructed, induced unsatisfactory air flow conditions at the after end, and its length was definitely on the short side for operating these modern aircraft from a comparatively slow speed ship.

Loss of Avenger

Avenger was lost on 15 November 1942 when she blew up after being hit by a torpedo.

The cause of the disaster, which was the subject of a special DNC enquiry, was put down to the fact that bombs and depth charges had been stowed right out against the ship's side and blew up due to splinters from the torpedo hit.

The action taken in all ships that were in hand and subsequent escort carriers both RN and USN was to rearrange the bomb room so that no bombs or depth charges were stowed within 10-15ft of the ship's side. This was done by working in two longitudinal bulkheads set in this distance from the ship's sides.

This had the effect of restoring confidence in this class of carrier.[5]

[5] It was not only bomb stowage but also petrol arrangements (loss of *Dasher*) which caused a lack of confidence in this group: see Cdr R M Crosley, *They Gave me a Seafire* (Shrewsbury 1986).

[6] As 1. There was considerable ill feeling over what some USN officers saw as unnecessary delay.

Tracker Class

This class was a follow-on from the BAVGs (*Avenger* Class) being converted also from the Maritime Commission C-3 cargo hull. With the conversion, started much earlier in the construction however, it was possible to improve the watertight subdivision and so provide better resistance to damage, as well as embodying many lessons learned in the earlier ships - particularly on the air side. Discussions on the details of the design went on throughout the conversions, changes being introduced as opportunity offered.

The flight deck as in previous ships was wood covered, but in this class the ship side above the main deck was plated in up to flight level to provide enclosed space for workshops, auxiliary machinery and hangar.

Subdivision in this class was improved, and between the fore peak and after peak bulkheads the ship was subdivided by nine main, transverse, watertight bulkheads extending to the main deck. There were also two transverse watertight bulkheads extending to the second deck and various watertight bulkheads between lower decks for further compartmentation.

Two lifts were installed, one forward and one aft. Both lifts were 42ft x 34ft, and the after lift was athwartships as in *Avenger* class; they were balanced for 12,000lb working loads. Lift time cycle was 50-55 seconds.

Type HII accelerator was fitted and the hangar accommodation was sufficient for twelve TBRs and six fighters.

Typical armament for a ship of this class in 1944 was:

2-4in HA/LA guns

4 twin Bofors mountings

8 Oerlikon twin-powered mountings

6 single Oerlikons

Machinery

The main propelling machinery was as designed for the C-3 cargo vessel with changes in type and number of auxiliaries necessary to suit the new service. The machinery consisted of one high pressure turbine and one low pressure and astern turbine with double reduction gear driving a single propeller. Two 'D' type watertube forced draught boilers were fitted in separate boiler room.

Propeller particulars:

Diameter	21ft 8in
Pitch	21ft 8in
Developed blade area	166sq ft

The auxiliary machinery arrangements were improved in this class and the outfit for a typical ship included:

3-250kW TGs in engine room

2-300kW DGs

1-100kW DG

Distilling capacity amounted to 24,000 gall/day.

Smiter Class

Late 1942 the need for a large number of these auxiliary carriers became evident, and to assist in meeting the situation the Maritime Commission undertook the design and construction of a group of auxiliary carriers which became known in British circles as the 'Kaiser' class. As some of these were tentatively assigned to us, endeavour was made to study the design and consider what modifications would be necessary for British operational service. The Admiralty's requirements for this class of ship had by now crystallised to a considerable extent, and it was clear the modifications would be considerable.

It was made plain to us that rapid production by the standardisation methods adopted by the 'Maiso' organisation was the over-riding consideration, and that no changes could be considered to meet the Admiralty's views. As it would have been impossible to take these ships in hand for modification in the UK, discussions were opened with the British Admiralty Technical Mission in Canada, on the possibility of carrying out the modifications in Canada. Before the necessary arrangements had been completed, we were informed that none of the 'Kaiser' class would be assigned to us, but that we should be assigned further C-3 types, then converting on the West Coast. These were a revised *Tracker* class, but as far as we were concerned the problem of carrying out the modifications was not materially altered.

The arrangements for modifying the ships after completion were continued with the Canadian authorities and a successful programme drawn up.

The ships (*Smiter* class) were to be turned over to us at fortnightly intervals and new facilities were provided at Vancouver, by converting a commercial wharf, to enable three ships to be handled at one time. To avoid the ships piling up it was necessary for the modification programme to be planned at six weeks per ship.[6]

General particulars of the *Smiter* class were:

Displacement (deep)	15,160 tons
Displacement (light)	9170 tons
Oil fuel	3160 tons
Diesel oil	130 tons
Petrol	43,200gall

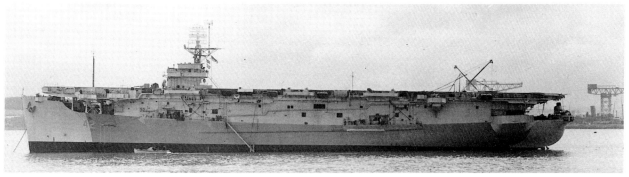

Empress, *a later US built ship of the* Smiter *class, seen on 25 Aug 1944. These ships were taken to Vancouver on completion for a six week refit to incorporate British requirements.*

Aircraft Arrangements

The hangar in this class was 260ft in length x 62ft in breadth and had a clear height of 18ft. Stowage arrangements were made for nine fighters and fifteen TBRs.

Two lifts were installed, one forward and one aft, each 42ft x 34ft and balanced for a 14,000lb working load.

The accelerator was a US type HIV designed for a maximum load of 16,000lb at 74kts. The arrester gear, which consisted of nine wires and three barriers, was also designed for this loading.

Two 12,000lb derricks were fitted.

Armament in *Smiter* class consisted of:
2-5in/38 HA/LA guns
8 twin Bofors
14 twin Oerlikons
7 single Oerlikons

The inclining experiment on *Smiter* gave the following results:

	Extra Deep Condition	Extreme Light Condition
Metacentric height	3.7ft	1.9ft
Angle of max stability	48°	44°
Range	over 90°	70°
Displacement	15,160 tons	9170 tons

General

The programme of escort carriers built in the USA between March 1941 and June 1944 saw the evolution of this type from the relatively simple *Archer* to the latest of the *Smiter* class, which were in many respects small editions of the fleet carrier.

The important modifications made to the original design during building of these classes included the lengthening of the flight deck and rounding down of the after end; larger hangar and improved aircraft arrangements; fitting of 1000-1300 tons of reinforced concrete ballast to improve stability, etc. To reduce the vulnerability of these ships, the amount of petrol actually carried was reduced to approximately one quarter of

the original stowage, and in the case of the *Tracker*s and *Smiter*s was confined to one tank - the remaining tanks being filled with water. Later it was approved to fit the British stowage system of separate cylindrical tanks.

An extra bombroom was fitted and protective bulkheads were fitted to them and to the depth charge rooms also; the magazines remained unprotected.

Inductor ventilation arrangements were fitted in the hangar, and the electrical system in the hangar was made safe.

Other items carried out or progressed included fighter direction and fitting out for cold weather operations.

At the end of the war the ships were returned to the US authorities.

US Classification	Ship	Completed
Avenger class		
BAVG 1	Archer	17 Nov 1941
BAVG 2	Avenger	1 Mar 1942
BAVG 3	Biter	5 May 1942
BAVG 5	Dasher	1 Jul 1942
Tracker class		
BAVG 6	Tracker	31 Jan 1943
AVG 6	Battler	15 Nov 1942
AVG 7	Attacker	10 Oct 1942
AVG 8	Hunter (ex Trailer)	11 Jan 1943
AVG 10	Chaser	9 Apr 1943
AVG 14	Fencer	20 Feb 1943
AVG 15	Stalker	30 Dec 1942
AVG 17	Pursuer	14 Jun 1943
AVG 19	Striker	29 Apr 1943
AVG 22	Seacher	8 Apr 1943
AVG 24	Ravager (ex Charger)	26 Apr 1943
Smiter Class		
CVE 32	Slinger	11 Aug 1943
CVE 33	Atheling	1 Aug 1943
CVE 34	Khedive	23 Aug 1943
CVE 35	Ameer	20 Jul 1943
CVE 36	Begum	3 Aug 1932

CVE 37	*Trumpeter*	4 Aug 1943
CVE 38	*Empress*	13 Aug 1943
CVE 39	*Emperor*	6 Aug 1943
CVE 40	*Speaker*	20 Nov 1943
CVE 41	*Nabob*	7 Sep 1943
CVE 42	*Premier*	3 Nov 1943
CVE 43	*Shah*	27 Sep 1943
CVE 44	*Patroller*	25 Oct 1943
CVE 45	*Rajah*	17 Jan 1944
CVE 46	*Ranee*	8 Nov 1943
CVE 47	*Trouncer*	31 Jan 1944
CVE 48	*Thane*	19 Nov 1943
CVE 49	*Queen*	7 Dec 1943
CVE 50	*Ruler*	22 Dec 1943
CVE 51	*Arbiter*	31 Dec 1943
CVE 52	*Smiter*	20 Jan 1944
CVE 53	*Puncher*	5 Feb 1944
CVE 54	*Reaper*	21 Feb 1944

Merchant Aircraft Carriers (MAC Ships)

As their name implies, these vessels were merchant ships so constructed to enable them to carry aircraft as defensive armament. The use of these vessels for escort purposes enabled air cover to be provided over a blind spot in the Atlantic through which convoys had previously sailed without air protection. As these ships were dual-purpose ships combining the carriage of cargo with the flighting of aircraft, they retained their identity as merchant ships and continued to be commanded by Merchant Navy Masters.

It was not until the beginning of 1942 that merchant ship aircraft carriers were first considered officially, and towards the middle of that year their immediate need became both apparent and urgent.

The preliminary naval staff requirements were for vessels of 14-15kts with dimensions capable of providing for a flight deck not less than 490ft length x 62ft breadth, and a hangar space for the housing of at least six fighters. As those vessels building or in service which could have satisfied these requirements were already allocated for other equally important duties, modified staff requirements were prepared based on the conversion of a standard tramp. These later requirements called for a flight deck of minimum dimensions 390ft x 62ft, a hangar for the accommodation of four Swordfish aircraft, and a speed in fair weather of more than 11kts. The MAC ships were designed and constructed under the auspices of the merchant shipbuilding and repair organisation set up during the war and the experience which had been gained by the Admiralty in escort

carrier conversions was made freely available. The special precautions as to stowing and handling of petrol and explosives and fire prevention in the hangars, incorporated in HM ships were applied to the similar problems in the MAC ships.

There were two types of merchant ships adapted for this role - cargo or grain ships and oil tankers.

Grain Ship Merchant Aircraft Carriers

Six grain ships were converted while building – *Empire McAlpine*, *Empire MacAndrew*, *Empire MacRae*, *Empire MacKendrick*, *Empire MacDermott* and *Empire MacCallum*. The dimensions of these ships varied with the builders but the general particulars for *Empire MacCallum*, a typical ship, were as follows:

Length overall	444ft 7in
Length between perps (on waterline)	425ft 0in
Breadth on waterline	57ft 9in
Mean draught loaded	24ft 6in
Freeboard to flight deck	30ft 1in
Displacement	13,000 tons

Machinery

There were no restrictions laid down as to the type of propelling machinery for these vessels, but it was accepted by all from their conception that only diesel machinery could be accepted.

The diesel machinery installed was rated as 3300bhp, *ie* 800hp above the normal standard tramp machinery. This was estimated to give an extra 1½kts to their speed. Single screws were fitted.

Generators installed were two 125kW DC type.

Aircraft Arrangements

The flight deck dimensions were 424ft 4in length x 62ft breadth and the hangar which was situated aft was 142ft x 38ft x 24ft in height. The hangar was served by a middle line single platform lift aft, 42ft x 20ft overall, electrically operated and capable of lifting a fully loaded plane from hangar to flight deck in fifty seconds.

Hangar stowage was provided for four Swordfish aircraft.

The arresting gear fitted was of the type fitted in the escort carriers and was, in fact, made available from the equipment ordered in anticipation of a considerable increase in the escort carrier programme. The four arrester wires were spaced at 30ft intervals; no safety barrier fitted.

Armament consisted of two Bofors and four Oerlikons and 1-12pdr HA/LA gun.

General arrangement of a tanker MAC ship

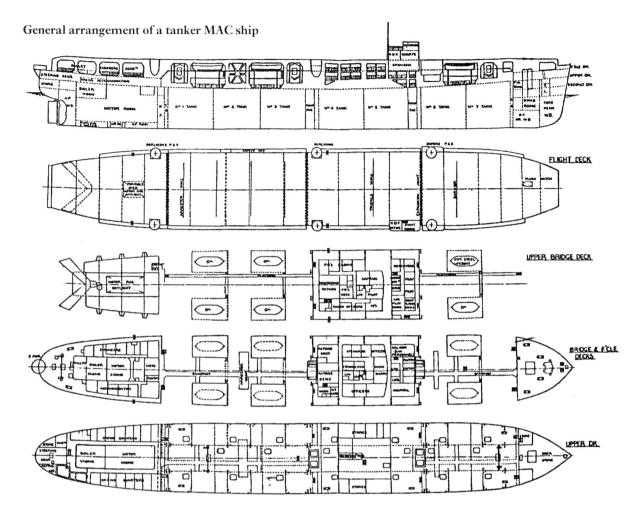

Stability

A number of stability problems resulted from the conversion of these ships, not the least being those associated with the large increases in top weight, due to the fitting of a flight deck. The optimum safe figure for the metacentric height in these vessels was considered to be about 4ft; the actual figures obtained in the various conditions of these ships were not less than this.

The first vessel - *Empire MacAlpine* - was ordered in June 1942, laid down in August 1942, launched in December 1942 and handed over completed in April 1943 - a truly creditable achievement.

Oil Tanker Merchant Aircraft Carriers

Proposals for the conversion of tankers were considered concurrently with the grain ship proposals, but little progress was made because of the difficulty in obtaining suitable modern ships; further, most of the tankers of the type required were engaged in carrying low flash-point fuel which with the operation of aircraft would be rather dangerous. Later, in 1942, however, it was decided to convert nine existing tankers and complete as

merchant carriers four tankers still under construction.

The vessels involved were: *Rapana*, *Amastra*, *Acavus*, *Ancylus*, *Miraldo*, *Alexia*, *Adula*, *Macoma*, *Gadila* and *Empire MacKay*, *Empire MacColl*, *Empire MacMahon* and *Empire MacCabe* respectively.

The principal difference between the two types of merchant aircraft carriers was that the tanker type was not fitted with a hanger. The increased length of flight deck provided some compensation for this omission but introduced other problems.

The flight deck was not a strength member, but was arranged in four sections with an expansion joint between each. This enabled the deck together with all its supports to be designed for prefabrication.

The dimensions of *Empire MacKay*, a typical oil tanker merchant aircraft carrier, were:

Length overall	479ft 6in
Length between perps	460ft 0in
Breadth on waterline	61ft 0in
Mean draught loaded	27ft 2¾in
Freeboard to flight deck	31ft 6in
Displacement	16,967 tons

[7] R D Layman, & S McLaughlin, *The Hybrid Warship* (London 1991).

Machinery
The fact that a number of existing vessels were included in this tanker programme precluded the possibility of increasing the propelling power of the new vessels; but all were capable of fulfilling the specified 11kt speed on diesels rated at 3300bhp driving single screws.

Three generators were installed in each ship, 2-30kW and 1-35kW.

Stability
The metacentric height for the conversion MAC tankers was about 2ft; that for the new construction tankers of 61ft beam was 3ft.
The average time taken for the conversion work on existing tankers was six months; while the extra time taken to complete the new tankers to the aircraft carrier design was about three months.

Armament consisted of two Bofors, six Oerlikons and 1-12pdr HA/LA gun.

Aircraft Arrangements
The flight deck dimensions of the class were approximately 460ft 0in x 62ft breadth, and a stowage and parking area for four Swordfish was arranged at the after end of the flight deck. This space 100ft in length was closed in by an arrangement of hinged wind screens fitted on each side of the deck, and by a palisade of portable screens placed across the fore end of the space.

The arrester gear was a repeat of that in the grain ships with an additional unit to operate the trickle wire and safety barrier.

General
The ability to operate aircraft from these ships was conditioned largely by the speed of ship and length of flying-off deck. In both types of MAC ships these factors approached the minimum simultaneously, and the resultant aircraft carrier was limited to the operation of relatively slow-flying aircraft, of a type which had, however, demonstrated its value for anti-submarine patrols.

These MAC ships sailed regularly with ocean convoys and made such a contribution to the anti-submarine production that fewer of the fully equipped escort carriers were necessary.

The Battleship, Cruiser and Destroyer /Carrier Designs

Early in 1941, with the growing difficulty of operating naval forces within striking distance of enemy land air bases, it was suggested by the Director of Plans that a more determined effort should be made to produce a design of battleship in which an additional 'defence armament' of aircraft could be carried. The suggestion was adopted to the extent that DNC was asked to prepare sketch designs for battleship, cruiser and destroyer/carriers.

The main dimensions of the designs prepared are listed below.

When circulated for comment, the designs met with very strong criticism from the Naval staff and no further action was ever taken.[7]

| | Battleship/Carrier | Cruiser/Carriers | | Destroyer/Carriers | | |
		A	B	B & E	C	D
Length on WL	800ft	670ft	690ft	560ft	680ft	650ft
Breadth of hull	112ft	83ft	83ft	66ft	76ft	76ft
Mean Draught (std)	30ft	22ft	22ft 3in	15ft 7in	17ft 6in	17ft 9in
Deep Displacement	51,000	23,000	24,300	10,600	17,500	17,000
Shp	130,000	120,000	120,000	80,000	90,000	90,000
Speed (kts)	28	30¾	30?	31	31	30¾
Main armament	6 x 16in	6 x 8in	9 x 8in	4 x 5in	4 x 5in	4 x 5in
	16 x 5.25in	12 x 4in	12 x 4in			
No of aircraft	12	14	12	12	12	12
Length of flight deck	500ft	380ft	340ft	530ft	630ft	600ft

Liner Conversions

In 1942 some consideration was given to converting the liners *Queen Mary* and *Queen Elizabeth* into aircraft carriers. The designs were prepared by Messrs John Brown in conjunction with DNC. The scheme was eventually abandoned as the two ships were taken up for trooping duties after the Americans came into the war.

The proposed conversions to aircraft carriers included:

Flying-off platform	500ft x 66ft minimum
Landing space	416ft x 125ft
Two hangars (one each side of the ship)	670ft x 45ft
Lifts (2)	45ft x 34ft
Armament	4-4in twins
	5 4-barrelled 2pdr pom-poms

CHAPTER 6

Cruisers

Editorial Note

The continuity of style in British cruiser design is due to the long term involvement of Charles Lillicrap as head of section from Adventure *in the early 1920s through to Assistant Director in the 1930s, following Goodall as DNC in 1944. Part of his style is apparent in the knuckle in every cruiser except* Birmingham *where it was omitted for comparison.*[1] *The development from* Adventure – Kent – York – Exeter – Leander – Amphion *and* Arethusa – Southampton – Fiji *is clear.*

The wartime cruiser programmes are difficult to follow as ships were ordered, deferred or cancelled and re-ordered many times.[2] *There were many other designs which were developed and not pursued, such as very big ships with 9.2in or 8in guns, abandoned when it was realised that their building time was about the same as a battleship. The* Fiji – Tiger *concept was further developed with later marks of 6in mountings with greater elevation and rate of fire. Towards the end of the war the cruiser was seen primarily as part of the carriers' AA screen and smaller ships, mounting improved 5.25in guns in triple mounts were favoured. There is a detailed account of British cruisers by Roberts and Raven.*[3]

[1] No record has been found of any comparison of *Birmingham* with sisters having a knuckle but there is a memo from Controller just before the war directing that *Birmingham*'s bow be re-built with a knuckle.

[2] An article by G Moore to appear in *Warship 1996* should clarify these programmes.

[3] A Raven and J Roberts, *British Cruisers of World War II* (London 1980).

Four classes of light cruiser built during the 1914–18 war survived to give good service in the 1939–45 war. They were of the 'C', 'D', 'E' and *Raleigh* classes. Particulars are given in the *Records of Warship Construction, 1914–18.*

'C' Class

Thirteen ships, viz *Calypso, Caledon, Caradoc, Curacoa, Coventry, Curlew, Ceres, Cardiff, Colombo, Carlisle, Cairo, Calcutta* and *Capetown*, remained at the end of the 1914–18 war. A number of these were earmarked for scrapping under the London Naval Treaty 1930, but were eventually retained.

In 1935 it was approved in principle to convert 'C' class cruisers to A/A ships fitted with HA guns only. The first ships to be so fitted were *Coventry* and *Curlew*. The whole of the 6in and 3in armament and torpedo tubes were removed and replaced by ten 4in HA guns in single mountings, two 8-barrelled pom-poms in *Coventry* and two 4-barrelled pom-poms in *Curlew*. Ballast was added to preserve stability.

In 1938 and 1939, *Cairo* and *Calcutta* were converted to A/A ships with slightly different armament, only eight 4in HA guns being fitted and one 4-barrelled pom-pom. *Carlisle* and *Curacoa* were converted to A/A ships in 1939 and *Colombo* and *Caledon* in 1942–3.

Curacao was sunk in 1942 after collision with RMS *Queen Mary*. *Cairo* was sunk in a Malta convoy on 12 August 1942 and *Coventry* was sunk on 10 October 1942. *Calypso* was also sunk. The rest of the class were scrapped at the end of the war, *Caledon* being used by the Ship Target Trials Committee before being scrapped.

Curlew, one of the prototype anti-aircraft cruisers. The HA 4in guns are very much in evidence, and one of the multiple pom-poms can be seen clearly on the superstructure forward of the bridge.

[4] These ships were very fast as built – *Emerald* made 32.9kts on trial – and may well have been the fastest RN cruisers during World War II.

[5] Replaced by four twin 4in mounts just before the war.

[6] It was not, in fact, uncharted but was a pinnacle rock, concealed by the navigator's pencil line.

[7] The depth, keel-to-deck, was increased at d'Eyncourt's suggestion to reduce stresses and hence weight which led to their distinctive high freeboard and airy mess decks.

'D' Class

Eleven ships of this class were originally ordered, but only eight were built, viz *Danae*, *Dauntless*, *Dragon*, *Delhi*, *Durban*, *Dunedin*, *Despatch* and *Diomede*. Subsequent to the approval in 1935 to convert 'C' class cruisers to A/A ships, 'D' class were earmarked for similar treatment, but this never really materialised.

Delhi was rearmed in 1940 in the USA with American 5in HA guns and American fire control arrangements etc, in view of the favourable and enthusiastic reports on these guns.

Dragon was loaned to the Polish Navy in 1942 under the terms of the additional protocol to the Anglo-Polish Naval Agreement. She received severe damage in August 1944 and was replaced by *Danae*, which was renamed ORP *Conrad*. *Danae* had had alterations to her armament in July 1942, which alterations included the removal of No 3 6in gun and the addition of two 4in HA/LA guns.

Dunedin was sunk in the South Atlantic on 24 November 1941, and *Durban* was used as a blockship in the invasion of France in 1944. The rest of the class was scrapped after the war.

'E' Class

There were three vessels, viz *Emerald*, *Enterprise* and *Euphrates*, in the class which was designed towards the end of 1917. *Emerald* and *Enterprise* were completed in 1926.[4] *Euphrates* was never completed.

Between 1934 and 1936, catapults and cranes were fitted. Previously they had had aeroplane platforms.

Reports from sea in 1940 under war conditions said that it was unsafe for men to work on the upper deck in heavy weather and that damage to boats was inevitable. Accordingly, the forecastle deck was extended aft to 127 station and the ship's side enclosed to upper deck level from 86 to 127 station.

The A/A armament was improved during 1942 and 1943 as a result of war experience. In 1944 the aircraft and catapult were removed and six additional Oerlikons fitted.

Both *Emerald* and *Enterprise* were scrapped after the war, *Emerald* first being used by the Ship Target Trials Committee.

Raleigh Class

Four vessels of this class, viz *Raleigh*, *Frobisher*, *Hawkins* and *Effingham*, were ordered in 1915, and a fifth, *Cavendish*, in April 1916.

Cavendish was subsequently converted into an aircraft carrier and renamed *Vindictive*. In 1936 *Vindictive* was converted into a seagoing cadet training ship to accommodate 285 cadets. She was again converted in 1940, this time to a repair ship.

Raleigh was lost by grounding in 1922.

Frobisher was converted in 1932 into a seagoing cadet training ship for 165 cadets. She was demilitarised in 1936 under the terms of the London Naval treaty and all the guns removed. A 4.7in gun was fitted for training purposes only. She was rearmed during the period 1939-42 as a 7.5in gun cruiser, being modernised as far as possible. In 1944-5 she was reconverted to a seagoing cadet training ship and made non-operational.

Hawkins was also demilitarised in 1936, but in 1939 she was taken in hand for rearming as a 7.5in gun cruiser and fitted with seven 7.5in guns, four 4in HA guns, and four pom-poms. During a refit in 1942, the bulge was extended to improve the stability.

Effingham was rearmed in 1936 as a 6in gun cruiser and was fitted with nine 6in BL guns, four 4in HA guns,[5] two 8-barrelled pom-poms. One funnel was removed and aircraft and a catapult fitted. She was lost off Norway when she struck an uncharted reef.[6]

Hawkins, *Frobisher* and *Vindictive* were scrapped at the end of the war, *Hawkins* first being used in ship target trials.

Kent Class

These cruisers were ordered in a special building programme in 1923-4. Their displacement was limited to 10,000 tons by the Washington Naval Treaty. Weights were drastically cut during the design stages and no margins were allowed for contingencies.[7]

The design particulars approved were:

Length BP	590ft 0in
Length overall	630ft 0in
Breadth extreme	68ft 3in
Legend draught	15ft 3in F / 17ft 3in A
Displacement	10,000 tons
Shp of engines	80,000
Speed	31½kts light / 30½kts deep
Complement (as private ship)	784

Armament
8–8in guns in twin turrets
4–4in HA guns
2 Mark 'M' pom-poms
2 AW quadruple torpedo tubes

Protection was limited to 160lb armour on 15lb magazine bulkheads, 120lb over magazines, 40lb protective plating to bulkheads of shell rooms and machinery spaces, 40lb protective plating over shell rooms and two thicknesses of 27½lb plating over machinery spaces and steering gear. An external bulge was fitted for underwater protection.

A revolving catapult for aircraft was installed before completion.

Seven ships were built, viz *Kent*, *Suffolk*, *Berwick*, *Cumberland*, *Cornwall*, *Australia* and *Canberra*. All were completed in 1928. The last two were for the Australian Navy.

In 1935 improvements were made to the armament and protection. A belt of 180lb NC armour was fitted on each side over the length of machinery spaces. The single 4in HA mountings were replaced by twin mountings and the Mark 'M' pom-poms by 2pdr Mark VII 4-barrelled pom-poms. Both sets of torpedo tubes were landed and the revolving catapult and crane replaced by a fixed catapult, hangar for two aircraft and a crane P & S. *Kent*, however, still kept the revolving catapult. The pole masts were replaced by light steel tripod masts.

During subsequent refits additions such as radar, Oerlikons, etc were fitted.

Canberra was sunk off the Solomon Islands on 9 August 1942, and *Cornwall* was sunk in the Indian Ocean on 5 April 1942. *Kent*, *Suffolk* and *Berwick* were scrapped at the end of the war. *Cumberland* was converted for use as a trials cruiser.

Cost: £2,000,000 per ship (ex guns).

London Class

Four ships of this class were ordered in the 1925-6 Programme, viz *London*, *Devonshire*, *Sussex* and *Shropshire*. They were completed in 1929. As in the case of the *Kent* class, they were limited to 10,000 tons standard displacement by the Washington Naval Treaty.

As designed, they were modified *Kents*, having the same overall length and a slightly reduced beam. The machinery, oil fuel capacity, protection to machinery, magazines, shell rooms, etc were as in the *Kent* class. The armament was the same, but a catapult and seaplane were provided for in the design. The chief respects in which the ships differed from the *Kents* were in the omission of the bulge and the introduction of protection to the transmitting station and its principal low power room.

Great difficulty was experienced in keeping the displacement down to the treaty limit and this was only possible by the most rigid economy of weight. It was necessary to specify light alloys for decks, stanchions, etc.

Shropshire in 1935, showing the classic profile of inter-war British 10,000-ton cruisers. The rather old-fashioned appearance of three funnels and high freeboard was misleading, and the ships actually incorporated a number of original features. (Wright & Logan)

London, the only ship of the County *classes to receive a full modernisation. Seen after the Yangtse action, September 1949, in support of* Amethyst *where she received extensive damage.*

The design particulars were as follows:

Length BP	595ft 0in
Length overall	630ft 0in
Breadth extreme	66ft 0in
Legend draught	16ft 0in F / 18ft 0in A
Displacement	10,000 tons
Shp of engines	80,000
Speed	32¼kts light / 31¼kts deep
Complement (as private ship)	785 (later reduced to 657)

Armament

8-8in guns in twin turrets
4-4in HA guns
2 Mk 'M' pom-poms
2 AW quadruple torpedo tubes
Catapult and Fairey III D seaplane

The magazines forward and aft had side protection of 160lb and roofs of 120lb armour. The amidships magazine had side protection of 120lb

and roof of 80lb armour. 40lb protective plating was fitted round shell rooms, transmitting station and LP supply room. 55lb protective plating was fitted over machinery and 60lb around the steering gear. 40lb plating was fitted on bulkheads and ships sides round machinery spaces in way of the waterline.

During 1936-7 all ships of the class were fitted with four additional single 4in HA guns.

London was reconstructed in 1938-9. A 140lb armour belt 8ft deep was added in way of machinery spaces, two vertical funnels replaced the three raking funnels with consequent modifications to the uptakes etc, the eight single 4in HA guns were placed by four 4in twin mountings, two 8-barrelled pom-poms were fitted on top of the hangars with their directors on the outboard sides and a 0.5in machine gun fitted one each of 'B' and 'Y' turrets. Aircraft hangars were fitted forward with a fixed D IV H catapult between the funnels and two cranes for handling aircraft and boats. The bridge structure was rebuilt on modern lines and radar was fitted. The pole masts were replaced by tripod masts, because of increased weight of aerials, etc.[8]

The catapult and aircraft were removed during later refits and additional close-range armament fitted.

The remaining three ships were not reconstructed but were rearmed. 'X' turret was removed in *Devonshire* and *Sussex*, and twin mountings replaced the 4in HA single mountings in all three. The catapult and aircraft were removed from all ships and the torpedo tubes from *Sussex*.

In 1942, *Shropshire* was transferred to the Australian Navy to replace *Canberra*, which had been lost in action. *London* and *Sussex* were scrapped in 1949. *Devonshire* was converted to a cadet training ship.

Cost
£2,000,000 per ship (ex guns).

Dorsetshire and *Norfolk* (Class 'A' Cruisers)

These two cruisers of the 1926 programme were to have been reproductions of the *London* class, but approval was given to incorporate a later type of 8in gun mounting and a revised disposition of magazines and shell rooms and their protection. They were completed in 1930.

The main features of the design are as *London*. The protection was as *London* except that the sides of the shell rooms forward and aft were of 160lb armour and the crowns of 120lb armour. 40lb protective plating was fitted to the sides and 30lb to the floors of the gun-houses.

Dorsetshire, at refit in 1937, and *Norfolk*, at a later refit, had additional secondary and close range armament added. The single 4in mountings were replaced by twins, and the Mark M pom-poms by 8-barrelled Mark VI pom-poms. Radar was also added and the wooden masts were replaced by steel tripod masts so that radar aerials could be carried.

In 1944, 'X' turret was removed to provide compensation of the fitting of additional close-range armament, radar, fire control systems, etc.

Dorsetshire was sunk in the Indian Ocean on 5 April 1942, and *Norfolk* was scrapped after the war.

York (Class 'B' Cruiser)

This vessel was ordered in the 1926 programme and completed in 1930. The design was prepared for a cruiser with six 8in guns arranged in two twin turrets forward and one twin turret aft, with as many of the characteristics of the 1925-6 improved *Kent*s as possible. The standard displacement was to be reduced to 8000 tons but it was found that with the consequent smaller length, the same engine power would be required to give the same maximum speed of 32kts.

The greater proportion of the saving of 2000 tons was made in the weight of the hull. The arrangement of decks was similar to that used in 'E' class and earlier cruisers, and the space available for accommodation was considerably less than in the *Kent*s.

The design particulars were:

Length BP	540ft 0in
Length overall	575ft 0in
Breadth extreme	57ft 0in
Legend draught	16ft 0in F / 18ft 0in A
Displacement	8425 tons
shp of engines	80,000
Speed	32¼kts standard / 31¼kts deep
Complement (as private ship)	628

Armament

6-8in guns in twin turrets
4-4in HA guns
2 Mk 'M' pom-poms
2 AW triple torpedo tubes
Revolving catapult and a catapult for a light type aircraft

The protection in way of machinery was 120lb protective plating on the sides, 100lb and 40lb on the bulkheads and 60lb on the deck over. The magazines had 160lb armour sides, 120lb (NCD) armour bulkheads and deck over. 40lb protective plating was worked around the fire control, LP supply room, lower steering position, and torpedo head and sub-calibre magazines. 60lb protective plating was fitted to the deck over the steering gear. The gun-house roofs and sides were of 40lb (NCD) armour and the bottom of the turret of 100lb (NCD). The cordite hoist structure was of 80lb (NCD) and the turret roller protection of 40lb (NCD).

The height of the funnels was determined from the results of trials carried out at the National Physical Laboratory in order that smoke and haze should not cause interference to the after control position.

Only one catapult was eventually fitted and this was fitted amidships; the catapult for the light type aircraft was omitted.

York was lost off Crete in 1941.

Exeter (Class 'B' Cruiser)

This ship of the 1927 programme was to be a substantial repeat of *York*, but allowing for the additions of weight made to *York* for the 8in mountings and modifications to bridge and control towers. To cope with this increase in weight the beam was increased and the lines slightly modified to correct trim. *Exeter* was built at Devonport and completed in 1931.

The design particulars were:

Length BP	540ft 0in
Length overall	575ft 0in
Breadth extreme	58ft 0in
Legend draught	16ft 0in F / 18ft 0in A (later reduced to a mean draught of 16ft 9in and 8400tons corresponding displacement by Controller's directions)
Displacement	8589 tons
Shp of engines	80,000
Speed	32¼kts standard / 31¼kts deep
Complement (as private ship)	628

Armament

  6-8in guns in twin turrets
  4-4in HA guns
  2-Mk 'M' pom-poms
  2-AW triple torpedo tubes
  2 catapults

The machinery was protected by 120lb protective plating on the sides, 100lb and 40lb on the bulkheads and 60lb on the deck over. The magazines and handing rooms had 200lb on the bulkheads and deck over, all being on 20lb D1 plating. The transmitting station, LP supply room, lower steering position, torpedo head and sub-calibre magazine had 40lb protective plating and the deck over the steering gear 60lb protective plating. The 8in gun-house roofs and sides were of 40lb NC armour, as was the turret roller protection. 100lb NC armour was fitted to the bottom of the turret

and 80lb to the cordite hoist structure. Doubling of 20lb D1 plating was fitted to the ring bulkheads to give more protection to the mounting.

The Mark 'M' pom-poms were replaced during building by single 2-pdr pom-poms. Two heavy type fixed catapults were fitted amidships.

Careful consideration was given to designing a bridge which would not be subject to smoke from the funnel or violent wind currents, which had been the cause of adverse criticism of the bridges of the *Kent* and *London* classes. A roof was fitted over the bridge to obtain general experience on covered bridges.

During subsequent refits the 4in single mountings were replaced by twins, and 8-barrelled pom-poms fitted in lieu of the singles. Two 4-barrelled machine guns were added and radar was fitted. The pole masts were replaced by tripod masts.

Exeter took an important part in the Battle of the River Plate in 1940 and sustained considerable damage. She was sunk in action in the Java Sea on 1 March 1942.

Leander

This design was prepared as a smaller type of cruiser with the function of supporting destroyer attack, repelling destroyer attacks, night attacks, and shadowing. *Leander* was ordered in the 1929 programme, built at Devonport and completed in 1933.

To meet the requirements a ship of 6000 tons standard displacement with a speed of about 31kts was taken as the basis for the design. In view of the length required for this speed, the hull had to be robust and the side and deck plating amidships in way of machinery was 1in thick.

The requirements called for the magazine protection to be sufficient to make them immune from 6in shell and withstand destroyer gun fire.

Investigation showed that if an increase of 400-500ton was permissible a better all-round design could be produced.

Exeter, the last British 8in cruiser to complete, after repairs to the damage caused by Graf Spee. *Vertical funnels were introduced to make it more difficult to determine her course. The low bridge was copied in later cruisers.*

The original design had two engine rooms and two boiler rooms. In October 1929, Board approval was given to modify the design to provide increased subdivision in the machinery compartments, viz. three boiler rooms and three machinery spaces, the centre one being mainly for gears. A new legend received approval.

A series of resistance experiments at Haslar on the model of a 6in gun cruiser fitted with a bulbous bow of varying degrees of fullness indicated that a bulbous bow with an area of about 4% of midship section would be advantageous, giving a reduction in resistance of about 1¼% and a consequent gain in speed of about ⅛kt at 25-32kts. The fitting of a bulbous bow was approved.[9]

With certain modifications to the original layout of machinery it was found possible to provide a total of 72,000shp, an increase of 9000shp over that in the approved legend. An increase of 50 tons in weight was necessary, but no increase in space was required. An increase of 1kt at standard displacement was expected.

Also, since the previous legend had been approved, the protection had been under consideration and it was proposed to improve this. A further new legend was approved.

The final revised particulars were:

Length BP	522ft 0in
Length overall	554ft 3in
Breadth extreme	55ft 2in
Legend draught	{ 15ft 2in F { 17ft 2in A
Displacement	7154 tons
Shp of engines	72,000
Speed	{ 32½kts standard { 31kts deep
Complement (as flag ship)	627

Armament
8-6in guns in 4 twin turrets
4-4in HA guns
4-0.5in machine guns
2 quadruple AW torpedo tubes
1 extending heavy type catapult
1 S/R and 1 F/R seaplanes

The machinery spaces were protected by 120lb NC armour on 40lb D1 plating on the sides, 50lb D1 plating overhead and 60lb D1 plating on the end bulkheads. The magazines had 140lb NC armour sides, 80lb NC armour crowns and 100lb NC armour and bulkheads. The shell rooms, transmitting station, forward LP switchboard room, thrust block recesses, turret trunks and ammunition lobbies had 40lb D1 plating as protection. The steering gear compartment had 50lb

D1 overhead and 60lb D1 on the sides and end bulkheads.

Leander was designed with only one funnel and consequently had a rather curious appearance at the base of this funnel where the uptakes merged in.

The accommodation was arranged as for a flagship.

In 1937 the 4in HA single mountings were replaced by 4in HA twin mountings.

Action damage repairs were carried out in the USA between January 1944 and 1946. During this period 'X' turret was removed as compensation for topweight, two quadruple Bofors (later reduced to twins) and Oerlikons were added and RP 50 4in HA mountings replaced the twin mountings. Sided 4in directors and barrage directors were fitted. The catapult and aircraft were landed. Emergency diesel generators were added and Asdic and radar fitted.

Leander was used for ship target trials at the end of the war before being scrapped.

Cost: £1,613,000 (ex guns)

Leander Class

This design was similar to that of *Leander* as modified for increase of shp to 72,000, but with the addition of air-preheating arrangements in one boiler room to obtain increased fuel economy at cruising speeds. The design had a beam of 55ft 8in overall (keeping the beam at the upper deck unaltered) in order to provide a further margin of stability. The bulbous bow was not fitted.

Three ships, *Achilles*, *Neptune* and *Orion*, were ordered in the 1930 programme and one, *Ajax*, in the 1931 programme. *Achilles* completed at the end of 1933, and *Neptune* and *Orion* early in 1934. *Ajax* completed in 1935.

All four ships of the *Leander* class were constructed as flagships but only *Leander* and *Orion* were fitted as such.

A heavy (S/R) type of seaplane was carried in place of a light seaplane, but provision was made for carrying a spare F/R type light seaplane.

The particulars were:

Length BP	522ft 0in
Length overall	554ft 3in
Breadth extreme	55ft 8in
Legend draught	{ 15ft 1in F { 17ft 1in A
Displacement	7184 tons
Shp of engines	72,000
Speed	{ 32½kts standard { 31kts deep

[9] It is believed that this was not fitted.

Ajax as completed. The profile of the Leander *class, with its single funnel was considered odd when it first appeared – it could also confuse the enemy, the captain of the* Graf Spee *being convinced that* Ajax *and* Achilles *were destroyers when they attacked him in company with the* Exeter *off the River Plate in 1939.*

Armament: As *Leander*.

The protection was similar to that fitted in *Leander*. During building the plating over the transmitting station and LP switchboard room was increased from 40lb to 60lb D1. In *Achilles* this was done by fitting 20lb plating on top of the existing 40lb. In the other ships 60lb plating was worked.

During 1937, *Neptune*, *Achilles* and *Orion* were rearmed with 4in twin HA mountings in place of the single mountings. This was carried out in *Ajax* in 1940.

In 1942 the catapult and aircraft were removed and radar was installed. The pole masts were replaced by steel tripod masts.

Achilles was again rearmed during 1943-4 when 'X' turret was removed as compensation for additional close range weapons. Sided 4in HA directors and 6in barrage directors were fitted. Emergency diesel generators and more radar was installed. The directors and diesel generators were added to *Ajax* in 1942.

Neptune was sunk on 19 December 1941. *Achilles* was transferred to the Royal Indian Navy and *Orion* and *Ajax* were used for ship target trials purposes after the war.

Arethusa Class

Sketch designs for these cruisers were started shortly after the signing of the London Naval Treaty, 1930. This treaty stipulated that the total new tonnage of cruisers, carrying a gun not exceeding 6.1in calibre, to be laid down in the years 1930-33 should not exceed 90,720 tons. The Naval staff requirement was for fifty cruisers by 31 December 1936, and in order to reach this figure the new construction cruisers had to number fourteen, and as fourteen ships of the previous design (*Leander* class) would have caused the total tonnage to be exceeded, the requirement arose for a smaller cruiser of about 5000 tons displacement.[10]

The first sketch designs were arranged with both engine rooms adjacent and abaft the boiler rooms as in previous cruiser designs. Then, in order to reduce the vulnerability of the main machinery, a sketch design was prepared with the machinery spaces divided into two units, arranged boiler room, engine room, boiler room, engine room. In this arrangement two boilers were placed abreast in the forward boiler room and two fore and aft in the after boiler room, to allow the forward pair of shafts to run outside the longitudinal bulkheads abreast the boiler room.[11] The power of the boilers had to be substantially increased to enable a four-boiler system to be worked.

Two ships, *Arethusa* and *Galatea*, were ordered in the 1931 programme, one *Penelope*, in the 1933 programme and one, *Aurora*, in the 1934 programme. *Aurora* completed as a flagship for Commodore (Destroyers).

The particulars were as follows:

Length BP	480ft 0in
Length overall	506ft 0in
Breadth extreme	51ft 0in
Draught	13ft 3in F / 15ft 3in A
Displacement	5444 tons
Shp of engines	64,000
Speed	32¼kts standard / 30¾kts deep
Endurance, clean bottom	5500 miles at 15kts
Complement	500

[10] See note 3 for a detailed account of the origin of the *Arethusas*.

[11] The wing spaces abaft the after boiler room were to prove a major hazard in this and later classes. Before the introduction of the computer it was virtually impossible to calculate the effect of major, asymmetric flooding. Simple calculations showed that the heel produced if one of these wing spaces was flooded was small but experience was to show that if a torpedo hit flooded three main machinery spaces and one wing space (as was quite likely) the effect of the heeling moment on the much reduced stability was catastrophic.

Armament

6-6in guns in three twin mountings
4-4in HA guns in single mountings
2-0.5in multiple machine guns
2 triple revolving AW torpedo tubes
1 light type catapult
1 seaplane

The ships' side protection was of 90lb NC armour. The upper deck had 40lb D1 worked structurally. The magazines were protected by 120lb NC sides and 80lb NC ends and crowns. The ring bulkheads were of 30lb D1 plating. The steering gear was protected by 25lb D1 plating on the sides and 40lb D1 on the ends and the deck over.

Each of the four boilers developed 16,000shp at a working pressure of 350lb/sq in and 200°F superheat. A small auxiliary boiler was fitted in the forward boiler room for harbour service use.

The machinery was a four shaft arrangement of single reduction geared turbines working at 300lb/sq in and 200°F.

The calculated maximum bending moments amidships on the standard wave were 130,500ton ft hogging and 106,750ton ft sagging, giving stresses of the order of 7-9ton/sq in.

Arethusa was the first cruiser on which electric welding was employed to join main structural members.[12] The stem casting was replaced by a fabricated structure and the whole of the foremost 60ft of the shell plating was all-welded. Riveting was maintained for important longitudinal strength members, *eg* upper deck, armour, protective plating and portions of structure likely to be subjected to blast or vibration. The decks, superstructure, bulkheads etc were generally welded,

but the shell plating was riveted abaft the all-welded fore end.

In order to improve the armament, the later ships were fitted with 4in HA twin mountings in place of the 4in HA single mountings before completion. Twin mountings were eventually fitted in other ships of the class.

Various changes were carried out mainly during the war years. The aircraft, catapult, crane, etc were removed, radar added, and close range armament fitted. The pole masts were replaced by steel tripod masts to carry the radar aerials.

Galatea was sunk by torpedo on 15 December 1941, and *Penelope*, also by torpedo, off Anzio on 18 February 1944. *Arethusa* was used for ship target trial purposes after the war, and *Aurora* was sold to the Chinese Navy in 1948.

Cost
£1,200,000 (ex guns)

Modified *Leander* Class

A modified arrangement of machinery, considered to be an improvement on the *Leander* from the point of view of operation, protection and subdivision, was incorporated in this design. The disadvantage was that it necessitated an increase in displacement to 7250 tons standard. Four boilers in two boiler rooms separated by the forward engine room were substituted for the six in three boiler rooms in *Leander* and developed 18,000shp each. The four turbines were all of equal power, 18,000shp, instead of more power being on the outer shafts as in *Leander*. The different arrangement necessitated the side armour being extended

12 C E Sherwin, (later, himself DNC), 'Electric Welding in Cruiser Construction', *Transactions of the Institution of Naval Architects* 78 (1936).

Penelope, one of the small cruisers of the Arethusa *class, running trials. The ship is already fitted with twin 4in (on the superstructure aft of the second funnel), later retrofitted to the earlier ships of the class.*

to the upper deck level over a length of 141ft instead of 84ft as in *Leander*.

Three ships of the class were built in the 1932 programme. They were named *Amphion, Apollo* and *Phaeton*. *Phaeton* was transferred to the RAN during building and renamed *Sydney*. *Amphion* and *Apollo*, after service with the Royal Navy, were transferred to the RAN and were renamed *Perth* and *Hobart* respectively. They all completed in 1935.

The particulars were as follows:

Length BP	530ft 0in
Length overall	562ft 3in
Breadth extreme	56ft 8in
Draught	15ft 3in F / 17ft 3in A
Displacement	7197 tons
shp of engines	72,000
Speed	32½kts standard / 31kts deep
Endurance, clean bottom	7000 miles at 16kts
Complement	570

The protection and general arrangements of the ship were as *Leander*.

The fitting out of the *Leander* and *Arethusa* classes showed that it was difficult to accommodate all the ships' company and for this class, Controller instructed departments to make a careful survey of fittings to see what they could do without. Only essentials were to be fitted.

The after director control tower, as in the *Leander* class, was replaced by a non-revolving after control position, with one of the machine guns on top.

During 1938-9 the 4in single mountings were replaced by 4in HA twin mountings.

Hobart was further rearmed in Australia in 1944. The catapult, aircraft and sided 44in searchlights were removed, and more close range armament, directors and radar fitted.

Perth and *Sydney* were sunk during the war, the latter off Western Australia on 20 November 1941.

Southampton Class

In 1933, when these ships were designed, a total of about 23,400 tons remained to be allocated amongst the cruisers according to the tonnage stipulations of the London Naval Treaty, 1930. Previous 6in gun cruisers were of the smaller *Leander* and *Arethusa* types, and the *Southampton* class were designed to meet the need for more heavily armed and protected ships.

Several sketch designs were produced and eventually a sketch design for a ship of 9100 tons

standard displacement mounting twelve 6in guns and with a speed of 32kts was approved by the board on 9 November 1933.[13]

Two ships, *Southampton* and *Newcastle*, were ordered in the 1933 programme and three, *Glasgow, Birmingham* and *Sheffield*, in the 1934 programme. Three more, *Liverpool, Manchester* and *Gloucester*, were ordered in the 1935 programme, but these were modified slightly from the original design, as described later.

The particulars were as follows:

Length BP	558ft 0in
Length overall	591ft 6in
Breadth extreme	61ft 8in at WL / 64ft 2in at upper deck
Draught to AWL	16ft 0in F / 18ft 0in A
Displacement	8988 tons
Shp of engines	75,000
Speed	32kts standard / 30½kts deep
Endurance, clean bottom	8900 miles at 16kts
Complement (as squadron flagship)	791

Armament

12-6in Mk XXIII guns mounted in four triple turrets, maximum elevation 45° and maximum depression 5°
8-4in QF HA guns in four twin mountings
2-2pdr 4-barrelled pom-poms
2-0.5in multiple machine guns
4-3pdr Hotchkiss guns for saluting
2 triple 21in revolving torpedo tubes, with 6 torpedoes
A fixed reversible type catapult
3 aircraft – 2 in hangars and 1 on the catapult
2 electric cranes for aircraft and boats

Staff requirements called for protection against 6in shell fire. To meet this 180lb C armour was worked on the ship's side with 50lb D1 worked structurally on the upper and lower decks. The citadel end bulkheads were of 100lb NC armour. The magazines were protected 180lb C armour at the sides, 100lb NC at the ends and 80lb NC on the crowns. The steering gear protection consisted of 60lb D1 on the sides and ends and 50lb D1 on the crown. The bulkheads were of 80lb D on the sides and 40lb D fore and aft, with a barbette ring at the weather deck of 80lb NC at the sides and 40lb NC fore and aft. 20lb and 15lb protective plating was fitted on the bridge.

The three ships of the 1935 programme (*Liverpool, Manchester* and *Gloucester*) were modified slightly, the beam being increased by 8in at

the waterline to provide for fitting heavier armour to the 6in turrets. The protective plating on the upper deck was increased from 50lb to 60lb and extended in area.

The machinery was arranged on the unit system with a total shp of 75,000. This was increased to 82,500shp in the 1935 programme ships by working the machinery at 10% overload. The turbines were fitted as a four-shaft arrangement in two compartments and had single reduction gearing. The working pressure was 300lb/sq in and the superheat 250°F. The shp with cruising turbines in use was about 18,000. Four boilers were fitted, two in each of two boiler rooms. The working pressure was 350lb/sq in and superheat 250°F. A small auxiliary boiler, with a working pressure of 125lb/sq in, was fitted in the forward boiler room for harbour service use. This was later removed and two 200kW turbo driven electric generators fitted instead.

The propellers were of 11ft 0in diameter and worked at 300rpm. In the earlier ships the pitch was 13ft 5in on the inner and 13ft 9in on the outer propellers with a developed area of 67sq ft. The 1935 programme ships had 12ft 4in pitch on the inner and 12ft 7in on the outer propellers with a developed area of 70sq ft.

After sea trials it was estimated that with the designed shp of 75,000 the ships should get 32.7kts in the standard condition and 31.7kts in the deep condition.

The electric generating plant consisted of four 300kW DC generators, two diesel-driven and two turbo-driven. This was later increased by the addition of two 200kW turbo-driven generators when the auxiliary boiler was removed.

Staff requirements called for all armament to be manned simultaneously and, as designed, the complement was fifty-four officers and 737 ratings as a squadron flagship.

In the deep condition as designed, 11,193 tons displacement and 20ft 1in mean draught, the GM was 5.48ft and the maximum GZ 4.18ft. The angle of maximum GZ was 46½° and the vanishing angle over 90°. In the average action condition the GM was reduced to 4.58ft.

The calculated maximum bending moments amidships when balanced on the standard wave were 222,600ton ft hogging and 224,500ton ft sagging, giving maximum stresses of between 6 and 8ton/sq in.

Welding was used in the construction of these vessels as in the *Arethusa* class.

The ships were modified since design. The major alterations took place during the war and were as follows:

Fitting of radar
Modernisation of W/T
Removal of aircraft arrangements and one crane
Fitting accommodation, cinema and action information arrangements in the vacated hangars
Fitting additional close range armament
Removal of 'X' 6in turret as compensation for topweight additions

Southampton, Manchester and *Gloucester* were sunk during the war, *Southampton* on 12 January 1941 in the Mediterranean, *Manchester* on 12 August 1942 while escorting a convoy to Malta, and *Gloucester* on 26 May 1941 off Crete. Of the remainder, only *Sheffield* is still in service [eventually broken up in 1967]. The remainder were scrapped some years after the war.

Birmingham, one of the beautiful Southampton *class. Raking funnels were re-introduced by the Controller, Henderson, for aesthetic reasons. She was the only inter-war cruiser built without a knuckle bow; apparently the experiment was unsuccessful as, had war not intervened, her bow was to be rebuilt to the lines of her sisters.*

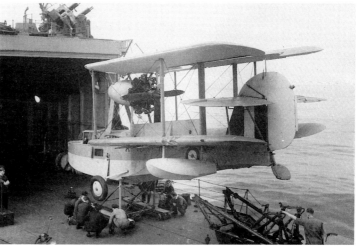

A Walrus aircraft outside the hangar of Sheffield *in 1940. Aviation arrangements took up a great deal of valuable upper deck space in capital ships and cruisers but were removed about 1943 as shore based patrol aircraft became more capable.*

Belfast Class

It was the original intention to design this class with sixteen 6in guns mounted in four quadruple turrets on a standard displacement of 10,000 tons, and a sketch design was prepared embodying these requirements. In the discussion on this design, it was ultimately decided by the Board that, in view of the difficulties in producing a sat-isfactory design of quadruple mounting, and as these ships were the last of the 9000-10,000 ton 6in gun cruisers allowed under the London Naval Treaty of 1930, it would be better to preserve homogeneity with the *Southampton* class and build the ships with four triple turrets. The weight so saved was used to increase the armour and protection.

The design in its broad outline was similar to the *Southampton* class cruisers, although of slight-ly larger dimensions.

Two ships, *Belfast* and *Edinburgh*, were ordered in the 1936 programme.

The particulars were as follows:

Length BP	579ft 0in
Length overall	613ft 6in
Breadth extreme	63ft 4in at AWL / 66ft 0in at upper deck
Draught to 'A' WL	16ft 3in F / 18ft 3in A
Corresponding displacement to AWL	9989 tons
Shp of engines	80,000
Designed speed	32½kts standard / 31kts deep
Endurance, clean bottom	10,000 miles at 16kts
Complement (as squadron flagship)	811

Belfast class
general arrangement as designed

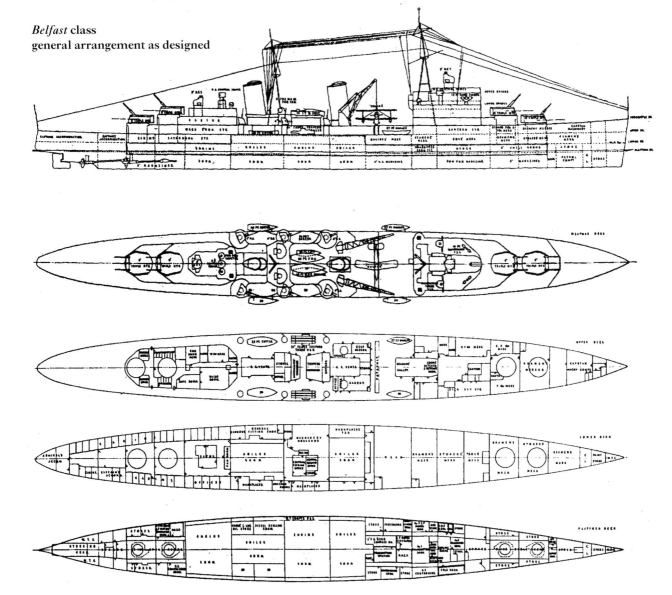

Armament

  12 BL 6in Mk XXIII guns mounted in four
    triple turrets, maximum elevation 45°,
    maximum depression 5°
  12 QF 4in Mk XVI guns mounted in six twin
    mountings
  2-2pdr 8-barrelled pom-poms
  4 QF 3pdr Hotchkiss guns for saluting
  2 triple 21in Mk IV AW revolving torpedo
    tubes with 6 torpedoes
  1 fixed type reversible catapult
  3 aircraft – 2 in hangars and 1 on the catapult
  2 electric cranes for aircraft and boats

The protection arrangements were similar to *Southampton* class, but more extensive. 180lb C armour was worked on the ships' side, with 80lb NC armour worked structurally on the upper deck and on the lower deck. The citadel end bulkheads were of 100lb NC armour. The magazines were covered by the citadel armour. The crowns of the shell rooms were of 120lb NC. The ring bulkheads were of 80lb D on the sides and 40lb D fore and aft and the barbette rings at the weather deck were correspondingly 80lb NC at the sides and 40lb NC fore and aft. The steering gear was protected by 60lb D plating on the sides and ends and 80lb NC armour on the crown. 20lb and 15lb protective plating was fitted on the bridge.

The machinery was arranged on the unit system with a total shp of 80,000. A four-shaft arrangement of geared turbines was fitted in two compartments. The working pressure of the turbines was 300lb/sq in and the temperature 250°F superheat. When using cruising turbines the shp was about 20,000. Four boilers were fitted, two in each of two boiler rooms and working at 350lb/sq in and 250°F superheat. A small auxiliary boiler was fitted in the forward engine room for harbour service use, but this was later removed and a 350kW turbo-driven electric generator fitted in its place.

The propellers worked at 300rpm and were 11ft 3in diameter, 13ft 9in pitch and had a developed area of 75sq ft.

During acceptance trials *Edinburgh* obtained a speed of 32.73kts with 81,630shp in the standard condition. *Belfast* obtained 32.98kts with 81,140shp in the standard condition and 32.01kts with 80,728shp in the deep condition. The fuel consumption in the standard condition was 0.718lb/shp/hour.

The electric generating plant consisted of four 300kW, 220 volt, DC generators, two turbo-driven and two diesel-driven. This was later increased by the addition of one 350kW turbo-driven generator in place of the auxiliary boiler as mentioned above.

The complement was fifty-eight officers and 753 ratings.

In the deep condition as designed, 12,672 tons displacement, 20ft 9in mean draught, the GM was 5.48ft and the maximum GZ 3.93ft. The angle of maximum GZ was 47° and the vanishing angle 88.4°. In the average action condition the GM was reduced to 3.8ft.

The maximum calculated bending moments amidships when balanced on the standard wave were 268,510ton ft hogging and 268,970ton ft sagging, giving stresses of between 5½ and 7½ton/sq in.

Welding was used extensively in construction as in the *Arethusa* and *Southampton* classes.

Edinburgh was sunk on 2 May 1942 while on a North Russian convoy. *Belfast* was badly damaged when mined in 1940 and subsequently underwent a large refit during which time a bulge 1ft 6in wide on each side, extending from just below the waterline to the upper deck, was added to improve the stability.

Other major modifications carried out on *Belfast*, mainly during the war years, were:

  Fitting of radar
  Modernisation of W/T
  Removal of aircraft arrangements and one
    crane
  Fitting of vacated hangars for accommodation,
    cinema and action information purposes
  Fitting of additional close range armament
  Removal of two 4in twin mountings as
    compensation for topweight added

Cost
£2,150,000 per ship (ex guns)

Dido Class

This design, prepared in 1936, was originally intended as a small cruiser of about 5000 tons for use as a flagship by Rear Admiral (Destroyers). It was evolved from the *Arethusa* class and expanded from the original intention into the *Dido* class. It met the need for a number of small cruisers of limited cost, which could operate with the Fleet and were equipped with anti-aircraft weapons. The small tonnage of the *Dido* enabled the large cruisers *Belfast* and *Edinburgh* to be built within the limits of the London Naval Treaty, 1930.

These ships, on a length and displacement comparable with the *Arethusa* class, were designed to carry a main armament of five twin 5.25in turrets, capable of HA or LA fire, thus disposing of the requirement for separate HA armament.

Dido class general arrangement as designed

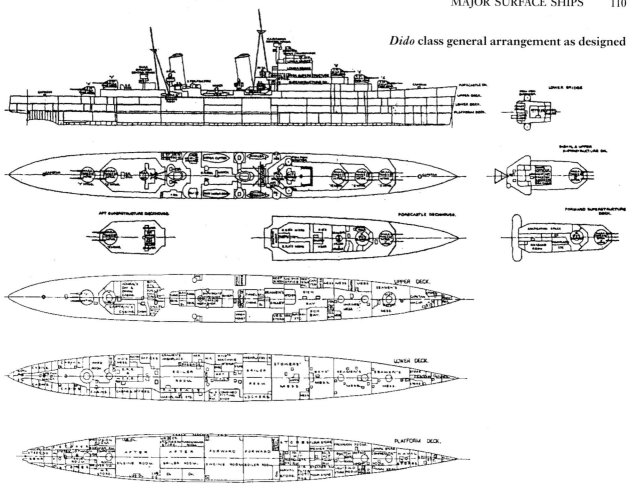

The original sketch design, after Board approval in June 1936, was subsequently modified to allow for a number of changes which were proposed during discussions. The shp was increased by 4000 and a different type of 5.25in mounting was used.

Sixteen vessels of this class were built, viz _Dido_, _Euryalus_, _Naiad_, _Phoebe_ and _Sirius_ in the 1936 programme; _Hermione_ and _Bonaventure_ in the 1937 programme; _Cleopatra_, _Charybdis_ and _Scylla_ in the 1938 programme; _Argonaut_ in the 1939 programme and _Spartan_, _Royalist_, _Bellona_, _Black Prince_ and _Diadem_ in the 1939 programme to a slightly modified design.

The particulars of the design were as follows:

Length BP	485ft 0in
Length overall	512ft 6in
Breadth extreme	50ft 6in
Draught	12ft 11in F / 15ft 6in A
Standard displacement	5450 tons
Shp of engines	62,000
Speed	32¼kts standard / 30¾kts deep
Endurance	5500 miles at 16kts
Complement (as private ship)	487

Armament

10-5.25in guns in HA/LA mountings
2 Mark 'M' 4-barrelled pom-poms
2-0.5in multiple machine guns
2 triple revolving 21in torpedo tubes and 6 torpedoes
6 depth charges

The five 5.25in mountings were arranged three forward and two aft, superimposed above each other.

The original (Mark I) 5.25in twin mounting was a 'between deck' mounting, and ammunition supply from the separate magazines and shell rooms being by means of separate external hoists. A 'long trunk' (Mark II) version was evolved for this class, in which the revolving structure of each turret extended down to the level of the magazines. These revolving trunks contained all the necessary hoists for supply of shell and cartridges, and owing to the adoption of metal cartridges with flashtight caps, it was decided to omit flashtight arrangements, off the mountings, and to combine the magazines and shell rooms. Flashtight arrangements were, however, fitted in the trunks. A more economical stowage of ammunition was thus obtained and an increased number of rounds

per gun stowed. The change from Mark I to the Mark II mounting also resulted in a decrease in complement, estimated at about sixty men.

A 5.25in director control tower was fitted on the upper bridge for LA control of main armament. An HA director tower was fitted immediately abaft and above the DCT for HA fire on forward bearings, while a similar director aft, but adapted for either HA or LA control, was fitted to cover after bearings.

The ship's small [*sic*, but must mean 'side'] armour was 120lb NC. Box protection was omitted from around the magazines in favour of a complete 80lb NC armour deck over the magazines and shell rooms. The ends of the magazines were protected by 80lb NC armour. This arrangement conserved weight and gave increased protection from aircraft. The deck over and bulkheads at the end of machinery spaces were of 40lb D plating. The gun supports and trunks were of 20lb D and D1. The turret sides and tops were of

40lb bullet-proof plating and the bridge was protected by 15lb and 20lb bullet-proof plating in exposed positions.

As in previous cruisers, the main machinery was arranged in two separate units, with the forward engine room between the two boiler rooms.

The propelling machinery consisted of a four-shaft arrangement of geared turbines, each shaft being driven by two main turbines arranged in series and power being transmitted through double helical gearing. An astern turbine was incorporated in the exhaust casing of each LP turbine. The shp of each set was 15,500 at 350rpm. The total HP developed when cruising was about 15,000. Working pressure at the turbines was 350lb/sq in at 250°F superheat.

Two boilers were arranged in each of the two boiler rooms. They were of the three-drum small-tube type working at 400lb/sq in. An auxiliary boiler was added in the forward boiler room for harbour service use, when it was decided that all

Dido, in 1944, with the design armament of five twin 5.25in guns prominently displayed. These mountings were slow to complete and several ships (including Dido) completed with a turret missing.

Two of the Didos, including Scylla, seen here in 1942, were given an armament of four twin 4.5in due to delays in the 5.25in mounting. The 4.5in armament was a much superior AA weapon but had less hitting power in surface action. The reduced armament gave more space for accommodation and they often served as flagships.

the main generators should be turbo-driven instead of diesel driven. The need for this subsequently lapsed when an 'emergency' diesel generator was fitted, and no auxiliary boiler was included in the modified 1939 *Dido* class.

The propellers were of 9ft 6in diameter.

The original scheme for electric power was to fit two turbo-generators in the engine rooms and two diesel generators in separate generator rooms, but it was ultimately decided to fit four turbo-generators, each of 300kW at 220 volts DC. An 'emergency' diesel generator was fitted later.

The fitting of Denny-Brown stabilising gear was investigated in order to provide a steady gun-platform, but the consequent loss of space and reduction in oil fuel capacity were unacceptable and the stabiliser was not fitted.

A mock-up of the bridge was constructed at Portsmouth, on which layout of instruments etc was worked out in detail.

Tripod masts were fitted instead of pole masts in order to avoid 'wooding' the directors. This was fortunate as it enabled the loading of the masts to be considerably increased on the advent of radar.

Welding was used extensively in the construction of these ships. The stem was completely fabricated and welding entirely replaced riveting and bolting for minor work, but riveting was maintained for important longitudinal strength members, armour, protective plating and proportions of structure subject to shock of vibration. Structural castings were reduced to a minimum by the adoption of fabricated welded structure.[14] The stern casting was reduced to the portion extending from the after cut-up to the rudder bearing.

Reports from sea praised the performance and layout of main machinery and the electrical supply, except that it was recommended that the main switchboard should be behind armour. The design was considered 'a great step forward', but the limitation of size was a handicap. The performance of the 5.25in armament was 'impressive' but the mountings were considered cramped.[15] The low freeboard was criticised. As a result of such reports, efforts were made to put their recommendations into effect in as many ships as possible. The lower deck sidelights were blanked before completion as a general wartime policy, and some improvement of the ventilation system was necessary. Wartime increases of complement also made themselves felt.

The rate of completion of the class was largely dependent on the supply of 5.25in mountings and by 1939 it was apparent that two of the ships would be unacceptably delayed because of this. The design of *Scylla* and *Charybdis* was therefore modified to take four 4.5in twin mountings as main armament. The weight and space gained by this enabled enlarged superstructures to be provided, with consequently more accommodation, and made these two vessels particularly suitable as flagships.

During the period June to October 1940, following the evacuation of Dunkirk, work was suspended on five of the six 'repeat' *Dido*s ordered in the 1939 Emergency Programme owing to division of labour and materials. Advantage was taken of this opportunity to modify the design in accordance with recommendations from sea and to embody certain additions arising from war experience and technical advances in these five ships when building resumed.

Modifications were made to the layout of accommodation, officers and men being more evenly distributed through the ship and near their action stations. The wardroom and officers' cabins were arranged in the forward superstructure. Additional 30lb DKM splinter protection was fitted on the ships' side over the full extent of the combined magazines and shell rooms and more protection was fitted to vital positions on the bridge. Increases in topweight were compensated by the omission of 'Q' 5.25in mounting, and a third multiple pom-pom was fitted in its place. The magazine was retained as a reserve 5.25in magazine.

By the omission of 'Q' mounting, it was possible to lower the forward superstructure by one complete deck and move the bridge structure forward. This permitted the fitting of vertical masts and funnels. The general result of this reduced the silhouette and saved topweight, which compensated for increased requirements in the bridge.

In the remainder of the class, the close-range armament changed and increased considerably as the effect of air attack was felt. Considerable numbers of radar sets and aerials were fitted and the pressure for more close-range armament together with the increase of topweight eventually resulted in the decision to remove 'Q' mounting from all ships and revert to the armament arrangements of the 1939 modified *Dido* class.

Fighter direction systems and action information organisation arrangements were added as opportunity offered, but the complete arrangements had only been fitted in *Euryalus*, *Argonaut* and *Cleopatra* when hostilities ended.

In 1943-4 arrangements were provided in *Royalist* and *Scylla* to equip them for duty as escort carrier flagships. This involved more radar and increased accommodation.

The complement of these vessels as designed was twenty-nine officers and 455 men, but due to increases during the war for close-range armament, radar, AIO, etc, the complement when carrying a flag was approximately fifty officers and 550 ratings. This increase together with the demand for more radar offices, power rooms, etc meant considerable discomfort. Every available space was appropriated for messes or cabins and many single cabins were converted to two-berth cabins.

These ships saw considerable action during the war and suffered casualties.[16] *Naiad*, *Hermione*, *Bonaventure*, *Charybdis* and *Spartan* were all sunk, the first four by torpedo and the last by glider bomb. *Dido*, *Phoebe*, *Argonaut* and *Cleopatra* sustained considerable damage at various times and were repaired and refitted in the USA. *Dido* was struck by a bomb on the starboard side of 'B' turret and considerable structural damage resulted. She was out of action for five months. *Phoebe* was hit by torpedo in 1941 and again in 1942, causing severe damage and she was out of action for eight months on each occasion. *Argonaut* was struck by torpedoes at bow and stern late in 1942 off Tunisia. The extreme fore end and after ends were blown away. She made port without assistance and after fitting a temporary bow at Gibraltar, managed to reach America for permanent repairs. She was out of action for ten months. *Cleopatra* was damaged by torpedo in 1943 and this resulted in machinery in the forward engine room and boiler room being extensively damaged. *Scylla* was damaged by a mine which, while wrecking all machinery in the ship, left all structural work intact though distorted. *Sirius* was damaged by enemy action whilst building.

Cost
£1,600,000 per ship (ex guns).

Fiji Class (*Uganda*, *Minotaur* and *Tiger* Classes)

This class succeeded *Southampton* class cruisers, but due to limitation in aggregate cruiser tonnage allocated to Britain, it was desired to retain in essence the speed and armament etc characteristics of *Southampton* on a substantially reduced size and displacement. Thus at the very outset the design was handicapped in meeting staff requirements and providing for eventualities.

The leading requirements were for a ship:

Standard displacement	8000/8130 tons
Length on waterline	550ft
Beam	62ft (extreme)
Draught	16ft 6in
Power	72,500shp
Speed (standard)	31½kts
Endurance at 16kts	8000 miles

Armament

4 triple 6in mountings	16 close range guns
4 twin 4in HA mountings	Torpedoes - 6 tubes
	Aircraft - 3

Several alternative designs were worked out, in all of which considerable difficulty was experienced in keeping within the desired displacement. Ultimately a design giving a standard displacement of 8170 tons was adopted, this being exclusive of torpedo armament. The Board, in accepting the design, gave directions that endeavours were to be made during construction to save sufficient weight to permit the fitting of torpedo armament within the approved displacement.

One important decision was to increase the power to a maximum of 80,000shp in lieu of

[16] These ships were known as Stanton's Follies after the head of the design section, referring to the way in which they capsized rapidly if torpedoed in way of the wing spaces alongside the after boiler room.

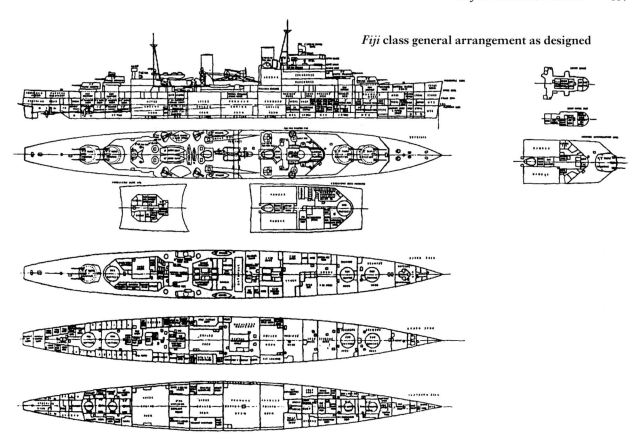

Fiji class general arrangement as designed

72,500shp. This involved additional weight of over 100 tons which was obtained mainly at the expense of protection. The design was finally approved by the Board in a minute dated 4 November 1937.

The leading particulars as calculated were:

Length overall	555ft 6in
Length on waterline	550ft 0in
Length between perps	538ft 0in
Breadth extreme	62ft 0in
Depth amidships (to UD at side)	32ft 0in
Displacement (standard)	8253 tons
Displacement (deep)	10,354 tons
Draughts (deep)	17ft 10½in F
	21ft 2½in A
	19ft 6½in Mean
Power	72,500shp, with 80,000shp available on the high rate of boiler forcing
Speed (max) in deep condition	30½kts and 31¼kts
Oil fuel capacity	1700 tons
Endurance at 16kts	8000 miles
Complement (as squadron flagship)	738 officers and men

Group Weights

Hull	3819 tons
Equipment	643 tons
Armament	1188 tons
Protection	1289 tons
Machinery	1413 tons
Aircraft equipment	174 tons
Oil fuel	1700 tons
RFW	123 tons
	10,354 tons

Structural Arrangements

The ship was built on the 'longitudinal' system, orthodox methods of construction being used and welding extensively employed. Broadly speaking, all structure not subjected to considerable structural, vibrational or gun shock stresses was welded, including all deck plating under 25lb, main transverse and longitudinal bulkheads, flats and associated beams, girders and stiffeners. In addition, the whole of the structure forward of about 30 station was welded.

All material contributing to the main structural strength was of 'D' quality plating, the remainder being MS generally, except where worked in conjunction with protection.

Arrangements were made to increase, considerably, the amount of welding in the two latest ships of the class, for which reason D1 plating was being replaced by plating of DW quality. This however was not implemented as the two ships were cancelled at the end of the war.

An interesting feature of the *Fiji* class was the transom stern, adopted primarily to give a slightly higher speed without increasing the length and displacement; it was also advantageous in giving greater space at the after end in way of the Admiral's apartments etc.

Protection

Armour protection was fitted on the ships' sides, 3½in NC abreast the magazines and 3¼in NC abreast machinery spaces. The citadel ends were enclosed by 60lb NC transverse bulkheads.

80lb NC deck protection was worked structurally at upper deck over the midship portion, and at lower deck over the remainder of the citadel; 80lb NC bulkheads being fitted transversely at the steps from upper to lower decks.

Steering gear was protected by 60lb D quality plating. Turret fronts were 2in NC, sides and rear 1in NC and roofs 2in NC.

Local splinter protection 15lb was fitted to bridges.

Armament consisted of:

12-6in guns in triple turrets
8-4in HA guns in twin mountings
2 Mk 'M' 2pdr quadruple pom-poms
2-0.5in machine guns

The 6in guns were controlled from the DCT forward or from the hood on 'X' turret; arrangements were made for dividing the control when necessary. All the 4in guns could be controlled by the HA/LA director aft. In addition, the two starboard 4in mountings could be controlled by the starboard HA/LA director and the two port by the port HA/LA director. Each pom-pom mount-ing was controlled by a director close to the mounting.

Ammunition stowage arrangements were on the scale of 200 rounds per gun for the 6in and 4in guns and 1800 rounds per barrel for the pom-poms. 5000 rounds of machine-gun ammunition was also stowed.

Six depth charges were carried.

Space was provided for torpedo armament but fitting was deferred until late in the building; then two triple 21in torpedo tubes were fitted. The hoped-for saving of weight during building to enable the torpedo arrangements to be fitted was not effected but, as part compensation for fitting these arrangements, the boat complement was reduced and two accommodation ladders, sheet anchor and bridge awnings were omitted. Further compensation was obtained by omitting ship-side lining except in way of cabins and living spaces.

Aircraft Arrangements

Three Walrus aircraft were provided for in the original design. This design also included a type D1H catapult, but as this catapult discharged on one side of the ship only it was decided to fit a type D4H catapult in lieu; this discharged on either side.

The aircraft arrangements were subsequently removed from completed ships and omitted for ships building.

Machinery

Two engine and two boiler rooms were provided, the forward engine room being between the boiler rooms. The main machinery compartments were adjacent except that the after boiler room and after engine room had 27ft fore and aft separation due to the amidships 4in magazines.

From a design point of view this separation should obviously have been between the forward

Nigeria, *a* Fiji *class cruiser in near original condition in June 1943. Note the transom stern, re-introduced in this class.*

Bermuda, *with many wartime alterations in 1945. 'X' turret has been removed as weight compensation and to provide space for additional close range AA guns and other items such as radar.*

engine room and the after boiler room, but this was not practicable owing to space requirements of aircraft arrangements, catapult, etc. The aircraft arrangements were subsequently removed or omitted, but the design was far too committed to make any change even in ships building.

Each of the four shafts had an HP and LP turbine in series transmitting through double helical reduction gearing.

Cruising and astern turbines were fitted.

Four main boilers were fitted, each of the three-drum small type, working at 400lb/sq in. Two were fitted side by side in 'A' boiler room and two in tandem in 'B' boiler room.

'A' boiler room and engine room worked as one unit, and 'B' boiler room and engine room as another, each unit being completely independent but cross-connected for emergency service. 'Closed' boiler rooms and forced draught was used, employing eight turbo fans.

In the earlier ships an auxiliary boiler was fitted in 'A' boiler room for harbour service; this was omitted in later ships to provide for additional generators.

Stability Particulars
The first ship of the class to complete, *Fiji*, was inclined with the following results:

	Deep Condition	Light Condition
Metacentric height	3.4ft (fl)	1.5ft
Max GZ	2.51ft	0.88ft
Angle of max GZ	43°	33½°
Range	80°	54°
Displacement	10,724 tons	8524 tons

The considerable difference between the displacement and stability as completed was due almost entirely to the extensive war additions which were considered imperative, it being observed that war broke out about nine months before the first ship, *Fiji*, was completed.

Propeller particulars:

Four 3-bladed propellers
Diameter	11ft 0in
Pitch	14ft 3in
Developed blade area	70sq ft

Electrical power was provided by four 300kW turbo generators. No diesel generators were provided in the original design.

The earlier ships of the *Fiji* class completed with types 279 or 281 radar sets.

Strength
The ship as originally designed was balanced on a standard trochoidal wave.

Deck armour was included, but side armour omitted, in calculating the moduli of the strength sections. All material in tension was reduced by 2/11 to allow for rivet holes.

The stresses were as follows:

	Hogging	Sagging
Max bending moment	209,000ton ft	190,000ton fit
Stress in upper deck	6.05ton/sq in	6.45ton/sq in
Stress in upper deck	6.48ton/sq in	4.93ton/sq in
Displacement	10,354 tons	9253 tons

General
As was inevitable, demands for further weighty equipment (*eg* additional radar, close-range armament, electrical equipment) arose as soon as the ships went into service, and it became necessary to insist on compensation being provided by landing the less essential gear. Difficulty arose in finding the required compensation and it became necessary to adopt unpopular expedients, *eg* omission of wood deck, etc. Experience also showed that important modifications were necessary to the existing and subsequent ships of the class, particularly in respect of close-range armament.[10]

Cost
£2,230,000 per ship (ex guns)

Uganda Class

It was not possible to find sites in existing ships for new close-range weapons without removal of some main armament. The three ships building at that time were accordingly redesigned to carry three triple 6in mountings instead of the original four; 'X' mounting being omitted and close-range armament fitted on the site vacated. These three ships became known as the *Uganda* class. At the same time important improvements to 'Warning' and other radar were introduced involving the appropriation of space for the necessary offices and the provision of a third HACP on the platform deck forward. The control hood fitted on 'X' turret in earlier ships was omitted and arrangements made for the after HA/LA tower to control 'Y' turret and also give emergency control of all 6in armament.

Opportunity was also taken in the redesigned *Uganda* to increase the auxiliary power to four 350kW turbo generators and to stagger breaker rooms and reposition the switchboard room more centrally, this with the object of reducing vulnerability.

Simple aircraft direction arrangements were also fitted, these being the forerunner of the important AIO system ultimately adopted.

Other features included the rearrangement of accommodation to enable personnel to be near their action stations, and the fitting of limited splinter protection to exposed positions; sliding protective doors were fitted abreast torpedo tubes, these being mainly to give protection from rising splinters to the 4in guns crew over the tubes.

These alterations resulted in a slight improvement in the stability of *Uganda* class, but the position was still unsatisfactory because, although the ships were perfectly stable, there was little margin to cater for major damage.

Stability particulars for *Uganda* as built were:

	Deep Condition	Light Condition
Metacentric height	3.65ft (fl)	1.3ft
Max GZ	2.7ft	1.04ft
Angle of max GZ	43°	34½°
Range	82½°	57°
Displacement	10,840 tons	8573 tons

Armament of the *Uganda* class as built was:

9-6in guns in triple turrets
10-4in HA guns in twin turrets
3-2pdr 'M' quadruple pom-poms
16 Oerlikons

Minotaur Class *(Swiftsure)* and *Tiger* Class

In order to maintain stability in later ships, in the face of continuously growing demands involving added topweight, the beam of the ships was increased from 62ft to 63ft in the *Minotaur* class (three ships; beam, of one ship only, increased to 64ft during building) and to 64ft in the *Tiger* class (five ships ordered, two cancelled).

Tiger Class
Group weights for *Superb* (the only ship of *Tiger* class completed to the original design) were:

Hull	4730 tons
Equipment	776 tons
Armament	1220 tons
Armour and protection	1310 tons
Machinery	1587 tons
Oil fuel	1941 tons
Deep displacement	11,564 tons

HMCS Ontario, *in June 1956, the last of the* Fiji *derivatives to complete during the war. Her beam was increased to 63ft to maintain stability whilst she completed without 'X' turret, receiving an extra twin 4in in lieu.*

Stability particulars for *Superb* were:

	Deep Condition	*Light Condition*
Metacentric height	4.55ft (fl)	2.86ft
Max GZ	3.23ft	1.37ft
Angle of max GZ	45°	36½°
Range	86°	62½°
Displacement	11,564 tons	9066 tons

Strength

	Hogging	*Sagging*
Max bending moment	209,300ton ft	211,900ton fit
Stress in keel	6.02ton/sq in	7.14ton/sq in
Stress in upper deck	6.38ton/sq in	5.44ton/sq in

Armament

9-6in guns in triple mountings
10-4in HA guns in twin mountings
4-2pdr quadruple pom-poms
2 single pom-poms
4-40mm Bofors
8-20mm Oerlikons in twin mountings
2 single 20mm Oerlikons

The stresses in the hogging condition were slightly less than the figures for the original *Fiji* design, but the increase in the stresses for the sagging condition were high and it was considered that the displacement of this class should be limited to 11,700 tons.

Cruisers – Particulars of Designs

	KENT.	LONDON.	YORK.	EXETER.	LEANDER.	LEANDER CLASS. (ACHILLES)	MODIFIED LEANDER CL. (SYDNEY)	ARETHUSA.	SOUTHAMPTON.	BELFAST.	DIDO.
LENGTH. B.P.	590' - 0"	595' - 0"	540' - 0"	540' - 0"	522' - 0"	522' - 0"	530' - 0"	480' - 0"	558' - 0"	579' - 0"	485' - 0"
LENGTH OVERALL.	630' - 0"	630' - 0"	575' - 0"	575' - 0"	554' - 3"	554' - 3"	562' - 3"	506' - 0"	591' - 6"	613' - 6"	512' - 0"
BREADTH EXTREME.	68' - 3"	66' - 0"	57' - 0"	58' - 0"	55' - 2"	55' - 8"	56' - 8"	51' - 0"	61' - 8" A.W.L. 62' - 4" UPPER DK	63' - 4" AT A.W.L. 66' - 0" UPPER DK	50' - 6"
DRAUGHT FORWARD.	15' - 3"	16' - 0"	16' - 0"	16' - 0" (LATER 16' - 9" MEAN 8400 TONS)	13' - 8"	15' - 1"	15' - 3"	13' - 3"	16' - 0"	16' - 3"	12' - 11"
DRAUGHT AFT.	17' - 3"	18' - 0"	18' - 0"	18' - 0"	17' - 2"	17' - 1"	17' - 3"	15' - 3"	18' - 0"	18' - 3"	15' - 6"
CORRESPONDING DISPLACEMENT.	10,000 TONS.	10,000 TONS	8,425 TONS.	5,588 TONS	7,164 TONS.	7,184 TONS	7,197 TONS.	5,444 TONS.	8,988 TONS.	9,989 TONS.	5,450 TONS.
FREEBOARD TO TOP OF DECK AT SIDE FOR'D	33' - 0"	32' - 0"	29' - 9"	29' - 9"	29' - 10"	29' - 11"	29' - 9"	27' - 9"	30' - 8½"	30' - 7"	24' - 1"
AMIDSHIPS	27' - 3"	26' - 6"	15' - 0"	15' - 0"	15' - 4"	15' - 5"	15' - 8"	14' - 3"	16' - 3"	16' - 3¼"	11' - 5"
AFT.	29' - 0"	28' - 0"	16' - 9"	16' - 9"	17' - 10"	17' - 11"	17' - 2"	15' - 3"	17' - 10½"	17' - 9"	12' - 7"
DEEP DRAUGHT (MEAN)	21' - 0"	21' - 3"	20' - 6"	20' - 4"	19' - 11		19' - 5"	17' - 10"	20' - 1"	20' - 9"	16' - 10"
DEEP DISPLACEMENT.	13,810 TONS.	13,438 TONS.	10,649 TONS.	10,798 TONS.	9,452 TONS.		9,278 TONS.	6,896 TONS.	11,193 TONS.	12,672 TONS	6,836 TONS.
S.H.P. OF ENGINES.	80,000	80,000	80,000	80,000	72,000	72,000	72,000	64,000	75,000	80,000	62,000
SPEED AT STANDARD DISP.T	31½ KNOTS (LIGHT)	32¼ KNOTS.	32¼ KNOTS.	32¼ KNOTS	32½ KNOTS.	32½ KNOTS.	32½ KNOTS.	32¼ KNOTS.	32 KNOTS.	32½ KNOTS.	32¼ KNOTS.
" " DEEP	30½ KNOTS.	31¼ KNOTS.	31¼ KNOTS.	31¼ KNOTS.	31 KNOTS.	31 KNOTS.	31 KNOTS.	30¾ KNOTS.	30½ KNOTS.	31 KNOTS.	30¾ KNOTS.
OIL FUEL CAPACITY.	3,424 TONS.	3,222 TONS.	1969 TONS.	1,923 TONS.	1,785 TONS.	1,800 TONS.	1,837 TONS.	1,127 TONS.	1,943 TONS.	2,256 TONS.	1,100 TONS.
ENDURANCE		9,900 MLS/12 KT.	7,850 MLS/12 KTS	7850 MLS/12 KTS.	8000 MLS/12 KTS.		7,000 MLS/16 KTS	5,500 MLS/16 KTS	8,900 MLS/16 KTS	1,000 MLS/16 KTS	5,500 MLS/16 KTS
COMPLEMENT (AS PRIVATE SHIP)	784	785 (LATER 657)	628.	628.	627 (AS FLAGSHIP)		621	500.	791 (AS FLAGSHIP)	811 (AS FLAGSHIP)	487.

ARMAMENT.-	KENT. NUMBER	KENT. ROUNDS PER GUN	LONDON. NUMBER	LONDON. ROUNDS PER GUN	YORK. NUMBER	YORK. ROUNDS PER GUN	EXETER. NUMBER	EXETER. ROUNDS PER GUN	LEANDER. NUMBER	LEANDER. ROUNDS PER GUN	ACHILLES NUMBER	ACHILLES ROUNDS PER GUN	SYDNEY NUMBER	SYDNEY ROUNDS PER GUN	ARETHUSA. NUMBER	ARETHUSA. ROUNDS PER GUN	SOUTHAMPTON. NUMBER	SOUTHAMPTON. ROUNDS PER GUN	BELFAST. NUMBER	BELFAST. ROUNDS PER GUN	DIDO. NUMBER	DIDO. ROUNDS PER GUN
MAIN ARMAMENT.	8 - 8"	150	8 - 8"	150	6 - 8"	150	6 - 8"	150	8 - 6"	200	8 - 6"	200	8 - 6"	200	6 - 6"	200	12 - 6"	200	12 - 6"	200	10 - 5.25"	360 P. 340 A.
H.A. GUNS.	4 - 4"	200	4 - 4"	200	4 - 4"	200	4 - 4"	200	4 - 4"	200	4 - 4"	200	4 - 4"	200	4 - 4"	150	8 - 4"	200	12 - 4"	250	-	-
POM POMS.	16 2 MK.M	1,000	16 2 MK.M.	1,000	16 2 MK.M.	1,000	8 2 MK.M.	1,500	-				-		-		2-4 BARREL	1,800	2-8 BARREL	1,800	2-4 BARREL	1,800

	KENT.	LONDON.	YORK.	EXETER.	LEANDER.	LEANDER CLASS. (ACHILLES)	MODIFIED LEANDER CL. (SYDNEY)	ARETHUSA.	SOUTHAMPTON.	BELFAST.	DIDO.
21" TORPEDO TUBES.	2 QUADRUPLE A.W.	2 QUADRUPLE A.W.	2 TRIPLE A.W.	2 TRIPLE A.W.	2 QUADRUPLE A.W.	2 QUADRUPLE A.W.	2 QUADRUPLE A.W.	2 TRIPLE A.W.	2 TRIPLE A.W.	2 TRIPLE A.W.	2 TRIPLE A.W.
21" TORPEDOES.	9	9	6	6	8	8	8.	7.	6.	6	6.
AIRCRAFT.	-	1.	2	2	2	2.	2.	2.	3	3.	-
PROTECTION.											
SHIP'S SIDE IN WAY OF M/Y.	1"	1"	3"	3"	3" ON 1"	3" ON 1"	3" ON 1"	2¼"	4½"	4½"	3"
DECK PROTECTION OVER M/Y.	1⅜"	1⅜"	1½"	1½"	1¼"	1¼"	1¼"	1"	1¼"	1"	1"
MAGAZINE SIDES.	4" ON ⅜"	3" AMID. 4" F.&A.	4"	5½" ON ½"	3½"	3½"	3½"	3"	4½"	4½"	-
MAGAZINE END.	4" ON ⅜"	- -	3"	2½" ON ½"	2½"	2½"	2½"	2"	2½"	2½"	2"
MAGAZINE CROWN	3"	2" AMID. 3" F.&A.	3"	2½" ON ½"	2"	2"	2"	2"	2"	3"	2"
STEERING GEAR COMPARTMENT SIDES.	-	1½"	-	-	1½"	1½"	1½"	⅝"	1½"	1½"	-
END	-	1½"	-	-	1½"	1½"	1½"	1"	1½"	1½"	-
CROWN	1½"	1½"	1½"	1½"	1¼"	1¼"	1¼"	1"	1¼"	2"	-
WEIGHT GROUPS:-	TONS	TONS.	TONS.	TONS	TONS.	TONS	TONS.	TONS	TONS.	TONS.	TONS.
HULL.	5,600	5,480	4,254	4,338	3,835		3,679	2,581	4,282	4,734	2,521
EQUIPMENT	570	570	491	523	507		473	421	580	610	406
ARMAMENT.	1,000	1,004	901	990	688		693	622	1,053	1,240	730
PROTECTION.	1,000	960	1,017	1,020	871		906	633	1,431	1,861	718
MACHINERY.	1,830	1,826	1,755	1,750	1,504		1,393	1,221	1,492	1,498	1,146
AIRCRAFT EQUIPMENT	-	-	-	-	43		53	41	109	126	-
STANDARD DISPLACEMENT.	10,000	9,840	8,418	8,621	7,448.		7,197	5,419	8,947	10,069	5,521
FUEL	3,424	3,222	1,969	1,923	1,785		1,837	1,327	1,943	2,256	1,105
RESERVE FEED WATER ETC.	180	165	165	165	134		148	116	148	157	122
EXTRA EQUIPT (INCL. AIRCRAFT EQ.T)	100	100	64	56	63		73	20	126	156	39
EXTRA ARMAMENT.	106	111	33	33	22		23	14	29	34	49
DEEP DISPLACEMENT.	13,810	13,438	10,649	10,798	9,452		9,278	6,896	11,193	12,672	6,836
COST. VOTE 8 COST (I.E. EXCLUDING GUN BARRELS, AIRCRAFT)	£2,084,200	£1,966,550			£1,613,220			£1,193,040.	£1,835,129.	£2,151,220	£1,574,450.

Other improvements which were incorporated in *Swiftsure* and *Superb* were the fitting of two 150kW diesel generators one each end of the ship on the platform deck, and the installation of two 1000ton turbo-driven salvage pumps, one in each boiler room, to pump out the machinery spaces. These pumps were independent of the main suction and firemain.

Accommodation
Fiji class, as originally designed, carried practically the same armament as *Southampton* class and had similar speed, so it was inevitable that accommodation for both officers and ship's company should become a serious problem.

The designed complement as a flagship was 738 total, but at the outbreak of war a considerable increase at once took place. Concurrently, severe inroads into available accommodation space were made by the necessity of finding space for the wartime additions, such as radar, damage control spaces, diesel generator compartments etc. As a result the accommodation fell far below the standard of 20sq ft per man that DNC had striven to maintain.

Some relief was obtained by the removal of the aircraft arrangements and 'X' turret but the majority of the space gained was immediately absorbed by AIO etc.

Towards the end of the war these ships became heavily congested and were running with complements of 900 or more. Every effort was made to alleviate conditions by increasing artificial ventilation and providing amenities such as cool drinking tanks, additional DARs etc. A certain amount of air conditioning was also fitted. Considerable improvement to lagging of accommodation spaces was effected, sprayed limpet asbestos lagging being ultimately fitted generally and extended to such positions as exposed action stations, galleys etc.

Special arrangements were made to meet Arctic conditions.

Experience on Service
The reports received from the first ships to go on service naturally contained a number of criticisms; these did not reflect on general design but rather dealt with matters of detail, many of which had already been anticipated as the inevitable result of carrying so much equipment on such a relatively light displacement. The ships stood up very well to the structural shocks produced by the continuous steaming at speed in all weathers and the frequently prolonged use of main or other armament. The ships handled well at all speeds and vibration was very small.

The arrangement of the bridge was a subject of criticism but the modifications suggested from sea were not unanimous. In the early ships the fore end of the bridge was rounded, and a wheel house fitted on the lower bridge; the wheel house was abolished early in the war. Ultimately the bridge was completely redesigned following a large 'mock up' at Portsmouth, and *Superb* was fitted with the new arrangements which were subsequently described as undoubted improvements.

The intention after the war was to eventually modernise completed ships with the most modern equipment available as far as practicable within the permissible limits of stability and strength, but the final nature of this modernisation would of course depend largely upon economic considerations.

Programme	Ship	Builder	Laid Down	Launched	Completed
Kent Class					
1924	*Cumberland*	Vickers Armstrongs	18 Oct 1924	16 Mar 1926	23 Jan 1928
1924	*Berwick*	Vickers Armstrongs	15 Sep 1924	30 Mar 1926	15 Feb 1928
1924	*Cornwall*	Devonport	9 Oct 1924	11 Mar 1926	8 May 1928
1924	*Suffolk*	Portsmouth	30 Sep 1924	16 Feb 1926	31 May 1928
1924	*Kent*	Chatham	15 Nov 1924	16 Mar 1926	22 Jun 1928
London Class					
1925	*London*	Portsmouth	23 Feb 1926	14 Sep 1927	31 Jan 1929
1925	*Devonshire*	Devonport	16 Mar 1916	22 Oct 1927	18 Mar 1929
1925	*Sussex*	Hawthorn Leslie	1 Feb 1927	22 Feb 1928	19 Mar 1929
1925	*Shropshire*	Beardmore	24 Feb 1927	5 Jul 1928	12 Sep 1929
1926	*Norfolk*	Fairfields	8 Jul 1927	12 Dec 1928	30 Apr 1930
1926	*Dorsetshire*	Portsmouth	21 Sep 1927	29 Jan 1929	30 Sep 1930
1926	*York*	Palmers	16 May 1927	17 Jul 1928	1 May 1930
1927	*Exeter*	Devonport	1 Aug 1928	18 Jul 1929	23 Jul 1935
1929	*Leander*	Devonport	8 Sep 1930	24 Sep 1931	24 Mar 1933

Programme	Ship	Builder	Laid Down	Launched	Completed
Leander Class					
1930	Achilles	Cammell Laird	11 Jun 1931	1 Sep 1932	6 Nov 1933
1930	Orion	Portsmouth	26 Sep 1931	24 Nov 1932	17 Jun 1934
1930	Neptune	Portsmouth	24 Sep 1931	31 Jan 1933	22 Feb 1934
1931	Ajax	Vickers Armstrongs	7 Feb 1933	1 Mar 1934	12 Apr 1935
Modified Leander Class					
1932	Phaeton	Swan Hunter	8 Jul 1933	22 Sep 1934	24 Sep 1935
1932	Apollo	Devonport	15 Aug 1933	9 Oct 1934	13 Jan 1936
1931	Amphion	Portsmouth	26 Jun 1933	27 Jul 1934	6 Jul 1936
Arethusa Class					
1931	Arethusa	Chatham	25 Jan 1933	6 Mar 1934	23 May 1935
1932	Galatea	Scotts	2 Jun 1933	9 Aug 1934	14 Aug 1935
1933	Penelope	Harland & Wolff	30 May 1934	15 Oct 1935	13 Nov 1936
1934	Aurora	Portsmouth	23 Jul 1935	20 Aug 1936	12 Nov 1937
Southampton Class					
1933	Newcastle	Vickers Armstrongs	4 Oct 1934	23 Jan 1936	5 Mar 1937
1933	Southampton	John Brown	21 Nov 1934	10 Mar 1936	6 Mar 1937
1934	Sheffield	Vickers Armstrongs	31 Jan 1935	23 Jul 1936	25 Aug 1937
1934	Glasgow	Scotts	16 Apr 1935	20 Jun 1936	9 Sep 1937
1934	Birmingham	Devonport	18 Jul 1935	1 Sep 1936	18 Nov 1937
1935	Manchester	Hawthorn Leslie	28 Mar 1936	12 Apr 1937	4 Aug 1938
1935	Liverpool	Fairfields	17 Feb 1936	24 Mar 1937	2 Nov 1938
1935	Gloucester	Devonport	22 Sep 1936	19 Oct 1937	31 Jan 1939
Belfast Class					
1936	Edinburgh	Swan Hunter	30 Dec 1936	31 Mar 1938	6 Jul 1939
1936	Belfast	Harland & Wolff	10 Dec 1936	17 Mar 1938	3 Aug 1939
Dido Class					
1937	Bonaventure	Scotts	30 Aug 1937	14 Sep 1939	24 May 1940
1936	Naiad	Hawthorn Leslie	26 Aug 1937	3 Feb 1939	24 Jul 1940
1936	Dido	Cammell Laird	20 Oct 1937	18 Jul 1939	30 Sep 1940
1936	Phoebe	Fairfields	2 Sep 1937	25 Mar 1939	30 Sep 1940
1937	Hermione	Stephens	6 Oct 1937	18 May 1939	25 Mar 1941
1936	Euryalus	Chatham	21 Oct 1937	6 Jun 1939	30 Jun 1941
1938	Charybdis	Cammell Laird	9 Nov 1938	17 Sep 1940	3 Dec 1941
1938	Cleopatra	Hawthorn Leslie	5 Jan 1939	27 Mar 1940	5 Dec 1941
1936	Sirius	Portsmouth	6 Apr 1938	18 Sep 1940	6 May 1942
1938	Scylla	Scotts	19 Apr 1939	24 Jul 1940	12 Jun 1942
War	Argonaut	Cammell Laird	21 Nov 1939	6 Sep 1941	8 Aug 1942
War	Spartan	Vickers Armstrongs	21 Dec 1939	27 Aug 1942	10 Aug 1943
Modified Dido Class					
War	Royalist	Scotts	21 Mar 1940	30 May 1942	10 Sep 1942
War	Bellona	Fairfields	30 Nov 1939	29 Sep 1942	29 Oct 1943
War	Black Prince	Harland & Wolff	2 Nov 1939	27 Aug 1942	20 Nov 1943
War	Diadem	Hawthorn Leslie	15 Dec 1939	26 Aug 1942	6 Jan 1944
Fiji Class – 1937 Programme (4–6in triple turrets, 62ft beam)					
	Fiji	J Brown	30 Mar 1938	31 May 1939	17 May 1940
	Nigeria	Vickers Armstrongs	8 Feb 1938	18 Jul 1939	23 Sep 1940
	Kenya	Stephens	18 Jun 1938	18 Aug 1939	27 Sep 1940
	Mauritius	Swan Hunter	31 Mar 1938	19 Jul 1939	1 Jan 1941
	Trinidad	Devonport	31 Apr 1938	21 Mar 1940	14 Oct 1941

Programme	Ship	Builder	Laid Down	Launched	Completed
1938, 1939 Programmes					
	Gambia	Swan Hunter	24 Jul 1939	30 Nov 1940	21 Feb 1942
	Jamaica	Vickers Armstrongs	28 Apr 1939	16 Nov 1940	29 Jun 1942
	Bermuda	J Brown	30 Nov 1939	11 Sep 1941	21 Aug 1942

Uganda Class – 1938, 1939 Programmes
(3-6in triple turrets, 62ft beam)

	Ship	Builder	Laid Down	Launched	Completed
	Newfoundland	Swan Hunter	9 Nov 1939	19 Dec 1941	20 Jan 1943
	Uganda	Vickers Armstrongs	20 Jul 1939	7 Aug 1941	31 Jan 1943
	Ceylon	Stephens	27 Apr 1939	30 Jul 1942	13 Jul 1943

Minotaur Class (Renamed *Swiftsure* Class) – 1941 Programme
(3-6in triple turrets, 63ft beam)

	Ship	Builder	Laid Down	Launched	Completed
	Swiftsure	Vickers Armstrongs	22 Sep 1941	4 Feb 1943	22 Jun 1944
	Ontario (originally *Minotaur*)	Harland & Wolff	20 Nov 1941	29 Jul 1943	25 May 1945
	Bellerophon (renamed *Tiger* 64ft beam)	J Brown	1 Oct 1941	25 Oct 1945	17 Mar 1959

Tiger Class 1941 (Supp) and 1942 Programmes[18]
(3-6in triple turrets, 64ft beam)

	Ship	Builder	Laid Down	Launched	Completed
	Superb	Swan Hunter	23 Jun 1942	31 Aug 1943	16 Nov 1945
	Defence (renamed *Lion*)	Scotts	24 Jun 1942	2 Sep 1944	22 Jul 1960
	Tiger (renamed *Bellerophon*)	Vickers Armstrongs	Cancelled		
	Blake	Fairfields	17 Aug 1942	20 Dec 1945	18 Mar 1951
	Hawke	Portsmouth	1 July 1943	Cancelled	

[17] Goodall expressed surprise in his diary that these very cramped ships were so well received by the fleet.

[18] The original text has been altered very slightly to take account of subsequent re-namings, etc.

CHAPTER 7

Fast Minelayers

Editorial Note

These ships were invaluable in war as high speed transports for stores and men – and, occasionally, for minelaying. Their speed has been, and still is, the subject of fantastic exageration; as the text makes clear, 35.6kts was the highest speed ever achieved in seagoing condition.

Abdiel Class

The object of this design was to produce a vessel able to lay as many mines as possible by day and by night in waters which might be under the control of the enemy. It was required to lay mines without escort and therefore had to rely on speed to avoid action with hostile surface vessels. A maximum speed of 40kts in the standard condition was required, giving an expected 37-38kts in the deep condition.

No specific limitation on tonnage was given but it was considered that the vessel should be in the region of 2000-2500 tons standard displacement. She was to be as seaworthy as a destroyer.

The vessel was to be capable of carrying 100 Mark XIV or XV mines on Mark XV sinkers in the standard condition and to be able to carry an additional fifty mines of the above type, the reduction of speed being accepted. This involved fitting two short inner sets of rails at the after end of the ship and fitting the necessary points for switching from the inner to the normal outer sets of rails. Alternative arrangements to lay 150 H2/VIII or VIII* units by power at 12 hours notice were also required, but were never fitted as the H2 mines were considered obsolete. All the mines were to be under cover and capable of being laid in one operation, under all conditions that the ship could keep at sea. The speed of laying was not to exceed

Abdiel class general arrangement as designed

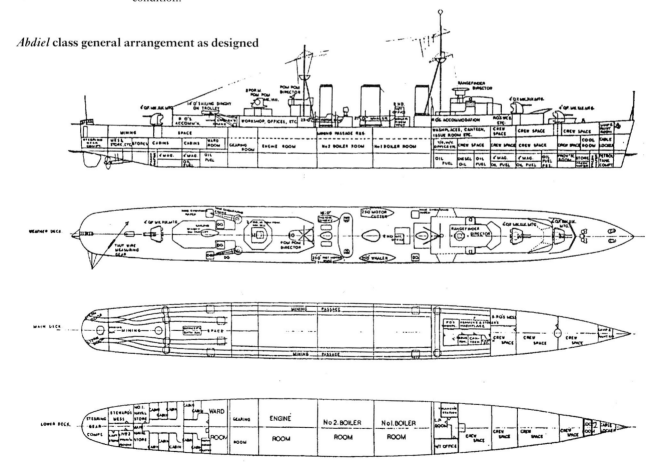

20kts and the spacing of the mines to be less than 120ft.

Six ships of this class were built in all, viz *Abdiel*, *Latona* and *Manxman* in the 1938 programme; *Welshman* in the 1939 programme; *Ariadne* and *Apollo* in the 1941 programme. The last two were 'Repeat *Abdiel*s' and embodied modifications found desirable in service.

The main particulars of the design were as follows:

Length BP	400ft 6in
Length overall	417ft 11in
Breadth extreme	40ft 0in
Draught to 'A' WL	10ft 0in F / 12ft 0in A
Displacement to 'A' WL	2640 tons
Shp of engines	72,000
Speed	40.2kts standard / 35.2kts deep

Armament

3-4in handworked twin mountings
1 4-barrelled 2pdr pom-poms
2-0.5in multiple machine guns
150 mines

The armament was primarily HA and allowed for one aircraft to be engaged by four guns.

The protection was limited to 10lb protective plating on the bridge. The necessity to keep down weight precluded fitting any other protection.

The machinery was designed to develop 72,000shp on two shafts. Single reduction geared turbines were fitted, the gearing being fitted in a separate gearing room. Both sets of machinery were fitted in one compartment. Separate cruising turbines were fitted, the shp when cruising being about 10,000.

Four boilers, each developing 18,000shp, were fitted, two in each of two boiler rooms. The working pressure was 300lb/sq in at 200°F superheat. A small vertical oil fired boiler, working pressure 30lb/sq in, was fitted for harbour service.

The propellers were of 11ft 6in diameter, 15ft 0in pitch and 97sq ft developed area and worked at 350rpm.

During sea trials on the measured mile at Arran, *Manxman* obtained a speed of 35.6kts with 73,000shp at 3450 tons displacement. These results were borne out by other ships of the class.

The endurance called for in the requirements was 5300-5500 miles at 15kts when six months out of dock. However, it was estimated from sea trials that only 4860 miles at 15kts could be achieved. The endurance, clean bottom, was estimated as 5810 miles at 15kts. These endurances assumed

that the diesel oil was burnt in the boilers as well as the oil fuel. 591 tons of oil fuel 58 tons of diesel fuel were carried.

Two 60kW diesel generators were provided in No 2 boiler room to supply the electrical power requirements.

The complement as designed was twelve officers and 224 men and the ship commissioned with this complement.

In the light condition as built, the GM was 1.76ft and the maximum righting lever 1.81ft. The angle of maximum righting lever was 61° and the vanishing angle over 90°.

The calculated maximum bending moments were 69,100ton ft in the hogging condition and 57,400ton ft in the worst sagging condition. These gave stresses in the deck and keel of between 5½ton/sq in and 7¾ton/sq in.

The large area of mining deck at the after end of the ship with no watertight subdivision constituted a danger in the event of damage. Loss of waterplane inertia and uncontrolled free water on the mining deck would cause loss of stability in both the transverse and longitudinal directions. In later tentative sketch designs it was proposed to split up the long mining deck by means of sliding watertight doors. As a compromise, the later ships of the class were fitted with portable watertight cofferdams across the mining deck.

In 1941 two ships, *Ariadne* and *Apollo* of the Repeat *Abdiel* class, were ordered. These ships were built to the same form as the original *Abdiel* class but incorporated several improvements and alterations as a result of sea experience. The armament was revised to:

2 twin 4in RPC mountings
3 Hazemeyer twin Bofors mountings
5 twin Oerlikons
150 mines

and the spacing of the masts was reduced to improve the arcs of fire. The fuel stowage was increased to 830 tons of oil fuel and 52 tons of diesel oil by fitting wing tanks in the boiler rooms etc. The diesel generators were separated, one being in No 2 boiler room and the other in the gearing room, to minimise the effect of damage. The mining arrangements were substantially the same, except that the two innermost after hatches, feeding the inner set of rails, were omitted, the inner rails being loaded by shunting from the outer rails.

Apollo cost £807,000 (ex guns, ammunition, etc).

Abdiel was sunk by mine when entering Taranto Harbour on 10 September 1943. *Latona* was sunk by bomb on 25 October 1941, and

Manxman. *These fast minelayers were invaluable for high speed store carrying, transport and minelaying. She was the only survivor of the original four ships and is seen here with late wartime modifications.*

Welshman by torpedo in the Mediterranean on 1 February 1943. *Manxman* was torpedoed whilst in the Mediterranean on 1 December 1942, the torpedo hitting abreast the engine room. It was considered that the movement of portions of the machinery across the ship caused the vessel to heel away from the damage and prevented the mining deck being flooded. It was this combination of circumstances which enabled the ship to be saved.

These ships were used on a large number of occasions during the war for carrying stores etc, especially when speed was necessary. For this purpose stores were carried on the mining deck and were limited to 200 tons. Restrictions to deck loading were also applied in order not to overstrain the light scantlings of these ships. At the end of the war all three remaining ships were placed in reserve, *Ariadne* still being in reserve to date. *Apollo* was refitted in 1951 as a flagship for C in C Home Fleet and finally scrapped in 1961. Since 1950 *Manxman* has had several refits for different duties, the latest being in 1961 when she was refitted as a CMS support ship for the Far East Squadron.

Particulars of Design

Length BP	400ft 6in
Length overall	417ft 11in
Breadth extreme	40ft 0in
Draught to 'A' WL	10ft 0in F
	12ft 0in A
Displacement to 'A' WL	2640 tons
Freeboard from AWL to upperdeck at side amidships	18ft 0in
Shp of engines	72,000
Speed at standard displacement (2650 tons)	40.2kts
Speed at deep displacement (3640 tons)	35.2kts
Oil fuel carried (including diesel oil)	749 tons

Armament

	No	Rounds per gun
HA armament	6-4in	250
Pom-poms	1-4-barrelled	1800
Mines		150

Group Weights

	Tons
Hull	1324
Equipment	200
Machinery	928
Armament	139
Mining gear	257
Fuel	749
Reserve feed water	46
Deep condition	3643

Building Particulars

Programme	Name of Ship	Builder	Date Laid Down	Date Completed
1838-9	*Abdiel*	J S White	29 Mar 1939	15 Apr 1941
	Latona	Thornycroft	4 Apr 1939	4 Apr 1941
	Manxman	Alex Stephen	24 Mar 1939	20 Jun 1941
1939-40	*Welshman*	Hawthorn Leslie	8 Jun 1939	25 Aug 1941
1941 (repeat *Abdiel*)	*Ariadne*	Alex Stephen	15 Nov 1941	9 Oct 1943
	Apollo	Hawthorn Leslie	10 Oct 1941	12 Feb 1944

CHAPTER 8

Destroyers

Editorial Note

At the end of World War I the British V & W class were the finest destroyers in service with any navy and, since there were large numbers available, there seemed no need for new designs. In 1925 C J W Hopkins produced a sketch design which was used as the basis of a loose specification from which Thornycroft and Yarrow developed the prototypes described below. These, in turn, were developed by the destroyer section into the A class which represented a considerable advance over the excellent wartime ships.

This basic design was used until the I class of 1935 and though there were improvements in hull design and, though there were experimental machinery and armament fits, the decade may be described as 'evolution from excellence to obsolescence'. The hulls were of rivetted, transverse frame construction, the main armament had a maximum elevation of 40°, with a very simple control system, and the machinery worked at comparatively low temperature and pressure and, in consequence was heavy, bulky, with high fuel consumption and requiring much maintenance. The machinery was not arranged in the unit system and hence the ships were easily disabled. Some of these points are expanded in the notes.

At the time, the reasons for accepting these old fashioned practices must have seemed strong. The story of welding is told in the introduction whilst there was intense opposition to both welding and longitudinal framing from shipbuilders (see note 5). Unit machinery was considered but rejected as it made the ships bigger and more costly. There were a number of attempts to produce more advanced machinery but there were not the design skill in industry to overcome the problems. A similar story can be told of attempts to develop a dual purpose gun but this lost urgency in 1931 when the RAF representative on the AA gunnery committee assured the navy that the dive bomber was an unlikely threat and that 40° elevation was quite satisfactory against high level bombers, flying straight and level. It seems likely that too much attention was paid to developments in potentially enemy navies and not enough to the enormous advances in US destroyers, particularly in machinery, which was light, compact, reliable and very economical. Note that the text is inconsistent on speed, some, such as the A - I classes are given in the deep condition, others in the standard with a difference of about 5kts.

By the time re-armament began it was too late to make many changes though A P Cole did manage to get longitudinal framing into the Javelin and later classes. The later Battle class introduced an effective armament whilst the Darings finally caught up with US features of a decade earlier. British Destroyers (by Edgar March), often considered the standard source, contains much useful information but should be read with care.

Construction during the inter-war period

The building of destroyers for the Royal Navy was in abeyance between the end of the 1914/18 War and 1925. During this period the Washington Naval Treaty (1921-22) was signed, but although no limitation was placed on destroyer construction by this Treaty, certain limitations were enforced by the succeeding London Naval Treaty of 1930. The standard displacement as defined by the Washington Naval Treaty was adhered to in destroyer design.

In 1925 two destroyers, *Amazon* and *Ambuscade*, were ordered to private designs.[1]

Amazon

Designed and built by Messrs Thornycroft & Co, having a standard displacement of 1350 tons, shp 39,500, designed speed 37kt (on trial 37.96kts) and endurance of 5250 miles at 11-12kts. Armament consisted of four 4.7in BL guns, two single 2pdr guns and two sets of triple R[otating] torpedo tubes. The vessel was employed as a fleet destroyer until 1943 when she was equipped for A/S duties and in late 1944 was relegated to flying training target duties.

Ambuscade

Designed and built by Messrs Yarrow & Co Ltd, with the same armament as *Amazon*. Standard displacement 1170 tons, shp 33,000, designed speed 37kts (on trial 37.19kts) and endurance 5000 miles at 11-12kts. The vessel was employed early in the war as an escort vessel and later was used as a trials ship for ahead thrown A/S weapons.

[1] It is interesting that the traditional Thornycroft and Yarrow approaches remain obvious. Thornycroft 'specials' always tended to be bigger and more powerful whilst Yarrow concentrated on lightweight construction of both hull and machinery. It is also interesting that the very high speed demanded of these ships was not repeated.

Amazon, the Thornycroft prototype, running trials when she reached very nearly 38kts.

Both of the above vessels were fitted with three boilers and twin screw geared turbines and were the first British destroyers fitted with a separate cruising turbine on each shaft. All hull structure contributing to strength was of the new Admiralty 'D' quality steel instead of HHT steel. The bridge of *Ambuscade* was constructed of aluminium alloy, and the scantlings of her hull structure were slightly lighter than those of *Amazon*.

Dimensions etc of *Amazon* and *Ambuscade* are given below:

		Amazon	*Ambuscade*
Length overall		322ft 0in	323ft 0in
Length on waterline		319ft 0in	319ft 0in
Breadth extreme		31ft 7in	31ft 1in
Standard displacement		1350 tons	1170 tons
Mean draught		12ft 7in	11ft 6in
Machinery		2 sets geared turbines	2 sets geared turbines
Shp		39,500	33,000
Speed (designed)		37kts	37kts
Speed (trials)		37.96kts	37.19kts
Endurance (15kts)		4820 miles	4,550 miles
Fuel oil		433 tons	386 tons
Complement		145 officers & men	145 officers & men
Metacentric height	deep	1.9ft (fl)	2.0ft (fl)
	light	2.15ft	2.6ft
Range of stability	deep	77½°	79½°
	light	68°	65°

A Class (1927 programme)

The Admiralty building programme was resumed in 1927 when the A class consisting of eight destroyers and a leader were provided for.

These destroyers were ordered during the stringent economy period between the two wars, and the original staff requirements were appreciably curtailed in order to reduce the cost. Their chief function was to replace existing flotillas for 'torpedo attack' with the fleet.

These ships represented a considerable improvement on previous Admiralty designed destroyers, and in this respect provision was made in the approved arrangements for a more powerful torpedo armament, improved main gun armament, new two-speed destroyer minesweeping arrangements, improved auxiliary machinery, and improved fire control arrangements.

General dimensions were:

Length overall	323ft 0in
Length between perps	312ft 0in
Extreme breadth	32ft 3in
Standard displacement	1330 tons
Deep displacement	1738 tons
Mean draught (deep)	10ft 3½in
Speed in deep condition	31½kts
Endurance at 15kts	4650 miles
Oil fuel	390 tons
Shp	34,000
Complement	145

Armament

4-4.7in QF guns (on centre line)
2-2pdr pom-poms
4 Lewis guns
2 sets quadruple torpedo tubes

Thirty depth charges were also carried, with three chutes and two throwers.

Propeller (2) Particulars

Diameter	9ft 6in
Pitch	13ft 0in
Developed blade area	53sq ft

The ships were designed with a considerable margin of stability to accommodate an estimated life of about sixteen years.

The standard strength calculations gave maximum stresses of about 8ton/sq in tension in the hogging condition and 6.4ton/sq in in the sagging condition.

Other improved items incorporated in these ships included improved accommodation and washing facilities, increased repair facilities in a small workshop, increased store room accommodation, oiling-at-sea arrangements, etc.

The requirements for the leader, *Codrington*, were similar to those for the flotilla except for an additional 4.7in gun, and the omission of minesweeping arrangements also increased accommodation. These additions involved a slight increase in dimensions, displacement and power, etc.

A total of eight ships were built (ex leader).

B Class (1928 Programme)

This was a repeat of A class design but the ships were fitted with Asdic and the two-speed destroyer sweep omitted. The flotilla leader *Keith* was built to the same lines as other destroyers of the flotilla. This restriction in size was opposed for tactical purposes, and to enable this to be done one 4.7in gun was dispensed with and part of Captain D Staff was borne in destroyers of the flotilla.

One flotilla (1 + 8 ships) was constructed.

C and D Classes (1929-1930 Programme)

A slight increase in length was necessary in these classes in order to obtain greater endurance and speed. To replace the 2pdr pom-pom a 3in HA gun was fitted. Protection was fitted to bridges and incorporated in the structure.

E and F Classes (1931-1932 Programme)

Both classes were built to the same form and a number of improvements were made on the C and D classes. The number of boiler rooms was increased from two to three, to give improved watertight subdivision, TSDS and asdics were fitted in all ships and the main armament elevation was increased to 40° (one gun 60°).

Esk and *Express* were fitted out as minelayers.

Two flotillas (1 + 8 ships) were built.

G, H and I Classes (1933-1935 Programme)

G class form was repeated for the H and I classes. A reduction in displacement and length was made and closer frame spacing adopted for these classes of destroyers. Construction was arranged for the ships to be rapidly converted to minelayers. The main differences in fitting out were:

(a) Oil fuel side or peace tanks were reduced from six to two.

(b) Two sets of quintuple torpedo tubes fitted in I class after experiments had been carried out in *Glowworm*; salt water ballast tanks were fitted as compensation.

The flotilla leaders of these classes were respectively *Grenville*, *Hardy* and *Inglefield*. They were slightly larger than the flotilla destroyers.

General particulars of G, H and I classes were:

Length overall	323ft 0in
Length between perps	312ft 0in
Moulded depth	19ft 3in
Breadth (extreme)	33ft 0in
Displacement (standard)	1350 tons
Displacement (deep)	1877 tons
Mean draught (deep)	10ft 9in
Power	34,000shp
Speed (max) deep condition	31½kts
Endurance at 15kts	5300 miles
Complement	147

Three flotillas, each 1 + 8 ships, were built.

Tribal Class (1935-1936 Programmes)

The importance of having a type of ship with good seakeeping qualities and a large radius of action to work in conjunction with cruisers and to give close support to destroyer flotillas were the main considerations which led to the ordering of sixteen vessels to this design.[2]

The principal features of the design involved in meeting these requirements were:

(i) High forecastle and freeboard to ensure good seakeeping qualities.

(ii) Large fuel capacity for increased endurance.

[2] There was a range of studies for a small cruiser or 'scout' in 1930 which led to the *Arethusa* class. The bottom of the range was very similar to the *Tribal*s.

Tartar, *one of the few survivors of the* Tribal *class, seen with later alterations - lattice mast and radar, enhanced close range armament and a twin 4in HA/LA mount in 'X' position.*

(iii) Accommodation to be suitable under all climatic conditions for the larger crews necessary.

(iv) Structure to provide for superimposed twin 4.7in mountings; stress being laid on the importance of concentrated forward fire.

(v) Fire control arrangements were fitted.[3]

Principal particulars of these ships were:

Length overall	377ft 0in
Length between perps	355ft 6in
Breadth (extreme)	36ft 6in
Moulded depth	21ft 6in
Displacement (deep)	2532 tons
Mean draught (deep)	11ft 3in
Power	44,000shp
Speed (max)	36kts
Endurance at 15kts	5200 miles
Complement	7 officers and 226 men

Group Weights

Hull	938 tons
Machinery	596 tons
Equipment	166 tons
Armament	272 tons
Oil fuel	521 tons
RFW	39 tons
Deep displacements	
	2532 tons

Machinery consisted of two sets of geared turbines and three boilers situated in three boiler rooms, for improved watertight subdivision.

The machinery was designed for 44,000shp and on trials gave 45,000shp (mean).

Propeller (2) Particulars

Diameter	10ft 3in
Pitch	13ft 1in
Developed blade area	70sq ft

Armament

The main armament consisted of four 4.7in twin mountings (two forward and two aft) and ammunition stowage was arranged on the scale of 250rpg.

The secondary armament was:

1-2pdr quadruple pom-pom
2-0.5in machine guns
4 Lewis guns

One set of quadruple 21in torpedo tubes were fitted and thirty depth charges were carried with two throwers and one rail.

Stability

An inclining experiment carried out on *Afridi* gave the following results:

	Light Condition	Deep Condition
Metacentric height	2.92ft	2.67ft (fl)
Maximum GZ	0.95ft	2.07ft
Range	67½°	over 90°
Displacement	1869 tons	2523 tons

The standard longitudinal strength calculation gave the following results:

	Hogging	Sagging
Maximum bending moment	41,700ton ft	35,135ton ft
Stress in upper deck	8.51ton/sq in	6.06ton/sq in
Stress in keel	6.44ton/sq in	6.86ton/sq in
Displacement	2478 tons	2389 tons

Sixteen vessels were ordered to this design. They proved very successful on trials, speeds of 37kts and over being obtained. These vessels also proved to be excellent sea boats.

The *Tribal* class destroyers were built to fulfil a definite function and could not be regarded as part of the normal development of destroyer design; the absence of minesweeping gear, the poor torpedo armament and their large size prevented them from fulfilling the normal functions of destroyers.

Cost

£452,000 per ship (ex guns).

J and K Classes (1936-1937 Programme)

The requirements for ships following the *Tribal*s specified a heavy torpedo armament and a gun armament which should enable them to engage enemy destroyers successfully, to defend themselves against air attacks and to contribute in as high a degree as possible to collective anti-aircraft security of the fleet. A ship smaller than the *Tribal*s was required.

The general particulars of the designs were:

Length overall	365ft 6in
Length between perps	339ft 6in
Beam (extreme)	35ft 8in
Moulded depth	20ft 6in
Displacement (standard)	1690 tons
Displacement (deep)	2320 tons
Mean draught (deep)	11ft 9in
Power (two sets geared turbines)	40,000shp
Speed (max)	36kts
Endurance at 15kts	5100 miles
Complement	7 officers and 211 men

[3] Prewar views on anti-aircraft gunnery and fire control have not been fully investigated. In 1931 the RAF told the navy that, though dive bombing was quite feasible, it required special aircraft which no air force could afford from a limited budget. The only way to attack an armoured ship was with large bombs dropped from a considerable height and for these to hit, the aircraft would have to fly straight and level. If this doctrine was accepted, it was perfectly sensible for screening ships to have a simple AA control system and only moderate elevation on their guns.

Kashmir (Kelly behind) in 1941, probably off Crete. She has radar at the mast head but is otherwise little changed.

Group Weights

Hull	876 tons
Machinery	530 tons
Equipment	142 tons
Armament	243 tons
RFW	45 tons
Oil fuel	484 tons
Deep displacement	2320 tons

Armament

3-4.7in QF twin mountings
1-2pdr quadruple pom-pom
2-0.5in machine guns
2 Lewis guns

Two pentad torpedo tubes were fitted and forty-five depth charges were carried with one rail and two throwers.

Stability

Particulars as a result of inclining *Javelin* were given as:

	Deep Condition	Light Condition
Metacentric height	2.37ft	2.48ft (fl)
Maximum GZ	1.92ft	0.90ft
Rangeover	90°	67½°
Displacement	2380 tons	1772 tons

The standard strength calculation gave the following results:

	Hogging	Sagging
Maximum bending moment	36,000ton ft	31,100ton ft
Stress in upper deck	8.23ton/sq in	6.01 ton/sq in
Stress in keel	6.28ton/sq in	6.34ton/sq in
Displacement	2244 tons	2190 tons

The design of this ship reverted to the two boiler room - one funnel arrangement,[4] and the 4.7in twin mountings were disposed two at the forward end superimposed and one on the after superstructure.

These ships were built to a system of longitudinal framing and may be regarded as the first class of destroyers to be designed in this manner.[5]

There was no special leader design for this and following classes.[6]

Cost

£520,000 per ship (ex guns)

L and M Classes (1937 and 1939 Programme)

The main differences between these classes and the J and K classes were that the main gun consisted of six 4.7in guns[7] mounted in three twin weatherproof mountings with a powered centre hoist. The guns were also capable of 50° elevation instead of 40° and of firing a 62lb shell. A combined HA/LA director control tower was also fitted in these classes. The additional weight of armament involved required a larger ship and the length and beam were increased and the freeboard slightly reduced, as compared with the J and K classes.

General particulars of the L and M were:

Length overall	362ft 6in
Length between perps	345ft 6in
Moulded depth	20ft 6in
Breadth (extreme)	35ft 9in
Displacement (standard)	1920 tons
Displacement (deep)	2630 tons
Mean draught (deep)	12ft 4in
Power (two sets geared turbines)	48,000shp
Speed (max)	37kts
Endurance at 15kts	5400 miles
Complement	7 officers and 171 men

N Class (1939 Programme)

During the Emergency period in 1939, eight repeats of the K class were ordered. These became known as the N Class. They were typical of the J and K classes except that one set of torpedo tubes was replaced by a 4in HA gun and the close-range armament increased by four Oerlikons.

The number of depth charges carried was increased to forty-five.

[4] This passage has been left as written; they were the first single funnel destroyers since *Fervent* and *Zephyr* of 1895. This was possible because A P Cole used influence through Mountbatten to persuade the Engineer-in-Chief to accept a two boiler plant.

[5] The Clydeside builders were so strongly opposed to longitudinal framing that they sent a delegation to the Controller asking him to dismiss Cole. Tenders for longitudinally framed ships were much more expensive than for transverse framing but building times suggest that there was little real difference, at least for follow-on ships. The true costs are concealed in the excess profits of the era. The only previous destroyer with longitudinal framing was the *Ardent* (Denny) 1913.

[6] One ship of each class did have an enlarged after superstructure as leader.

[7] Mk XXI gun in Mk XX mount.

Ship	Builder	Laid Down	Launched	Completed
A Class (1927 Programme)				
Codrington (F/Leader)	Swan Hunter	20 Jun 1928	8 Aug 1929	4 Jun 1930
Acasta	John Brown	13 Aug 1928	8 Aug 1929	11 Feb 1930
Achates	John Brown	11 Sep 1928	4 Oct 1929	27 Mar 1930
Acheron	Thornycroft	29 Oct 1928	18 Mar 1930	13 Oct 1931
Active	Thornycroft	10 Jul 1928	9 Jul 1929	9 Feb 1930
Antelope	Hawthorn Leslie	11 Jul 1928	27 Jul 1929	20 Mar 1930
Anthony	Hawthorn Leslie	30 Jul 1928	24 Apr 1929	14 Feb 1930
Ardent	Scotts	30 Jul 1928	26 Jun 1929	14 Apr 1930
Arrow	Vickers Armstrong	20 Aug 1928	22 Aug 1929	14 Apr 1930
B Class (1928 Programme)				
Keith (F/Leader)	Vickers Armstrong	1 Oct 1929	10 Jul 1930	20 Mar 1931
Basilisk	John Brown	19 Aug 1929	6 Aug 1930	4 Mar 1931
Beagle	John Brown	11 Oct 1929	26 Sep 1930	9 Apr 1931
Blanche	Hawthorn Leslie	29 Jul 1929	29 May 1930	13 Feb 1931
Boadicea	Hawthorn Leslie	11 Jul 1929	23 Sep 1930	7 Apr 1931
Boreas	Palmers	22 Jul 1929	11 Jun 1930	20 Feb 1931
Brazen	Palmers	22 Jul 1929	25 Jul 1930	8 Apr 1931
Brilliant	Swan Hunter	8 Jul 1929	9 Oct 1930	21 Feb 1931
Bulldog	Swan Hunter	10 Aug 1929	6 Dec 1930	8 Apr 1931
C & D Classes (1929-30 Programme)				
Kempenfelt (F/Leader)	J S White	18 Oct 1930	29 Oct 1931	31 May 1932
Crusader	Portsmouth DY	12 Sep 1930	30 Sep 1931	30 Apr 1932
Comet	Portsmouth DY	12 Sep 1930	30 Sep 1931	31 May 1932
Cygnet	Vickers Armstrong	1 Dec 1930	29 Sep 1931	1 Apr 1932
Crescent	Vickers Armstrong	1 Dec 1930	29 Sep 1931	15 Apr 1932
Duncan (F/Leader)	Portsmouth DY	25 Sep 1931	7 Jul 1932	31 Mar 1933
Defender	Vickers Armstrong	22 Jun 1931	7 Apr 1932	31 Oct 1932
Diamond	Vickers Armstrong	29 Sep 1931	8 Apr 1932	3 Nov 1932
Daring	Thornycroft	18 Jun 1931	7 Apr 1932	25 Nov 1932
Decoy	Thornycroft	25 Jun 1031	7 Jun 1932	17 Jan 1933
Dainty	Fairfields	20 Apr 1931	5 May 1932	22 Dec 1932
Delight	Fairfields	2 Apr 1931	2 Jun 1932	31 Jan 1933
Diana	Palmers	12 Jun 1931	16 Jun 1932	21 Dec 1932
Duchess	Palmers	12 Jun 1931	19 Jul 1932	27 Jan 1933
E & F Classes (1931-32 Programme)				
Exmouth (F/Leader)	Portsmouth DY	15 May 1933	30 Jan 1934	9 Nov 1934
Echo	Denny	20 Mar 1933	16 Feb 1934	22 Oct 1934
Eclipse	Denny	22 Mar 1933	12 Apr 1934	29 Nov 1934
Escapade	Scotts	30 Mar 1933	30 Jan 1934	30 Aug 1934
Escort	Scotts	30 Mar 1933	29 Mar 1934	30 Oct 1934
Esk	Swan Hunter	24 Mar 1933	19 Mar 1934	28 Sep 1934
Express	Swan Hunter	24 Mar 1933	29 May 1934	2 Nov 1934
Electra	Hawthorn Leslie	15 Mar 1933	15 Feb 1934	13 Sep 1934
Encounter	Hawthorn Leslie	15 Mar 1933	29 Mar 1934	2 Nov 1934
Faulknor (F/Leader)	Yarrow	31 Jul 1933	12 Jun 1934	24 May 1935
Fearless	Cammell Laird	17 Jul 1933	12 May 1934	19 Dec 1934
Foresight	Cammell Laird	31 Jul 1933	29 Jun 1934	15 May 1935
Foxhound	John Brown	15 Aug 1933	12 Oct 1934	21 Jun 1935
Fortune	John Brown	28 Jul 1933	29 Aug 1934	27 Apr 1935
Forester	J S White	15 May 1933	28 Jun 1934	19 Apr 1935
Fury	J S White	19 May 1933	10 Sep 1934	18 May 1935
Fame	Vickers Armstrong	5 Jul 1933	28 Jun 1934	26 Apr 1935
Firedrake	Vickers Armstrong	5 Jul 1933	28 Jun 1934	30 May 1935
G, H & I Classes 1933-35 Programme)				
Grenville (F/Leader)	Yarrow	29 Sep 1934	15 Aug 1935	1 Jul 1936
Gallant	Stephens	15 Sep 1934	26 Sep 1935	25 Feb 1936
Grenade	Stephens	3 Oct 1934	12 Nov 1935	28 Mar 1936

Ship	Builder	Laid Down	Launched	Completed
Garland	Fairfields	22 Aug 1934	24 Oct 1935	3 Mar 1936
Gipsy	Fairfields	4 Sep 1934	7 Nov 1935	22 Feb 1936
Glowworm	Thornycroft	15 Aug 1934	22 Jul 1935	22 Jan 1936
Grafton	Thornycroft	30 Aug 1934	18 Sep 1935	20 Mar 1936
Greyhound	Vickers Armstrong	20 Sep 1934	15 Aug 1935	1 Feb 1936
Griffin	Vickers Armstrong	20 Sep 1934	15 Aug 1935	6 Mar 1936
Hardy (F/Leader)	Cammell Laird	30 May 1935	7 Apr 1936	11 Dec 1936
Hasty	Denny	15 Apr 1935	5 May 1936	11 Nov 1936
Havoc	Denny	15 May 1935	7 Jul 1936	16 Jan 1937
Hereward	Vickers Armstrong	28 Feb 1935	10 Mar 1936	9 Dec 1936
Hero	Vickers Armstrong	28 Feb 1935	10 Mar 1936	21 Oct 1936
Hostile	Scotts	27 Feb 1935	24 Jan 1936	10 Sep 1936
Hotspur	Scotts	27 Feb 1935	23 Mar 1936	29 Dec 1936
Hunter	Swan Hunter	27 Mar 1935	25 Feb 1936	30 Sep 1936
Hyperion	Swan Hunter	27 Mar 1935	8 Apr 1936	3 Jan 1936
Inglefield (F/Leader)	Cammell Laird	29 Apr 1936	15 Oct 1936	25 Jun 1937
Icarus	John Brown	9 Mar 1936	26 Nov 1936	1 May 1937
Ilex	John Brown	16 Mar 1936	28 Jan 1937	7 Jul 1937
Imogen	Hawthorn Leslie	18 Jan 1936	30 Oct 1936	2 Jun 1937
Imperial	Hawthorn Leslie	29 Jan 1936	11 Dec 1936	30 Jun 1937
Impulsive	J S White	9 Mar 1936	1 Mar 1937	29 Jan 1938
Intrepid	J S White	6 Jan 1936	11 Dec 1936	30 Jun 1937
Isis	Yarrow	5 Feb 1936	12 Nov 1936	2 Jun 1937
Ivanhoe	Yarrow	12 Feb 1936	11 Feb 1937	24 Aug 1937

Tribal Class (1935-36 Programme)

Ship	Builder	Laid Down	Launched	Completed
Afridi	Vickers Armstrong	9 Jun 1936	8 Jun 1937	29 Apr 1938
Cossack	Vickers Armstrong	9 Jun 1936	8 Jun 1937	10 Jun 1938
Eskimo	Vickers Armstrong	5 Aug 1936	3 Sep 1937	30 Dec 1938
Mashona	Vickers Armstrong	5 Aug 1936	3 Sep 1937	30 Mar 1939
Ghurka	Fairfields	6 Jul 1936	7 Jul 1937	21 Oct 1938
Maori	Fairfields	6 Jul 1936	2 Sep 1937	30 Nov 1938
Mohawk	Thornycroft	16 Jul 1936	5 Oct 1937	7 Sep 1938
Nubian	Thornycroft	10 Aug 1936	21 Dec 1937	7 Dec 1938
Sikh	Stephens	24 Sep 1936	17 Dec 1937	12 Oct 1938
Zulu	Stephens	27 Aug 1936	23 Sep 1937	6 Sep 1938
Matabele	Scotts	1 Oct 1936	6 Oct 1937	25 Jan 1939
Punjabi	Scotts	1 Oct 1936	18 Dec 1937	29 Mar 1939
Ashanti	Denny	23 Nov 1936	5 Nov 1937	21 Dec 1938
Bedouin	Denny	13 Jan 1937	21 Dec 1937	15 Mar 1939
Somali	Swan Hunter	26 Aug 1936	24 Aug 1937	7 Dec 1938
Tartar	Swan Hunter	26 Aug 1936	21 Oct 1937	10 Mar 1939

J & K Classes (1936-37 Programme)

Ship	Builder	Laid Down	Launched	Completed
Jervis	Hawthorn Leslie	26 Aug 1937	9 Sep 1938	12 May 1939
Jackal	John Brown	24 Sep 1937	25 Oct 1938	13 Apr 1939
Javelin	John Brown	11 Oct 1937	21 Dec 1938	8 Jun 1939
Jaguar	Denny	25 Nov 1937	22 Dec 1938	12 Sep 1939
Juno	Fairfields	5 Oct 1937	8 Dec 1938	25 Aug 1939
Janus	Swan Hunter	29 Sep 1937	10 Nov 1938	5 Aug 1939
Jersey	J S White	20 Sep 1937	26 Sep 1938	28 Apt 1939
Jupiter	Yarrow	28 Sep 1937	27 Oct 1938	25 Jun 1939
Kelly	Hawthorn Leslie	26 Aug 1937	25 Oct 1938	23 Aug 1939
Kandahar	Denny	18 Jan 1938	21 Mar 1939	10 Oct 1939
Kelvin	Fairfields	5 Oct 1937	19 Jan 1939	27 Nov 1939
Khartoum	Swan Hunter	27 Oct 1937	6 Feb 1939	6 Nov 1939
Kashmir	Thornycroft	18 Nov 1937	4 Apr 1939	26 Oct 1939
Kimberley	Thornycroft	17 Nov 1938	1 Jun 1939	21 Dec 1939
Kingston	J S White	6 Oct 1937	9 Jan 1939	14 Sep 1939
Kipling	Yarrow	26 Oct 1937	19 Jan 1939	22 Dec 1939

Ship	Builder	Laid Down	Launched	Completed
L & M Classes (1937-39 Programme)				
Laforey	Yarrow	1 Mar 1939	15 Feb 1941	26 Aug 1941
Lance	Yarrow	1 Mar 1939	28 Nov 1940	13 May 1941
Larne	Cammell Laird	18 Oct 1938	8 Jul 1940	18 Feb 1941
Lively	Cammell Laird	20 Dec 1938	28 Jan 1941	20 Jul 1941
Legion	Hawthorn Leslie	1 Nov 1938	26 Dec 1939	19 Dec 1940
Lighting	Hawthorn Leslie	15 Nov 1938	22 Apr 1940	28 May 941
Lookout	Scotts	23 Nov 1938	4 Nov 1940	30 Jan 1942
Loyal	Scotts	23 Nov 1938	8 Oct 1941	31 Oct 1942
Milne	Scotts	24 Jan 1940	30 Dec 1941	6 Aug 1942
Marksman	Scotts	7 Jul 1939	18 Aug 1941	28 Jul 1942
Musketeer	Fairfields	7 Dec 1939	2 Dec 1941	5 Dec 1942
Myrmidon	Fairfields	7 Dec 1939	2 Mar 1942	5 Dec 1942
Matchless	Stephens	14 Sep 1940	4 Sep 1941	26 Feb 1942
Meteor	Stephens	14 Sep 1940	3 Nov 1941	12 Aug 1942
Marne	Vickers Armstrong	23 Oct 1939	30 Oct 1940	2 Dec 1941
Martin	Vickers Armstrong	23 Oct 1939	12 Dec 1940	4 Aug 1942
N Class (1939)				
Nerissa	John Brown	26 Jul 1939	7 May 1940	4 Nov 1940
Nizam	John Brown	27 Jul 1939	4 Jul 1940	8 Jan 1941
Noble	Denny	27 Jul 1939	25 Jun 1941	21 Feb 1942
Nonpareil	Denny	27 Jul 1939	25 Jun 1941	5 May 1942
Napier	Fairfields	26 Jul 1939	22 May 1940	11 Dec 1940
Nester	Fairfields	26 Jul 1939	9 Jul 1940	12 Feb 1941
Norman	Thornycroft	27 Jul 1939	30 Oct 1940	29 Sep 1941
Norseman	Thornycroft	9 Sep 1939	4 Dec 1941	29 May 1941

War Emergency Destroyers

O and P Classes (Intermediates)
(1st and 2nd Flotillas)

During the latter part of 1938 and the early part of 1939 there was some discussion on the desirability of building a destroyer intermediate in displacement between the I class and the J class. The gun armament of this intermediate type was to be a return to the single handworked 4.7in gun but firing a 62lb shell, and was to include a 2pdr multiple pom-pom.

A sketch design, with a machinery installation of 38,000shp to give a deep speed of 32kts, was accordingly submitted to the Board by DNC.

When an outbreak of war appeared imminent it was decided to modify the above design to facilitate rapid production. The 4.7in guns were made 50pdr as the 62pdr was still under development, and the machinery was changed to that of the K class developing 40,000shp. The fire control system was to comprise a combined HA/LA director control tower with fuse keeping clock and fire control box, the transmitting station being in the bridge immediately below the director.

A design embodying the above was submitted by DNC and approved by the Board on 21 December 1939.

The leading particulars of the design were:

Length overall	345ft 0in
Length between perps	382ft 9in
Breadth (extreme)	35ft 0in
Moulded depth	20ft 4in
Displacement (standard)	1570 tons
Displacement (deep)	2175 tons
Mean draught (deep)	11ft 4½in
Power	40,000shp
Speed (deep)	32¼kts
Endurance (20kts)	3850 miles
Complement	7 officers and 167 men

Group Weights

Hull	804 tons
Machinery	533 tons
Armament	174 tons
Equipment	129 tons
Oil fuel	497 tons
RFW	38 tons
Deep displacement	2175 tons

Protection

10lb protective plating was fitted round bridge, wheelhouse and transmitting station.

Onslaught *in 1942. She
was one of four of the first
sixteen wartime destroyers
completed with the intended
armament of four single
4.7in guns.*

Armament

The gun armament of this design was based on the primary requirement of low angle fire, the secondary A/A armament providing an insurance against air attack delivered from positions which the 4.7in guns, with their limited elevation of 40°, could not cover. This was considered satisfactory until the collapse of France and Norway exposed vessels in home waters to the dangers of dive and high level bombing. Consideration was then given to equipping fleet destroyers nearing completion with high angle main armament.

It was decided that eight vessels of O and P classes should complete with five 4in single HA guns and one set of quadruple torpedo tubes in lieu of the original armament of four 4.7in guns and two sets of torpedo tubes.[8] A new legend of particulars was accordingly prepared and submitted.

Early in 1941 four vessels were selected for completion such that they could be readily converted to minelayers should the necessity arise. Their gun armament was changed to 4in single mountings.[9]

Thus of the sixteen vessels of the O and P class only four completed with gun armament for which they were designed.

Seventy depth charges were also carried with two rails and four throwers.

Machinery

Two boilers arranged one in each of the two boiler rooms, the uptakes being led into a single funnel. Two sets of geared turbines (single reduction gearing) in main engine room and separate gearing room.

Propeller (2) Particulars

Diameter	10ft 6in
Pitch	13ft 3in
Developed blade area	65sq ft
Rpm	350

Stability

Based on the inclining experiment carried out on *Offa*, the stability particulars of the class were:

	Deep Condition	Light Condition
Metacentric height	2.37ft	2.8ft
Maximum GZ	2.02ft	1.0ft
Rangeover	90°	73°
Displacement	2220 tons	1618 tons

The standard strength calculation gave the following results:

	Hogging	Sagging
Maximum bending moment	30,255ton ft	27,940ton ft
Stress in upper deck	7.99ton/sq in	6.24ton/sq in
Stress in keel	5.83ton/sq in	6.25ton/sq in
Displacement	2110 tons	2074 tons

Q to C Classes
(3rd - 14th Emergency Flotillas)

Soon after the outbreak of war it became apparent that greater endurance was required in destroyers. Previously endurance had been considered in relation to the operating speed of 15kts, but with the increased submarine menace 20kts was regarded as the operating speed. To meet this

[8] The eight ships with 4in guns became the P class with some re-naming.

[9] The minelayers were *Opportune, Orwell, Obdurate* and *Obedient*.

[10] One has to repeat 'with old fashioned machinery'.

[11] It took a long while to get the Mk VI director into production and the completion of several ships was delayed in consequence.

requirement it was decided that Q and later classes of destroyers - known as Emergency Classes – should mount the same armament and machinery on a larger J class hull. A magazine and shell room were used to stow 125 tons more oil fuel, giving a nett additional endurance, compared with all earlier destroyers, of about 25%. This illustrated the high price that had to be paid for increased endurance in these destroyers.[10]

The change in design did not disturb output and the production of emergency destroyer flotillas was in full swing over the period 1940-42, the vessels entering the Fleet in 1942, 1943 and 1944. Ninety-six vessels (3rd-14th Flotillas) were ordered, thirty-two in 1940, forty in 1941 and twenty-four (part of the programme) in 1942.

With each successive flotilla new war requirements were embodied without change of dimensions or major structural alterations, the changes being made in each case with due regard to progress of construction. These improvements are given in the following paragraphs.

Armament
The need for a fully high angle armament was well realised but suitable mountings were not available, and not likely to be produced for some time.

The designed armament of Q class was the same as O class, *ie* four single 4.7in 40° elevation hand-worked mountings.

1 4-barrelled pom-pom
2-0.5in machine guns
2 quadruple torpedo tubes
5 pattern depth charge arrangements

Rapid in 1942. The second wartime order were given longer hulls based on the Javelin. In this picture, Rapid has a radar amidships but retains the original tripod mast.

Commencing with the 5th Flotilla 55° elevation mountings were installed. Commencing with 10th

Flotilla 4.5in guns took the place of the 4.7in guns in the 55° elevation mountings. Commencing with the 5th Flotilla a twin Bofors equipment with self-contained predictor control was mounted in lieu of the 4-barrelled pom-pom. From the 4th Flotilla onward four twin-powered Oerlikons were mounted as the close-range armament. Following experience in 1940 at Dunkirk and Norway a 4in HA gun was mounted in lieu of and as an alternative to the after set of torpedo tubes. Commencing with the 12th Flotilla remote power control was fitted to the main armament, one set of torpedo tubes being surrendered as compensation. From the 12th Flotilla onward a new design of HA/LA stabilised director, the Mk VI, was fitted.[11] From the 5th Flotilla onward endless chain hoists were fitted to improve rate of supply of ammunition.

With improved close-range armament the necessary arcs of fire were obtained by progressive reduction of the main aerial. In the later vessels the main mast was deleted.

The depth charge armament was increased to ten pattern as a normal armament. From the 4th Flotilla onward carrier-retaining depth charge throwers were fitted.

Alternative Armaments
Provision for three alternative armaments were made in these vessels, *ie*:

(i)   normal armament as above
(ii) fit fourteen pattern depth charge armament and land No 4 gun
(iii) Fit TSDS and land No 4 gun (destroyers only)

Provision was made for rapid conversion to these alternatives, all vessels normally completing to the design armament.

Protection: Zarebas were provided for all main and close-range armament in open mountings. Electric cables were lowered throughout machinery spaces and telemotor leads to steering gear lowered and duplicated.

Electric Power: Considerable improvements were effected in provision of electric power and distribution of the units. In the later emergency destroyers three 50kW diesels were fitted in addition to two 155kW turbo generators.

Pumping, Fire Fighting, etc. The pumping arrangements were reviewed on two occasions and with the final arrangements two 20ton electrically driven pumps were fitted, one forward and one aft, in addition to the 40ton steam-driven pump in machinery spaces. The main suction and firemain were subdivided into three sections and two 70ton portable pumps fitted, one of which could be diesel driven.

Form and Seaworthiness: A square-cut stern was introduced in Q class similar to that fitted in *Hunt*s. Based on sea experience in *Norman* an improved type of bow, similar to *Tribal* class, was introduced in the 5th and later Flotillas.[12] A

recessed bullring was also embodied in *Savage* and *Saumarez* for trial; this improved depression on No 1 mounting for ahead fire. A deeper bilge keel of Vee Type construction was fitted to all vessels to reduce rolling.

Habitability: In the *Hunt* class, officers were accommodated forward and early war experience showed that this was a desirable feature.[13] Accordingly, commencing with the 4th Flotilla, officers were accommodated mainly forward in all vessels. The crew were accommodated both forward and aft, roughly in proportion to the armament mounted at each end.

The improvements included the air lookout sights which were fitted on the bridge and in the searchlight sponsons.

Improved asdic equipment was also fitted in the 5th and later Flotillas (type 144) with the office in close proximity to the captain.

An improved plotting office was incorporated in the 4th to 10th Flotillas and AIO in later Flotillas.

Cost of a typical ship of C class was £627,000 (ex guns).

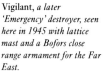

Vigilant, *a later 'Emergency' destroyer, seen here in 1945 with lattice mast and a Bofors close range armament for the Far East.*

12 A N Harrison, the very experienced constructor commander with the Home Fleet (later a DNC) did not believe that the shape of the bow made any difference to the comparative wetness of *Tribal*s and *J*s. Postwar research supports his views.

13 Catwalks were eventually built over the torpedo tubes which made it fairly safe to move fore and aft – but personal experience proved you still got wet.

Childers, *seen on 16 December 1945, had the standard 'Emergency' hull but her four 4.5in mounts were power worked – up to 18 rounds in one minute per gun – and controlled by the much better Mk VI director. Several ships were delayed in consequence of late delivery of these directors.*

Programme	Builder	Laid Down	Launched	Completed
1st Emergency Flotilla				
Oribi	Fairfields	15 Jan 1940	14 Jan 1941	5 Jul 1941
Offa	Fairfields	15 Jan 1940	11 Mar 1941	20 Sep 1941
Onslow	John Brown	1 Jul 1940	31 Mar 1941	8 Oct 1941
Onslaught	Fairfields	14 Jan 1941	9 Oct 1941	19 Jun 1942
Opportune	Thornycroft	28 Mar 1940	21 Jan 1942	14 Aug 1942
Obdurate	Denny	25 Apr 1940	19 Feb 1942	3 Sep 1942
Orwell	Thornycroft	20 May 1940	2 Apr 1942	17 Oct 1942
Obedient	Denny	22 May 1940	30 Apr 1942	30 Oct 1942
2nd Emergency Flotilla				
Panther	Fairfields	15 Jul 1940	23 May 1941	12 Dec 1941
Paladin	John Brown	22 Jul 1940	11 Jun 1941	12 Dec 1941
Pakenham	Hawthorn Leslie	6 Feb 1940	28 Jan 1941	4 Feb 1942
Penn	Vickers-Armstrong	26 Dec 1939	12 Feb 1941	20 Feb 1942
Partridge	Fairfields	3 Jun 1940	5 Aug 1941	22 Feb 1942
Pathfinder	Hawthorn Leslie	5 Mar 1940	10 Apr 1941	13 Apr 1942
Petard	Vickers-Armstrong	26 Dec 1939	27 Mar 1941	15 Jun 1942
Porcupine	Vickers-Armstrong	26 Dec 1939	10 Jun 1941	31 Aug 1942
3rd Emergency Flotilla				
Quentin	J S White	25 Sep 1940	5 Nov 1941	15 Apr 1942
Quiberon	J S White	14 Oct 1940	31 Jan 1942	22 Jul 1942
Quality	Swan Hunter	10 Oct 1940	6 Oct 1941	7 Sep 1942
Quickmatch	J S White	6 Feb 1941	11 Apr 1942	30 Sep 1942
Quilliam	Hawthorn Leslie	19 Aug 1940	29 Nov 1941	22 Oct 1942
Quadrant	Hawthorn Leslie	24 Sep 1940	28 Feb 1942	26 Nov 1942
Queenborough	Swan Hunter	6 Nov 1940	16 Jan 1942	10 Dec 1942
Quail	Hawthorn Leslie	30 Sep 1940	1 Jun 1942	7 Jan 1943
4th Emergency Flotilla				
Rotherham	John Brown	10 Apr 1941	21 Mar 1942	27 Aug 1942
Redoubt	John Brown	19 Jun 1941	2 May 1942	1 Oct 1942
Racehorse	John Brown	25 Jun 1941	1 Jun 1942	30 Oct 1942
Raider	Cammell Laird	16 Apr 1941	1 Apr 1942	16 Nov 1942
Relentless	John Brown	20 Jun 1941	15 Jul 1942	30 Nov 1942
Rapid	Cammell Laird	16 Jun 1941	16 Jul 1942	20 Feb 1943
Roebuck	Scotts	19 Jun 1941	10 Dec 1942	10 Jun 1943
Rocket	Scotts	14 Mar 1941	28 Oct 1942	4 Aug 1943
5th Emergency Flotilla				
Scorpion	Cammell Laird	19 Jun 1941	26 Aug 1942	11 May 1943
Savage	Hawthorn Leslie	7 Dec 1941	24 Sep 1942	8 Jun 1943
Saumarez	Hawthorn Leslie	8 Sep 1941	20 Nov 1942	1 Jul 1943
Scourge	Cammell Laird	26 Jun 1941	8 Dec 1942	14 Jul 1943
Success	J S White	25 Feb 1942	3 Apr 1943	6 Sep 1943
Swift	J S White	12 Jun 1942	15 Jun 1943	6 Dec 1943
Serapis	Scotts	14 Aug 1941	25 Mar 1943	23 Dec 1943
Shark	Scotts	5 Nov 1941	1 Jun 1943	18 Mar 1944
6th Emergency Flotilla				
Troubridge	John Brown	20 Nov 1941	23 Sep 1942	8 Mar 1943
Tuscan	Swan Hunter	6 Sep 1941	28 May 1942	11 Mar 1943
Tumult	John Brown	16 Nov 1941	9 Nov 1942	2 Apr 1943
Tyrian	Swan Hunter	15 Oct 1941	27 Jul 1942	8 Apr 1943
Teazer	Cammell Laird	20 Oct 1941	7 Jan 1943	13 Sep 1943
Termagant	Denny	25 Nov 1941	22 Mar 1943	18 Oct 1943
Tenacious	Cammell Laird	3 Dec 1941	24 Mar 1943	30 Oct 1943
Terpsichore	Denny	25 Nov 1941	17 Jun 1943	20 Jan 1944
7th Emergency Flotilla				
Grenville	Swan Hunter	1 Nov 1941	12 Oct 1942	27 May 1943
Ulster	Swan Hunter	12 Nov 1941	9 Nov 1942	30 Jun 1943
Urchin	Vickers-Armstrong	28 Mar 1942	8 Mar 1943	24 Sep 1943
Ulysses	Cammell Laird	14 Mar 1942	22 Apr 1943	23 Dec 1943
Undine	Thornycroft	18 Mar 1942	1 Jun 1943	23 Dec 1943
Urania	Vickers-Armstrong	18 Jun 1942	19 May 1943	18 Jan 1944
Ursa	Thornycroft	2 May 1942	22 Jul 1943	1 Mar 1944
Undaunted	Cammell Laird	8 Sep 1942	19 Jul 1943	3 Mar 1944

Programme	Builder	Laid Down	Launched	Completed
8th Emergency Flotilla				
Hardy	John Brown	14 May 1942	18 Mar 1943	14 Aug 1943
Venus	Fairfields	12 Jan 1942	22 Feb 1943	28 Aug 1943
Vigilant	Swan Hunter	31 Jan 1942	22 Dec 1942	10 Sep 1943
Virago	Swan Hunter	16 Feb 1942	4 Feb 1943	5 Nov 1943
Verulam	Fairfields	26 Jan 1942	22 Apr 1943	10 Dec 1943
Valentine	John Brown	8 Oct 1942	2 Sep 1943	28 Feb 1944
Vixen	J S White	31 Oct 1942	14 Sep 1943	5 Mar 1944
Volage	J W White	31 Dec 1942	15 Dec 1943	26 May 1944
9th Emergency Flotilla				
Kempenfelt	John Brown	24 Jun 1942	8 May 1943	25 Oct 1943
Wakeful	Fairfield	3 Jun 1942	30 Jun 1943	17 Feb 1944
Wizard	Vickers–Armstrong	14 Sep 1942	29 Sep 1943	30 Mar 1944
Wager	John Brown	20 Nov 1942	1 Nov 1943	14 Apr 1944
Whelp	Hawthorn Leslie	1 May 1942	3 Jun 1943	26 Apr 1944
Wessex	Fairfields	20 Oct 1942	2 Sep 1943	11 May 1944
Wrangler	Vickers–Armstrong	23 Sep 1942	30 Dec 1943	14 Jul 1944
Whirlwind	Hawthorn Leslie	31 Jul 1942	30 Aug 1943	20 Jul 1944
10th Emergency Flotilla				
Myngs	Vickers–Armstrong	27 May 1942	31 May 1943	23 Jun 1944
Zambesi	Cammell-Laird	21 Dec 1942	12 Nov 1943	18 Jul 1944
Zest	Thornycroft	21 Jul 1942	14 Oct 1943	20 Jul 1944
Zephyr	Vickers–Armstrong	13 Jul 1942	15 Jul 1943	6 Sep 1944
Zealous	Cammell-Laird	5 May 1943	28 Feb 1944	9 Oct 1944
Zebra	Denny	14 May 1942	8 Mar 1944	13 Oct 1944
Zodiac	Thornycroft	7 Nov 1942	11 Mar 1944	23 Oct 1944
Zenith	Denny	19 May 1942	5 Jun 1044	22 Dec 1944
11th Emergency Flotilla				
Caprice	Yarrows	24 Sep 1942	16 Sep 1943	5 Apr 1944
Cambrian	Scotts	14 Aug 1942	10 Dec 1943	17 Jul 1944
Cassandra	Yarrows	30 Jan 1943	29 Nov 1943	23 Jul 1944
Caesar	John Brown	3 Apr 1943	14 Feb 1944	5 Oct 1944
Carron	Scotts	26 Nov 1942	28 Mar 1944	6 Nov 1944
Cavalier	J S White	28 Feb 1943	7 Apr 1944	22 Nov 1944
Cavendish	John Brown	19 May 1943	12 Apr 1944	13 Dec 1944
Carysfort	J S White	12 May 1943	25 Jul 1944	20 Feb 1945
12th Emergency Flotilla				
Chevron	Stephens	18 Mar 1943	23 Feb 1944	23 May 1945
Chaplet	Thornycroft	29 Apr 1943	18 Jul 1944	24 Aug 1945
Chequers	Scotts	4 May 1943	30 Oct 1944	28 Sep 1945
Charity	Thornycroft	9 Jul 1943	30 Nov 1944	19 Nov 1945
Cheviot	Stephens	27 Apr 1943	2 May 1944	11 Dec 1945
Childers	Denny	27 Nov 1943	27 Feb 1945	19 Dec 1945
Chieftan	Scotts	27 Jun 1943	26 Feb 1945	7 Mar 1946
Chivalrous	Denny	27 Nov 1943	22 Jun 1945	13 May 1946
13th Emergency Flotilla				
Comet	Yarrows	14 Jun 1943	22 Jun 1944	6 Jun 1945
Cossack	Vickers–Armstrong	18 Mar 1943	10 May 1944	4 Sep 1945
Cockade	Yarrows	11 Mar 1943	7 Mar 1944	29 Sep 1945
Contest	J S White	1 Nov 1943	16 Dec 1944	9 Nov 1945
Constance	Vickers–Armstrong	18 Mar 1943	22 Aug 1944	31 Dec 1945
Consort	Stephens	26 May 1943	19 Oct 1944	19 Mar 1946
Comus	Thornycroft	21 Aug 1945	14 Mar 1945	8 Jul 1946
Concord	Thornycroft	18 Nov 1943	14 May 1945	20 Dec 1946
14th Emergency Flotilla				
Crescent	John Brown	16 Dep 1943	20 Jul 1944	21 Sep 1945
Crusader	John Brown	15 Nov 1943	5 Oct 1944	26 Nov 1945
Croziers	Yarrow	26 Oct 1943	19 Sep 1944	30 Nov 1945
Crystal	Yarrow	13 Jan 1944	12 Feb 1945	9 Feb 1946
Crispin	J S White	1 Feb 1944	23 Jun 1945	10 Jul 1946
Cromwell	Scotts	24 Nov 1943	6 Aug 1945	16 Sep 1946
Creole	J S White	3 Aug 1944	22 Nov 1945	14 Oct 1946
Crown	Scotts	16 Jan 1944	19 Dec 1945	25 Apr 1947

Battle Class Destroyers – 1942 Programme

During 1941 the problem of providing high angle gun fire in a destroyer without detriment to efficiency at low angles was actively reconsidered in relation to the destroyers to be ordered in the 1942 programme. This found final expression in the *Battle* class design, having a main armament of two twin 4.5in 80° mountings. The other main features of the design were as follows:

(a) Heavy medium and close-range armament
(b) Remote power control of the main armament
(c) Fitting of ship stabilisers
(d) Increased allowance of protection
(e) Length kept to a minimum to improve manoeuvrability
(f) Size limited for production reasons

The above clearly shows the influence of air attack on the design of such ships.[14]

The design was approved by the Board in June 1942 and the principal particulars were:

Length on waterline	319ft 0in
Length overall	322ft 0in
Breadth extreme	31ft 7in
Depth (USK to top of deck at side amidships)	22ft 0in
Displacement (deep)	3153 tons
(standard)	2332 tons
Shp	50,000
Speed(deep)	31¼kts
(standard)	35¾kts
Oil fuel capacity	700 tons
Endurance at 20kts (clean bottom and trial condition)	4400 sea miles

Legend of Weights

Hull	1157 tons
Machinery	655 tons
Armament (including stabilisers)	367 tons
Protection	21 tons
Electric generators	30 tons
Equipment	178 tons
Oil fuel	699 tons
RFW	46 tons
	3153 tons

Structure

The ships were longitudinally framed, but in way of the OF tanks forward and abaft the machinery spaces the spacing of the transverse framing up to the lower deck was decreased from 5ft to 21in spacing.

Armament

The main feature of the armament of this design was undoubtedly the high angle elevation of the 4.5in main armament.

The problem of increasing the elevation of the main armament above the 50° elevation attained in L class whilst keeping an enclosed mounting was solved by designing a BD (between deck) mounting suitable for use in a destroyer. Originally these mountings were to take 4.7in guns firing a 50lb projectile but early in design they were modified to take the 4.5in gun firing a 55lb projectile with separate ammunition. Trials were first carried out with a prototype fitted in the emergency destroyer *Savage*. These mountings were fitted with remote power control, and ammunition supply was by endless chain hoists from magazine and shell room to the gun working chambers below the mounting.

In order to provide fire at angles of depression the mountings were actually built in the ship on a semi-BD principle, and special strengthening was fitted in the vicinity of the opening where No 1 mounting passed through the forecastle deck. Around the periphery of this deck opening spring loaded rollers were fitted, and special weathering arrangements were provided to guard against water draining through to the deck below; special pumping arrangements were also fitted in case of flooding of the gun chambers.

In order to reduce wear on the main armament remote power control gear, it was considered desirable to provide means for reducing the amplitude of roll of the ship; for this purpose a Denny-Brown fin stabiliser was fitted.

The great weight of these mountings, together with the extra weight involved in fitting the stabiliser gear, resulted in an appreciable increase in displacement compared with earlier destroyers. To keep the displacement down to a reasonable limit a main armament of two mountings, both arranged forward, was accepted. The secondary armament was also rather heavy for this class of ship and consisted of four twin Bofors mountings arranged on the four-cornered principle. These mountings were far more elaborate than previous medium range AA weapons, being based on a triaxial system of movement and having a self-contained stabilising mechanism and predictor control (the Hazemeyer system).

At the time of designing, the submarine menace was at its height, and these ships were fitted with a heavy armament of depth charges.

Complete armament was:

2 twin 4.5in HA/LA in BD mountings
4 twin Bofors
4-20mm single Oerlikons
1-4in star shell gun

2-21in quadruple torpedo tubes (hand worked)

60 depth charges with four throwers and two rails

These ships were fitted with Asdics types 144Q and 147B.

Stabilisers

Subsequent to the approval of the design, the decision to fit stabilisers were reconsidered in the light of opinions from sea. While these opinions were far from unanimous a very common complaint was that they induced a 'jerky' motion to the ships, and, incidentally, increased the tendency to seasickness.[15] Further, it was generally considered that the space occupied by a stabiliser and its equipment could be more usefully employed as a stowage space for extra oil fuel.

It was finally decided in April 1942 that the Denny Brown stabilisers were not to be fitted in the *Battle* class destroyers, and the space made available used to stow an extra 60 tons of oil fuel. The manufacture of two sets of equipment was, however, well advanced, so they were completed and installed in *Camperdown* and *Finisterre* building at Messrs Fairfields.

Protection

Serious consideration was given during the design of these ships to providing protection against attack from the air. Magazines were protected by 10lb doubling plates fitted inside the hull plating along the waterline in way of the magazines and the decks over were increased in thickness from 6lb to 10lb plating. The bulkheads to the gun bays were also increased in poundage to 15lb while 15lb bulletproof plating was fitted round the bridge instead of the usual 10lb. Extra protection was also fitted to radar and WT offices, cable trunk and other important electric cables. 10lb

zarebras were fitted in way of close-range armament and 20lb plating to shields of 4.5in BD mountings.

Machinery

The machinery was based on that of the L class destroyer and designed to give 31¼kts at 320rpm in the deep condition, *ie* 3150 tons displacement. To achieve this the shp was increased from 48,000 to 50,000 while the steam pressure was increased from 300lb/in² to 400lb/in². The machinery layout was normal destroyer practice of two BR, ER and GR.

Propellers etc

Two shafts, propellers - three-bladed manganese bronze

diameter	11ft 6in
pitch	13ft 9in

Electrical Power

Two 200kW turbo generators and three 100kW diesel generators.

Radar

Originally fitted in these ships were types 275, 282P, 272 and 290.

The original design allowed for a type 'K' director with type 285 radar, but as this could not be adapted to take type 275 radar the heavier Mark 6 DCT had to be accepted instead.

Stability

	Light Condition	Deep Condition
Metacentric height	2.77ft	3.60ft (S)
Max value of GZ	1.15ft	3.07ft (F)
Angle of max GZ	33°	44°
Range	65°	over 90°
Displacement	2385 tons	3291 tons

Barfleur, *unusually for a* Battle, *in camouflage painting in January 1945. Note the 4in gun for star shell behind the funnel.*

[15] Modern research suggests that roll has very little effect on seasickness which is due primarily to vertical acceleration in the 0.15 - 0.3 Hz band. Roll, and particularly a jerky roll, is tiring and a tired man is more susceptible to sickness.

16 The Mk 37 system was probably the best AA fire control in any World War II navy.

These figures show an increase in displacement on the original design conditions.

Strength

From the standard longitudinal strength calculations the max bending moments and stresses were as follows:

	Hogging	Sagging
Maximum bending moment	49,930ton ft	39,890ton ft
Max stress in upper deck	8.02ton/in²	5.41ton/in²
Max stress in keel	5.93ton/in²	5.53ton/in²

Increase in Displacement

The displacements of these ships increased during building by about 140 tons on the design deep condition. This increase was accounted for and found to be mainly due to increase in oil fuel and electric cables, fitting for Arctic service (including sprayed limpet asbestos).

Complement

Twelve officers, 239 men.

Accommodation was provided both forward and aft and provision was made in the design for 15% supernumaries.

General

The first ship *Barfleur* was 80% fitted for Arctic service when it was decided to abandon the idea for this class. However, all the 1942 programme of this class were fitted with sprayed limpet asbestos lagging.

Bridge Arrangements

The many contending requirements for the limited space available on the bridge made satisfactory design a difficult matter, and it was decided that a full-scale mock-up of the 1942 *Battle* class bridge should be built with all important fittings in place and manned by Naval working parties. After approval, the arrangements as mocked-up were to be followed in every detail for the remaining vessels of the class.

As a basis for preliminary discussion, a ¹⁄₁₂th scale model was made in DNC department; this was used by Messrs Fairfields as a guide for the preparation of the full-scale mock-up on HMS *Camperdown*. The full-scale mock-up included, however, the requirements of an action information organisation, which had been approved for destroyers subsequent to the preparation of the model. The mock-up was inspected and approved in November 1943. The bridges of the remaining vessels of the class were built to these details, except for minor modifications which were per-

mitted where the dislocation caused was small and the advantage gained great.

Due to the large displacement of these ships and the consequential increased time to build compared with earlier destroyers, only sixteen ships (1st and 2nd Flotillas) were ordered in the 1942 programme.

1943 Programme

It was decided to repeat the *Battle* class design in the 1943 programme and twenty-six vessels were ordered to make up the 3rd, 4th, 5th and 6th flotillas.

In the 3rd and 4th flotillas increased broadside and torpedo armament were called for. These requirements were met by fitting a 4.5in Mark 5 single mounting with remote power control in lieu of the 4in star shell gun fitted in the 1942 *Battle*s, and pentad torpedo tubes in lieu of the quadruple tubes. Consideration was at first given to the provision of quick-reload torpedoes, but this was found to be no more economical in weight and space than the fitting of the extra tubes. As top-weight compensation one of the twin Bofors outfits and one twin Oerlikon were surrendered.

The design for the vessels to comprise the 5th and 6th flotillas incorporated a new upper deck type twin 4.5in gun mounting. This gun was under development at the time and had an increased rate of fire up to twenty rounds per minute. In these ships it was not considered necessary to fit the 4.5in single mounting, but the 4in star shell gun was retained. (This was subsequently replaced by two single Bofors in all flotillas.) To improve stabilisation of these ships the beams were increased to 41ft 0in.

The approved close-range armament of the 3rd-6th flotillas was to include the improved type of twin Bofors, viz the STAAG Mark 2, three in the 3rd-4th flotillas and four in the 5th-6th flotillas. Due to the large increase in the final weight of this mounting over the estimated weight the number of mountings to be fitted was finally reduced to two and three respectively.

Two vessels of this programme were built with fabricated shaft brackets.

Owing to the shortage of British Fire Control equipment all the vessels of this programme were fitted with an American computer system with a Mark 37 director.[16]

With the end of the war eighteen vessels of the 1943 programme were cancelled, including the whole of the 5th and 6th flotillas, the remainder being reconstituted into the 3rd flotilla.

Two vessels, which were repeats of the 5th and 6th flotilla design, were eventually built in Australia.

Battle class (1942 Programme)
general arrangement as designed

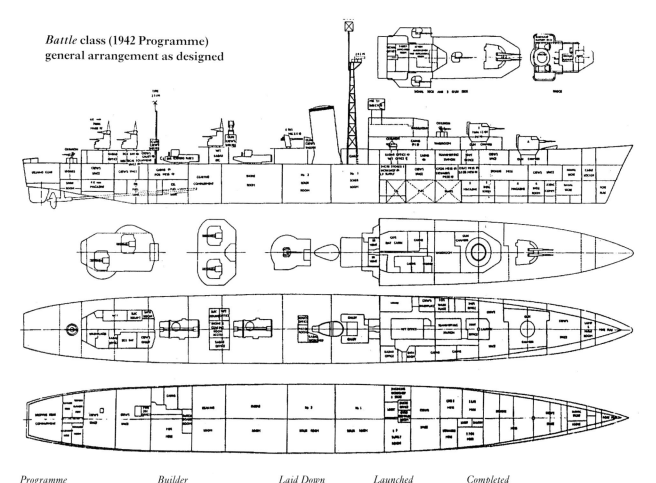

Programme	Builder	Laid Down	Launched	Completed
1942 Programme – *Battle* class				
1st Flotilla				
Barfleur	Swan Hunter	28 Oct 1942	1 Nov 1943	14 Sep 1944
Camperdown	Fairfields	30 Oct 1942	8 Feb 1944	18 Jun 1945
Trafalgar	Swan Hunter	15 Feb 1943	12 Jan 1944	23 Jul 1945
Hogue	Cammell Laird	6 Jan 1943	21 Apr 1944	24 Jul 1945
Finisterre	Fairfields	8 Dec 1942	22 Jun 1944	11 Sep 1945
Lagos	Cammell Laird	8 Apr 1943	4 Aug 1944	2 Nov 1945
St Kitts	Swan Hunter	8 Sep 1943	4 Oct 1944	21 Jan 1946
Gabbard	Swan Hunter	2 Feb 1944	16 Mar 1945	10 Dec 1946
2nd Flotilla				
Armada	Hawthorn Leslie	29 Dec 1942	9 Dec 1943	2 Jul 1945
Solebay	Hawthorn Leslie	3 Feb 1943	22 Feb 1944	11 Oct 1945
Cadiz	Fairfields	10 May 1943	16 Sep 1944	12 Apr 1946
Gravelines	Cammell Laird	10 Aug 1943	30 Nov 1944	14 Jun 1946
St James	Fairfields	20 May 1943	7 Jun 1945	12 Jul 1946
Saintes	Hawthorn Leslie	8 Jun 1943	19 Jul 1944	27 Sep 1946
Sluys	Cammell Laird	24 Nov 1943	28 Feb 1945	30 Sep 1946
Vigo	Fairfields	11 Sep 1943	27 Sep 1945	9 Nov 1946
1943 Programme – *Battle* class				
Dunkirk	Stephens	19 Jul 1944	27 Aug 1945	27 Nov 1946
Barrosa	John Brown	28 Dec 1943	17 Jan 1945	14 Feb 1947
Aisne	Vickers Armstrong	26 Aug 1943	12 May 1945	20 Mar 1947
Jutland	Stephens	27 Nov 1944	20 Feb 1946	30 Apr 1947
Corunna	Swan Hunter	12 Apr 1944	29 May 1945	6 Jun 1947
Agincourt	Hawthorn Leslie	12 Dec 1943	29 Jan 1945	25 Jun 1947
Matapan	John Brown	11 Mar 1944	30 Apr 1945	5 Sep 1947
Alamein	Hawthorn Leslie	1 Mar 1944	28 May 1945	21 May 1948

Weapon Class Destroyers (Intermediate) – 1943 Programme

In 1942 the general requirements for future Fleet destroyers were discussed at a meeting of the Future Building Committee and it was decided to include in the 1943 programme a certain number of 'Intermediate' type destroyers in addition to a repeat of the 1942 *Battle* class. It was fully appreciated that the full functions required of a destroyer could only be met by a design on the lines of the *Battle* class, but these ships were considered rather large for escort work and moreover too large to be built at all destroyer-building yards. The required functions of the smaller intermediate destroyers were similar to those of the larger Fleet destroyers but the limitations accepted were, as far as possible, without detriment to its A/S and A/A functions.

In order to produce a design capable of being built on any slip previously used for destroyers it was necessary to restrict the displacement to about 1800-1900 tons in the standard condition. With this limited displacement, consideration was given to fitting special design lightweight 4.5in 80° mountings, but in view of the relatively small number required this idea was abandoned and 4in 80° mountings were fitted instead. At one stage fixed ahead torpedo tubes were also considered;[17] tactical disadvantages and the fact that only one half of the torpedo armament was available on a beam resulted in revolving tubes being preferred, in spite of the increase in weight involved.

The design was approved by the Board in June 1943. The principal dimensions were:

Length between perps	341ft 6in
Length overall	365ft 0in
Breadth (extreme)	38ft 0in
Depth (USK to top of deck at side amidships)	20ft 9in
Displacement (deep)	2700 tons
Displacement (standard)	1965 tons
Shp	40,000
Speed (deep)	30kts
(standard)	34kts
Oil fuel capacity	620 tons
Endurance at 20kts (clean)	5000 miles

Legend of Weights	Deep
Hull	1009 tons
Machinery	570 tons
Armament	258 tons
Electric generators	30 tons
Equipment	163 tons
Oil fuel	620 tons
RFW	39 tons
Board margin	13 tons
	2702 tons

[17] The *Tyrian* was fitted with four ahead firing, fixed tubes for trial, possibly to see if the *Weapon*s should be so fitted.

Structure

These ships were longitudinally framed and built to the current destroyer building practices. An interesting and novel feature was the fitting of the forward funnel inside the lattice foremast. This allowed a shortening [*sic*, but sense must be 'lengthening'] of the forecastle with a corresponding improvement in seaworthiness. Of the ships built *Scorpion* was all-welded, the rest were partly welded. Aluminum alloy was fairly extensively used in the bridge and superstructure.

Armament

The most suitable armament for the restricted displacement (even though greater than that originally intended) was decided as being:

3 twin 4in HA/LA 80° mountings
2 twin Bofors
2 twin Oerlikons
2-21in quadruple torpedo tubes (hand worked)
50 depth charges, 2 rails and 2 throwers

Due to the Far Eastern war, a requirement to mount a heavier torpedo armament led to the fitting of two pentad torpedo tubes in lieu of the quadruple tubes.

In this design provision was also made for the mounting of five alternative armaments; these comprised increased depth charges, ahead throwing weapon, TSDS (two-speed destroyer sweep), and increased close-range armament. Subsequent difficulties encountered in mounting the ahead throwing weapon and retaining No 1 gun led to this alternative arrangement being deleted.

The main armament was under remote power control, and the ammunition supply was by endless chain hoists to the deck houses.

The ships were fitted with Asdics types 144Q and 147B.

Protection was very limited and consisted of 10lb splinter protection on the front and sides of the bridge and wheelhouse, and zarebas for the main and close-range armament.

Machinery

As a result of war experience, these ships were designed with the machinery in two units, with alternate boiler rooms and engine rooms. The units, each consisting of a boiler room and engine rooms, were separated by a 10ft OF block and 2ft air space, and cross connections between units were fitted for alternate 'pairings'. This machinery layout was considered to be the best arrangement to minimise the effects of heavy damage.

In order to economise on the use of fuel the machinery installation provided for higher pres-

Scorpion, in October 1947, a Weapon *class destroyer intended to be built on slipways too short for a* Battle. *They completed after the war with two Squids in place of one of the twin 4in mounts. The guns were controlled by an electronic system, 'Flyplane' which was very good for its day. The widely separated funnels show that, at last, the unit machinery layout had reached RN destroyers. The forward funnel is inside the lattice mast.*

sures than hitherto worked in destroyers, namely 400lb/in², and economizers were fitted to reduce temperature from 750° to 450°F at full power.

Stability Particulars

	Light Condition	*Deep Condition*
Metacentric height	2.20ft	2.76ft
Max value of GZ	0.97ft	1.98ft
Angle of max GZ	33°	44°
Range	63°	90°
Displacement	2080 tons	2837 tons

Electrical Power
Two 200kW turbo generators, one in each boiler room. Two 100kW diesel generators, one in each engine room.

The TG capacity was estimated to be sufficient to cover all requirements for action damage; while the DGs were capable of dealing with the action loads. Electric cooking facilities were fitted in this class.

Radar
Types 275, 242, 293, 262 and 253 ships were fitted with stabilised Mark 6 DCT.

Strength
From the standard strength calculation the maximum bending moments and stresses were:

	Hogging	*Sagging*
Maximum bending moment	42,635ton ft	34,520ton ft
Max stress in upper deck	8.04ton/in²	5.52ton/in²
Max stress in keel	5.98ton/in²	5.64ton/in²

Propellers etc

2 shafts, propellers	– diam 10ft 6in
	– pitch 12ft 11in

On speed trials the *Battleaxe* generated 39,700shp at 324rpm to give 30.7kts at a displacement of 2495 tons.

Increase in Displacement
As a result of the first ship of this class to be inclined, viz *Battleaxe*, it was estimated that the deep displacement was about 120 tons greater than the designed deep. The greater part of this weight was accounted for: hull structure, fittings etc 70 tons; electric cables 39 tons; etc.

Complement of 272 was accommodated partly forward and partly aft to enable armament and control positions to be rapidly manned from the living quarters.

General
Nineteen ships of this class were ordered in the original 1943 programme, the balance of twenty-six vessels being repeat *Battle*s. With the cessation of hostilities all but four of the *Weapons* class were cancelled, and in January 1946 it was approved to complete these four ships as leaders and Fleet A/S escorts, no provision to be made for alternative armament other than twin-speed destroyer sweep (TSDS). It was stipulated that in modifying the ships for escort duties, no structural alterations were to be made which would render them unfit for the ordinary and manifold duties of destroyers.

Each ship was fitted with a double squid in lieu of a 4in mounting; in two ships in place of 'B' mounting, and in the other two in place of 'X' mounting. The depth charge complement was reduced to fifteen. *Scorpion* was fitted with Type 160X asdics, while the remainder of the class were fitted with the seating for the 160X only. *Broadsword* was fitted with the Flyplane Predictor system.

The bridge layout in this class was based on that of the J class destroyers with improvements in detail resulting from war experience. The ships were not fitted out for Arctic service.

Programme	Builder	Laid Down	Launched	Completed
1942 Programme – *Weapon* class				
Scorpion	J S White	16 Dec 1944	15 Aug 1946	17 Sep 1947
Battleaxe	Yarrow	22 Apr 1944	12 Jun 1945	23 Oct 1947
Crossbow	Thornycroft	26 Aug 1944	20 Dec 1945	4 Mar 1948
Broadsword	Yarrow	20 Jul 1944	5 Feb 1946	4 Oct 1948

Daring Class Destroyers (1944 Programme)

In June 1943 staff requirements were issued calling for a new large Fleet destroyer to succeed the *Battle* class. They were in fact to be six–gun *Battle*s and were required to support and screen heavy ships, in particular the aircraft carrier groups of the future, against submarine, aircraft and E-boat attack, and be capable of attacking enemy forces under torpedoes and gunfire. Manoeuvrability was important as protection against torpedoes. The first design gave a ship 420ft x 45ft x 4800 tons deep, 72,000shp and 32kts. This was considered far too large and the staff requirements were revised and by adopting several weight-saving features it was found possible to meet the new requirements with a ship 390ft x 43ft x 3360 tons deep.

The design was approved by the Board in December 1944. Principal dimensions were:

Length between perps	366ft
Length overall	390ft
Breadth extreme	43ft
Depth (USK to top of deck at side)	22ft 9in
Displacement (deep)	3360 tons
Displacement (standard)	2594 tons
Shp	54,000
Speed deep and clean	31½kts
Endurance at 20kts (clean bottom and trial condition)	4400 miles

Legend Weights

Hull	1274 tons
Machinery	705 tons
Armament	435 tons
Equipment	241 tons
Electric generators	38 tons
Oil fuel	598 tons
RFW	43 tons
Board margin	26 tons
	3360 tons

All ships were fitted as leaders.

Structure

These vessels were the first destroyers to have been designed and specified for all welded prefabricated construction. The ships were longitudinally framed except at the ends where a close 21in system of transverse framing was adopted.[18]

Due to labour and space problems two of the builders had to depart from the all-welded prefabricated scheme; this resulted in three of the ships, viz *Daring*, *Diana* and *Decoy*, being erected plate by plate, with riveted longitudinals, beams and deck girders; the framing in these ships was increased slightly.

The approved scheme of erection whereby the main hull was split into about 100 units was followed with slight departures in the rest of the class. During construction the DNC Radiography team were actively employed and from their examinations the standard of welding was considered to be rather poor[19]. In comparing the results of the more important welded joints, *ie* shell crossovers, the percentage of cracking defects found in the various ships varied from 0% to 60%; for slag inclusions the percentages varied from 3% to 22%.

Arrangements were made for *Delight* to have a thorough radiographic summary before completion and for a subsequent survey after a spell in service.

An interesting feature in these ships was the box-like structural arrangements at the break of the forecastle. This structure was determined by a series of model experiments at NCRE and was essentially different from the breakdown in any previous destroyer.[20]

Aluminium plating was used extensively for minor bulkheads, superstructure decks, deckhouse sides, bridge flats and sides where clear of gun blast; all aluminium plating was riveted.

Armament

It was originally intended that the armament should consist of:

6-4.5 Mark V guns in three twin HA/LA mountings
6-40mm twin *Buster* mountings
4-20mm Oerlikons
2-21in pentad torpedo tubes
70 depth charges, 2 rails and 4 throwers

In 1946 the armament was modernised and the DCs were replaced by single squid and STAAGs

18 The ends of the ship are not stressed by the overall bending of the hull and the guideline is to stiffen plate panels across the shortest sides. The transition from longitudinal to transverse frames needs care.

19 The radiography (and other testing) of welds is a vital part of the process. For many years DNC's Radiography team were world leaders.

20 This structure at the break was successful but very heavy. In the postwar *Tribal* class it was found that a flush deck hull was lighter than one with a break.

Defender, *a* Daring *class ship, on completion. The general appearance is similar to the smaller* Weapon *class.*

were fitted in lieu of the *Buster* mountings. The armament as completed was:

3 twin 4.5 Mark 6 mountings
2 twin STAAGs
1 twin Mark V Bofors
2-21in pentad torpedo tubes (power worked)
1 single squid

Ships were designed to be fitted with types 166X, 147F and 162 Asdics.

Protection

The usual type of protection was fitted to gun houses, gun working chambers, viz 15lb; front and sides of bridge were fitted with 10lb. 10lb zarebas were fitted to close-range armament, transmitting station, wireless offices and cable trunks.

Machinery etc

The machinery in this class was split into two separate units of BR and ER separated by 12ft OB and air space; cross connections were arranged for use in overhaul of boilers and machinery and in emergency.

The boilers, each 27,000shp were arranged one in each BR and worked at 650lb/in², steam temperature of 850°F with economizers to reduce gas temperature to 450°F at full power.

The propelling machinery consisted of a two-shaft arrangement of turbines with three-bladed manganese bronze propellers 12ft diameter, 14ft 4in pitch.

Trials

On trials the maximum speed attained was 32.95kts with 54,300shp on a displacement of 3130 tons.

Electrical Power

Two 350kW turbo generators, one in each BR and three in no 150kW diesel generators, one in engine room and one forward.

Four ships of the class were fitted with an AC electrical supply. This was a departure from usual practice and it was considered that it would result in a saving in space, weight and complement. From experience in the early stages of fitting out it was doubtful whether this would be the case as certain of the AC machines were heavier than their DC counterparts.[21] However, the AC electrical machinery spaces were far cleaner and less congested than those containing DC machines.

Radar - types 293, 974 and 275.

Stability (from inclining experiment)

	Deep	Light
GM	3.44ft (fl)	3.21ft
Max GZ	2.45ft	1.55ft
Angle of max GZ	41°	34°
Range	82°	66°
Displacement	3608 tons	2818 tons

Strength

	Hogging	Sagging
Maximum bending moment	54,130ton ft	45,730ton ft
Max stress in upper deck	8.52ton/in²	6.11ton/in²
Max stress in keel	6.68ton/in²	6.62ton/in²

Increase in Displacement

The ship as built came out approximately 250 tons heavier than the deep design figure. It was estimated that this extra weight could be accounted for in: increases in oil fuel 30 tons, machinery 110 tons, general electrical and W/T equipment 50 tons, and general overall equipment 60 tons.

Complement

The complement of 329, including nineteen officers, were accommodated fore and aft. In order to ensure that maximum use was made of the space

21 It is common for the first use of a new approach to show no savings. It will usually be a very conservative design and the real value will appear in the second generation.

Daring class general arrangement as designed

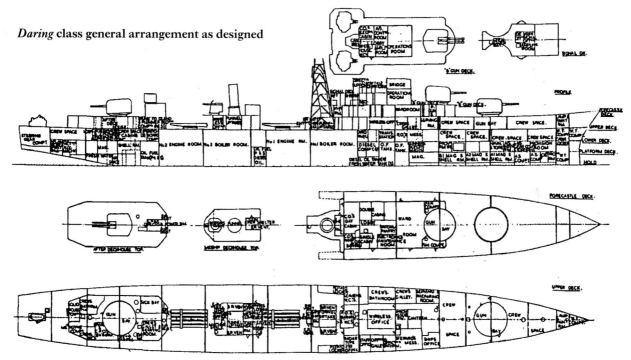

allocated for accommodation, the layouts of the compartments were planned on large scale drawings (1in = 1ft) showing everything in the compartments. The runs of ventilation trunking, piping, cable trays, rod gearing etc were determined and the resultant layout of accommodation rigidly adhered to during construction. This method of determining the layout of the messes proved to be a complete success.

General

As in the *Weapons* class destroyer the forward funnel was situated inside the lattice mast which, unlike that of the *Weapons*, was of all-welded tubular steel construction.

The ventilation arrangements were carefully designed with the fans positioned clear of the accommodation spaces. This was made possible by adopting a group system of ventilation for the fore end of the ship and a small number of large fans elsewhere. Advantage was taken of the saving in space by the use of 17½in and above axial flow fans.

Air conditioning was provided for the radar and main W/T offices by a 90,000btu air conditioning set.

During construction collective protection arrangements were made an extra requirement and, while it was not possible to fit air filtration units, the collective protection requirements were met by arranging gas citadels forward and aft of the machinery spaces.

Hunt Class Destroyers

At the time of the crisis in 1938 it was decided to press forward with the production of a large number of specially designed A/A, A/S escorts. For production reasons and to obtain the requisite numbers it was necessary that these should be simple, cheap and small. A consequence of their size was that their endurance would be limited to rather more than half that of a contemporary Fleet destroyer, and their speed would fall short of that of a Fleet destroyer by a few knots. A stabiliser was considered a necessary feature in a ship with a complete high-angled armament. The ships were required to perform the work of a modern escort vessel and be capable of carrying out manifold duties hitherto done by destroyers with the exception of attendances on a fleet.

The design of the *Hunt* class destroyers was rushed through in about three months, and was approved in January 1939.

The general particulars of the design, which became known as the Type I *Hunt* class were:

Length overall	280ft 0in
Length between perps	264ft 3in
Breadth extreme	29ft 0in
Depth (to UD at side)	17ft 2in
Displacement (deep)	1314 tons
Displacement (standard)	1000 tons
Mean draught (standard)	12ft 0in
Power	19,000shp
Max Speed (deep)	27kts
Oil fuel	243 tons
Endurance at 20kts	2300 miles
Complement	142

Group Weights

Hull	513 tons
Machinery	290 tons
Armament	108 tons
Equipment	91 tons
Oil fuel	243 tons
RFW	19 tons
Ballast	50 tons
Deep condition	1314 tons

In these ships the hull was designed on destroyer lines with some slight modifications to improve the performance at 20kts, this being accepted as an important speed from an endurance point of view.

Machinery consisted of geared turbines with the machinery compartments divided into separate engine and gearing rooms and two boiler rooms.

Propeller particulars:

Two 3-bladed propellers at 400rpm
Diameter	8ft 3in
Pitch	10ft 3in
Developed blade area	36sq ft

Auxiliary power was provided by 2-60kW turbo generators and two 20kW diesel generators.
Steering gear was of electro-hydraulic type.

The ships were constructed to normal Admiralty practices.
To improve accuracy of HA fire and to ensure good behaviour in a seaway, these ships were fitted with Denny Brown stabilisers. Reports from sea showed that a great deal of courage and enterprise was needed to get the best use out of the stabiliser, as the behaviour of the ship could become very alarming indeed. It was found that commanding officers were very loath to use the equipment and eventually pressed for its removal.

Armament (as designed) consisted of:

4-4in HA/LA guns in twin turrets[22]
1-2pdr multiple pom-poms (4-barrel)
2 Lewis guns
Magazine stowage for 4in armament was 250rpg.

Fifty depth charges were carried and each ship provided with one rail and two throwers.

Accommodation
Officers forward, A/A guns crews messed forward and aft immediately below the guns served.

Stability
The following stability particulars for *Atherstone*, a typical *Hunt* Type I, were obtained from an inclining experiment:

	Deep Displacement	*Light* Displacement
Metacentric height	1.9ft (fl)	1.7ft
Max GZ	1.98ft	1.07ft
Range	over 90°	over 90°
Displacement	1340 tons	1030 tons

These figures were obtained after 52 tons of solid ballast had been fitted to reduce the KG by 1.3ft.

22 The design armament was three twin 4in. An error was made in the design calculations and the Type I ships had to have the armament reduced and the bridge and funnel cut down to obtain sufficient stability. The later ships had increased beam. See J English, *The Hunt Class* (Kendal 1987).

Fernie a Type I Hunt *in original condition. Following the discovery of the design error referred to in the footnote, the armament was reduced to two twin 4in and the superstructure and funnel cut down.*

Strength

The standard longitudinal strength calculations gave the following results:

	Hogging	*Sagging*
Max. moment at Hard	14,850ton ft	12,100ton ft
Stress in upper deck	7.55ton/in²	5.25ton/in²
Stress in keel	5.95ton/in²	5.60ton/in²
Displacement	1307 tons	1257 tons

The need for improved stability and increased armament resulted in a redesign of the *Hunt* which became known as the *Hunt* Type II.

Hunt Type II

The general particulars were:

Length overall	280ft 0in
Length between perps	264ft 3in
Beam extreme	31ft 6in
Depth (to UD at side)	17ft 2in
Displacement (deep)	1430 tons
Displacement (standard)	1050 tons
Draughts (standard) F	9ft 10in
A	13ft 0in
Power	19,000shp
Max Speed (deep)	25¾kts
Oil fuel	277 tons
Endurance at 20 kts	2560 miles
Complement	164

The revised group weights became:

Hull	595 tons
Machinery	295 tons
Armament	136 tons
Equipment	111 tons
Oil fuel	277 tons
RFW	16 tons
Deep displacement	1430 tons

Armament in the Type II was increased to:

6-4in HA/LA guns in twin turrets
1-2pdr pom-pom (quadruple)
2 Oerlikons

Fifty depth charges were carried with one rail and two throwers.

The machinery was the same as for the previous design with a very slight change in the pitch dimension of the propellers.

Propeller dimensions:

Diameter	8ft 3in
Pitch	10ft 0in
Developed blade area	37.5sq ft

The new stability particulars of a typical *Hunt* Type II were:

	Deep Condition	*Light Condition*
Metacentric height	2.39ft (fl)	2.39ft
Max GZ	1.71ft	1.0ft
Range	69°	56°
Displacement	1413 tons	1074 tons

No ballast was fitted.

Hunt Type III

When it became clear that these vessels would have to take on certain duties belonging to destroyers and operate occasionally with the Fleet, it was decided to undertake another redesign incorporating torpedo armament as well as the 4in main armament.

Two separate designs were produced:
(a) a ship with twin torpedo tubes and 4-4in guns, on a waterline length of 272ft, and
(b) a ship with twin torpedo tubes and 6-4in guns, on a waterline length of 282ft.

Design (a) was approved, *ie* Hull, general arrangement and machinery as in previous *Hunt* II, excepting as influenced by torpedo requirements, but one 4in twin mounting less.

The dimensions of the ship remained the same and the weight of the Type III came to within 10 tons of that of the Type II.

It was necessary to fit 40 tons of permanent ballast in these ships.

Hunt Type IV

Two ships of this type were built to a design prepared by Thornycrofts. No stabilisers were fitted.

The general particulars were:

Silverton, with increased beam, could carry the planned armament of three twin 4in. Taken 15 December 1942.

The third batch of Hunts, *like* Easton, *had a twin torpedo tube mount in place of a twin 4in.*

Length overall	296ft 0in
Length on waterline	283ft 0in
Beam	33ft 5in
Depth to UD at side	16ft 3in
Deep displacement	1515 tons
Mean draught (deep)	10ft 3in
Power	19,000shp
Endurance at 20kts	2350 miles
Max Speed (deep)	25kts
Complement	167

Group Weights

Hull	655 tons
Machinery	305 tons
Armament	154 tons
Equipment	95 tons
Oil fuel	286 tons
RFW	20 tons
Deep displacement	1515 tons

As no stabilisers were fitted extra fuel was carried in one ship giving a total of 357 tons and a deep displacement of 1586 tons.

Armament as designed consisted of:

3 twin 4in HA/LA mountings
1 set of triple torpedo tubes
1-2pdr multiple pom-pom (quadruple)
4 Oerlikons
2 Lewis guns

Fifty depth charges were also carried, with two rails and four throwers.

Stability particulars of *Brissenden* were:

	Deep Condition	Light Condition
Metacentric height	1.48ft (fl)	1.06ft
Max GZ	2.6ft	1.0ft
Range	over 90°	77°
Displacement	1770 tons	1329 tons

Fifty-five tons of solid ballast were fitted.

A considerable increase in weight during building was experienced with the later ships of the *Hunt* class. This was mainly due to improvements in armament and additions as a result of war experience.

These particular ships were rather lightly built and suffered some damage forward due to pounding; some large areas of somewhat light plating required stiffening. The torpedo tubes also showed some disposition to move in a seaway and local stiffening was fitted to correct this.[23]

General

On the whole, the *Hunt* class destroyers, later known as escort destroyers - were a success in service. Their stability was not good, however, and they had to be ballasted and even then carefully watched in order to avoid unnecessary increase in top weight with further decrease in stability.

The Denny Brown stabilisers were always a source of trouble in these ships, mainly due to the fact that they were rarely, and then timorously, used by the COs. Further, the majority of ships were in effect carrying the stabilisers as ballast, and that compartment if used for oil fuel would give an increase of 22% in endurance. As war conditions were not conducive to further experimenting with stabilisers in ships on service, it was decided towards the end of building the Type III *Hunts* to omit the stabiliser and use the compartment for additional oil fuel.

Of the twenty-eight Type III *Hunts*, only fourteen had stabilisers. Four sets of gear were also removed from the Type II *Hunts*.

From time to time improvements were made in the armament in these ships; signal deck sponsons were fitted to carry Oerlikon guns, depth charge equipment was increased, and 2pdr pom-poms were fitted right forward as bow chasers primarily for anti-E-boat work.

The final gun armaments at the end of the war were:

[23] The Type IV ships were impressive and had many desirable features but were much bigger and more expensive than earlier types. One must doubt the wisdom of building such ships, particularly only two, in wartime.

Type I	*Type II*	*Type III*	*Type IV*
4-4in HA/LA guns	6-4in HA/LA guns	4-4in HA/LA guns	6-4in HA/LA guns
1-2pdr quadruple pom-pom	1-2pdr quadruple pom-pom	1-2pdr multiple pom-pom	1-2pdr multiple pom-pom
1-single 2pdr pom-pom	1 single 2pdr pom-pom	3 twin powered Oerlikon	2 Lewis guns 4 twin-powered Oerlikons
2 Oerlikons	2 twin Oerlikons		
2 Lewis guns			

The first ships in service experienced a number of troubles; steps were taken to overcome these faults in the later ships.

In Types II and III *Hunts*, the designs included a shortened bridge, set further aft, and lowered funnels. The wind currents from the bridge fronts swept the funnel gases over the bridge personnel and special deflectors had to be fitted with restriction plates in the funnel. The shape of the bridge fronts also affected the wind on personnel, and it was necessary to modify the bridge sides and sponsons to overcome the effects of side winds.

A total of eighty-six *Hunt* class escort destroyers were built, twenty-two Type I, thirty-four Type II, twenty-eight Type III and two Type IV.

Cost of a ship of *Hunt* class Type III was £352,000 (ex armament).

Programme	Builder	Laid Down	Launched	Completed
Hunt Type I				
Atherstone	Cammell Laird	8 Jun 1939	12 Dec 1939	23 Mar 1940
Fernie	John Brown	8 Jun 1939	9 Jan 1940	29 May 1940
Berkeley	Cammell Laird	8 Jun 1939	29 Jan 1940	6 Jun 1940
Hambledon	Swan Hunter	8 Jun 1939	12 Dec 1939	8 Jun 1940
Garth	John Brown	8 Jun 1939	14 Feb 1940	1 Jul 1940
Cattistock	Yarrow	9 Jun 1939	22 Feb 1940	4 Aug 1940
Holderness	Swan Hunter	29 Jun 1939	8 Feb 1940	10 Aug 1940
Eglinton	Vickers-Armstrongs	8 Jun 1939	28 Dec 1940	28 Aug 1940
Cleveland	Yarrow	7 Jul 1939	24 Apr 1940	18 Sep 1940
Quorn	J S White	26 Jul 1939	27 Mar 1940	21 Sep 1940
Mendip	Swan Hunter	10 Aug 1939	9 Apr 1940	12 Oct 1940
Pytchley	Scotts	26 Jul 1939	13 Feb 1940	23 Oct 1940
Exmoor	Vickers-Armstrongs	8 Jun 1939	25 Jan 1940	1 Nov 1940
Southdown	J S White	22 Aug 1939	5 Jul 1940	8 Nov 1940
Cotswold	Yarrow	11 Oct 1939	18 Jul 1940	16 Nov 1940
Tynedale	Stephens	27 Jul 1939	5 Jun 1940	2 Dec 1940
Blencathra	Cammell Laird	18 Nov 1939	6 Aug 1940	13 Dec 1940
Cottesmore	Yarrow	12 Dec 1939	5 Sep 1940	29 Dec 1940
Meynell	Swan Hunter	10 Aug 1939	7 Jun 1940	30 Dec 1940
Quantock	Scotts	26 Jul 1939	22 Apr 1940	6 Feb 1941
Whaddon	Stephens	27 Jul 1939	16 Jul 1940	28 Feb 1941
Brocklesby	Cammell Laird	18 Nov 1939	30 Sep 1940	9 Apr 1941
Hunt Type II				
Avonvale	John Brown	12 Feb 1940	23 Oct 1940	17 Feb 1941
Eridge	Swan Hunter	21 Nov 1939	20 Aug 1940	28 Feb 1941
Liddesdale	Vickers-Armstrong	22 Nov 1939	19 Aug 1940	3 Mar 1941
Blankney	John Brown	17 May 1940	19 Dec 1940	11 Apr 1941
Farndale	Swan Hunter	21 Nov 1939	30 Sep 1940	27 Apr 1941
Silverton	J S White	5 Dec 1939	4 Dec 1940	28 May 1941
Oakley	Vickers-Armstrong	22 Nov 1939	30 Oct 1940	17 Jun 1941
Heythrop	Swan Hunter	18 Dec 1939	30 Oct 1940	21 Jun 1941
Croome	Stephens	7 Jun 1940	30 Jan 1941	29 Jun 1941
Puckeridge	J S White	1 Jan 1940	6 Mar 1941	30 Jul 1941
Lamerton	Swan Hunter	10 Apr 1940	14 Dec 1940	16 Aug 1941
Badsworth	Cammell Laird	15 May 1940	17 Mar 1941	18 Aug 1941
Dulverton	Stephens	16 Jul 1940	1 Apr 1941	27 Sep 1941
Hurworth	Vickers-Armstrong	10 Apr 1940	10 Apr 1941	5 Oct 1941
Southwold	J S White	18 Jun 1940	29 May 1941	9 Oct 1941
Chiddingfold	Scotts	1 Mar 1940	10 Mar 1941	16 Oct 1941
Exmoor (ex *Burton*)	Swan Hunter	7 Jun 1940	12 Mar 1941	18 Oct 1941
Wheatland	Yarrow	30 May 1940	7 Jun 1941	3 Nov 1941
Beaufort	Cammell Laird	17 Jul 1940	9 Jun 1941	3 Nov 1941
Tetcott	J S White	29 Jul 1940	12 Aug 1941	11 Dec 1941
Calpe	Swan Hunter	12 Jun 1940	28 Apr 1941	11 Dec 1941

Programme	Builder	Laid Down	Launched	Completed
Hunt Type II *(continued)*				
Lauderdale	Thornycroft	21 Dec 1939	5 Aug 1941	24 Dec 1941
Middleton	Vickers-Armstrong	10 Apr 1940	12 May 1941	10 Jan 1942
Grove	Swan Hunter	28 Aug 1940	29 May 1941	5 Feb 1942
Ledbury	Thornycroft	24 Jan 1940	27 Sep 1941	11 Feb 1942
Wilton	Yarrow	7 Jun 1940	17 Oct 1941	18 Feb 1942
Hursley	Swan Hunter	21 Dec 1940	25 Jul 1941	2 Apr 1942
Blackmore	Stephens	10 Feb 1941	2 Dec 1941	14 Apr 1942
Oakley (ex *Tickhan*)	Yarrow	18 Aug 1940	15 Jan 1942	7 May 1942
Bedale	Hawthorn Leslie	25 May 1940	23 Jul 1941	9 May 1942
Bramham	Stephens	7 Apr 1941	29 Jan 1942	16 Jun 1942
Bicester	Hawthorn Leslie	29 May 1940	5 Sep 1941	18 Jun 1942
Zetland	Yarrow	2 Oct 1940	6 Mar 1942	27 Jun 1942
Cowdray	Scotts	30 Apr 1940	22 Jul 1941	29 Jul 1942
Hunt Type III				
Airedale	John Brown	20 Nov 1940	12 Aug 1941	8 Jan 1942
Aldenham	Cammell Laird	22 Aug 1940	27 Aug 1941	5 Feb 1942
Albrighton	John Brown	30 Dec 1940	11 Oct 1941	22 Feb 1942
Belvoir	Cammell Laird	14 Oct 1940	18 Nov 1941	29 Mar 1942
Bleasdale	Vickers-Armstrong	31 Oct 1940	23 Jul 1941	16 Apr 1942
Derwent	Vickers-Armstrong	29 Dec 1940	22 Aug 1941	24 Apr 1942
Glaisdale	Cammell Laird	4 Feb 1941	5 Jan 1942	12 Jun 1942
Catterick	Vickers-Armstrong	1 Mar 1941	22 Nov 1941	12 Jun 1942
Bolebroke	Swan Hunter	3 Apr 1941	5 Nov 1941	27 Jun 1942
Eskdale	Cammell Laird	18 Jan 1941	16 Mar 1942	31 Jul 1942
Border	Swan Hunter	1 May 1941	3 Feb 1942	5 Aug 1942
Hatherleigh	Vickers-Armstrong	12 Dec 1940	18 Dec 1941	10 Aug 1942
Blean	Hawthorn Leslie	22 Feb 1941	15 Jan 1942	23 Aug 1942
Penyland	Vickers-Armstrong	4 Jun 1941	17 Mar 1942	31 Aug 1942
Tanatside	Yarrows	23 Jun 1941	30 Apr 1942	4 Sep 1942
Holcombe	Stephens	3 Apr 1941	14 Apr 1942	16 Sep 1942
Welbreak	Swan Hunter	23 Jun 1941	5 Mar 1942	10 Oct 1942
Limbourne	Stephens	8 Apr 1941	12 May 1942	24 Oct 1942
Haydon	Vickers-Armstrong	1 May 1941	2 Aug 1942	24 Oct 1942
Wensleydale	Yarrow	28 Jul 1941	20 Jun 1942	30 Oct 1942
Rockwood	Vickers-Armstrong	29 Aug 1941	13 Jun 1942	4 Nov 1942
Goathland	Fairfield	30 Jan 1941	3 Feb 1942	6 Nov 1942
Modbury	Swan Hunter	5 Aug 1941	13 Apr 1942	25 Nov 1942
Easton	J S White	25 Mar 1941	11 Jul 1942	7 Dec 1942
Haldon	Fairfield	16 Jan 1941	27 Apr 1942	30 Dec 1942
Eggesford	J S White	23 Jun 1941	12 Sep 1942	21 Jan 1943
Stevenstone	J S White	2 Sep 1941	23 Nov 1942	18 Mar 1943
Talybont	J S White	28 Nov 1941	3 Feb 1943	19 May 1943
Hunt Type IV				
Brecon	Thornycroft	27 Feb 1941	27 Jun 1942	18 Dec 1942
Brissenden	Thornycroft	28 Feb 1941	15 Sep 1942	12 Feb 1943

Town Class Destroyers

These were American destroyers transferred to the Royal Navy under the Anglo-American Agreement of 2 September 1940.[24] Delivery commenced in September 1940. They were all First World War designed and completed between 1918 and 1920. The total number transferred was fifty, and comprised four classes, the *Burnham*, *Montgomery*, *Newport* and *Leeds* classes of twenty, eleven, sixteen and three vessels respectively. General particulars were as follows:

Burnham Class (known as the 'A' Type Town Class)

Displacement (standard)	1190 tons
Displacement (deep)	1725 tons
Mean Draught (deep)	12ft 10in
Length overall	314ft 4in
Maximum beam	31ft 8in
Shp	27,000
Speed (deep)	28½kts
Endurance	3425 at 15kts

[24] A Hague, *The Towns* (Kendal 1988).

Montgomery Class (known as the 'B' Type Town Class)

Displacement (standard)	1090 tons
Displacement (deep)	1530 tons
Mean Draught (deep)	11ft 11in
Length overall	314ft 4in
Maximum beam	31ft 0in
Shp	24,000-26,000
Speed (deep)	28¾kts
Endurance	2800 at 15kts

Newport Class (known as the 'C' Type Town Class)

Displacement (standard)	1060 tons
Displacement (deep)	1530 tons
Mean Draught (deep)	11ft 11in
Length overall	314ft 4in
Maximum beam	31ft 8in
Shp	25,000-27,000
Speed (deep)	27¾kts
Endurance	2400 at 15kts

Leeds Class (known as the 'D' Type Town Class)

Displacement (standard)	1020 tons
Displacement (deep)	1445 tons
Mean Draught (deep)	10ft 11½in
Length overall	315ft 6in
Maximum beam	31ft 2in
Shp	18,500
Speed	30kts
Endurance	2250 at 15kts

Two vessels, the *Lincoln* (Type B) and *St Albans* (Type C) were manned by the Royal Norwegian Navy. Seven vessels, from Type A and three Type C, were manned by the Royal Canadian Navy. The vessels, except *Leeds*, *Lewes* and *Ludlow* (Type D) were armed as follows:

4-4in LA guns
1-3in LA gun
12-18in torpedo tubes in triple mountings
8 DCs in trough
2-0.5in M/C guns

In order to improve the seaworthiness and fighting efficiency of the class (except *Leeds*, *Lewes* and *Ludlow* and the three A Type vessels *Stanley*, *Clare* and *Bradford*) 50 tons of permanent ballast was fitted, the depth of the bilge keels was increased and the armament finally modified to:

1-4in LA gun
1-12pdr HA/LA gun
3-20mm single Oerlikon guns
2-0.5in Browning machine guns
2 Lewis machine guns
1 set of triple torpedo tubes on CL
Single Hedgehog

Sixty depth charges were carried with two rails, four throwers and the depth charge mag.

The above armament was modified in five vessels fitted with HF/DF to:

1-4in LA gun
1-12pdr HA/LA gun
3-20mm single Oerlikons
2-0.5in Browning machine guns
2 Lewis machine guns
Single Hedgehog

Fifty depth charges were carried with two rails, four throwers and the depth charge mag.

Soon after these vessels were taken over consideration was given to converting them for long-range convoy escort duties and, as a result, the *Stanley*, *Clare* and *Bradford* ('A' Type vessels) were taken in hand. The conversion entailed considerable work which included converting the forward boiler room into additional oil fuel tanks and mess spaces; rearrangement and modification of mess spaces to accommodate the revised complement in accordance with normal British standards as far as practicable for this type of vessel; enlarging the after deck house and enclosing the space between the bridge and midship gun platform to provide extra WCs, washplaces, galleys, stores and sick bay, etc. The bridge was entirely rebuilt to include improved W/T, radar, anti-submarine and navigating facilities. In addition, the original armament was altered to:

1-4in LA gun
1-12pdr HA/LA gun
2-2pdr single pom-poms
2-0.5in Browning machine guns
2-.303 Hotchkiss machine guns
2 Lewis machine guns
1 set of triple torpedo tubes on CL

Eighty-eight depth charges carried in eight depth charge throwers, two depth charge rails and the depth charge magazine.

At a later date the 2pdr and Browning mountings were replaced by 20mm single Oerlikon mountings, a single hedgehog was fitted and four depth charge throwers removed to obtain a ten depth charge pattern.

The endurance of these three vessels after this conversion was approximately 4100 at 15kts.

Owing to the time involved in carrying out this conversion (approx 6 months), it was decided not to convert other *Town* class destroyers in a similar manner. Investigations were made and proposals promulgated for a less costly conversion of the remaining vessels of the class, but these arrangements were never put into effect owing, chiefly, to the employment of these vessels on urgent operational duties.

The *Leeds*, *Lewis* and *Ludlow* (D Type) were employed on East Coast escort duties and their original armament was modified to:

Ludlow   2–3in guns
           2–2pdr pom-poms
           2–20mm Oerlikon guns (single)
           2–0.5in Browning machine guns
           4 twin Lewis machine guns
           Twenty depth charges stowed in one rail, two throwers and the depth charge magazine.

Leeds   2–3in guns
           2–2pdr pom-poms
           2–20mm Oerlikon guns (single)
           2–0.5in Browning machine guns
           2–.303 Hotchkiss machine guns
           Twenty depth charges stowed in one rail, two throwers and the depth charge magazine.

Lewes   2–3in guns
           2–2pdr pom-poms
           2–0.5in Browning machine guns
           2–.303 Hotchkiss machine guns
           2–twin Lewis machine guns
           2–20mm Oerlikon guns (single)
           Twenty depth charges stowed in one rail, two throwers and the depth charge magazine.

Seven *Town* class destroyers were fitted out for service on the Arctic convoy routes during 1942.

Towards the end of 1944 consequent upon the availability of new construction destroyers, frigates and corvettes, nine *Town* class destroyers were transferred on loan to the Russian Government and the remainder removed from operational service.

Brighton, one of the Town *class lent to the Soviet Union, on her return to Britain in March 1949.*

All-welded Destroyers – built by Messrs J S White & Co Ltd

In June 1942 British shipbuilders were invited by the Admiralty to develop to the greatest possible extent the use of electric welding in the construction of warships and Messrs J S White were asked to take the lead in the structural design and construction of all-welded destroyers.

This firm's shipyard had suffered widespread damage by enemy bombing in the early part of 1942, and in rebuilding it was decided to modernise the yard layout to accommodate the more up-to-date methods of ship construction. The new ships and machinery layout were arranged in a manner suited to a prefabrication technique and considerable assistance was given by the Admiralty in the supply of equipment, such as Unionmelt welding machines and modern gas-cutting equipment, and in giving technical advice.

The required number of welding operators (both male and female) were given preliminary training at a welding school in Southampton; their training was completed in the shipyard itself.

Close liaison was maintained with the firm, and as it was not possible to appoint a permanent

25 Goodall noted in his diary, with horror, that at the end of the war one prominent destroyer builder thought he could return to rivetted construction.

welding overseer, periodic visits were made to the shipyard by the Admiralty Principal Welding Overseer and the constructor in charge of the Destroyer Design Section.

It was decided that the first two ships, viz *Cavalier* and *Carysfort*, were to be built to a 'hybrid' scheme, since most of the structural materials for these vessels had already been ordered; subsequent vessels *Contest*, *Craccher* [renamed *Crispin* 1946] and *Creole* were to be all-welded.

In accepting the principle of all-welded destroyers, the following points were made:

1. No welding was to be done on ship structure of less than 7lb.

2. All main transverse bulkheads were to be of 7lb thickness.

3. Where the upper deck and shell of the 'hybrids' were over 20lb D quality they were to be riveted; elsewhere they were to be flush welded.

4. No shell plating less than 9lb thickness was to be welded.

5. No thickness limitation was specified for the welding of deckhouses.

6. No D quality plating or rivets were to be used in future for destroyers, and strength requirements were to be met by the use of DW quality material.

7. In the all-welded vessels, the hull was to be prefabricated in units not exceeding 7 tons, this being the maximum lift of the cranes.

The following is a very brief description of the sequence of erection followed in the first all-welded vessels:

Vertical keel and (single) flat keel fabricated in the shop in suitable lengths.

Keel erected on the slip, together with the small middle-line bulkheads and transverse bulkheads outside machinery spaces.

Over approximately one-third length of the ship at amidships, formers were erected to the shape of the outside of shell as far as the outboard seam of C strake.

The garboard, B and C strakes were laid on the formers and welded, as much as possible by Unionmelt welding machine, the remainder by hand.

Frames, longitudinals and floors in the machinery spaces were welded together in the ship on the 'egg-box' principle and then erected at the ship.

Next machinery compartment bulkheads were erected, then shell panels, with frames and longitudinals welded thereto, working from amidships towards the end, and finally, flats and decks. To take account of slight inaccuracies, a closing shell strake running just below the lower deck edge was moulded at the ship.

In the first all-welded vessels, a number of joints of the main structure were subjected to radiographic examination just prior to launch.

Later all-welded vessels at Cowes had a different erection procedure based on experience with *Contest*, involving fabrication of 'blocks' of ship instead of panels, so as to improve rigidity.

In the 1944 programme *Daring* class the vessels were designed from the start as all-welded in order to restrict the displacement to certain limits. Of the eight vessels building, however, it was necessary to accept a small amount of riveting in those ships at Swan Hunters and Yarrow because of:

(a) inability of firms to handle large pieces on the slip.

(b) lack of facilities for making large all-welded fabrications.

(c) desirability that firm using the method of building by small pieces or plate by plate should employ riveting to hold the ship to form.

The extent of riveting consisted of longitudinals and deck girders only.[25]

Index